2000
Yearbook of
Astronomy

2000 Yearbook of Astronomy

edited by
Patrick Moore

MACMILLAN

First published 1999 by Macmillan
an imprint of Macmillan Publishers Ltd
25 Eccleston Place, London SW1W 9NF
Basingstoke and Oxford
Associated companies throughout the world
www.macmillan.co.uk

ISBN 0 333 76581 8

Copyright © Macmillan Publishers 1999

9 8 7 6 5 4 3 2 1

Typeset by Rowland Phototypesetting Ltd,
Bury St Edmunds, Suffolk
Printed and bound in Great Britain by
Mackays of Chatham plc, Chatham, Kent

Contents

Editor's Foreword

The 2000 *Yearbook* follows the established pattern. As always, Gordon Taylor has provided data for the monthly notes, and John Isles and Robert Argyle have contributed the sections on double stars and variable stars, respectively.

Some of our most valued contributors have again joined us: Dr Paul Murdin, Dr Fred Watson and Professor Chris Kitchin. There are observational articles from Nigel Bannister and Ron Arbour, and a leading representative of the younger school of astronomers, Chris Lintott, has provided the first article.

In one way, 1998 has been a sad time. To save money, the British Government ordered the closure of our flagship observatory, the Royal Greenwich Observatory, which was founded during the reign of Charles II and for well over three hundred years maintained its position as a leader of world astronomy. The last two articles deal with the history of the RGO and its final years.

PATRICK MOORE
Selsey, June 1999

Preface

New readers will find that all the information in this *Yearbook* is given in diagrammatic or descriptive form; the positions of the planets may easily be found from the specially designed star charts, while the monthly notes describe the movements of the planets and give details of other astronomical phenomena visible in both the northern and southern hemispheres. Two sets of star charts are provided. The **Northern Charts** (pp. 16 to 41) are designed for use at latitude 52°N, but may be used without alteration throughout the British Isles, and (except in the case of eclipses and occultations) in other countries of similar northerly latitude. The **Southern Charts** (pp. 42 to 67) are drawn for latitude 35°S, and are suitable for use in South Africa, Australia and New Zealand, and other locations in approximately the same southerly latitude. The reader who needs more detailed information will find *Norton's Star Atlas* an invaluable guide, while more precise positions of the planets and their satellites, together with predictions of occultations, meteor showers and periodic comets, may be found in the *Handbook* of the British Astronomical Association. Readers will also find details of forthcoming events given in the American magazine *Sky & Telescope* and the British monthly *Modern Astronomer*.

Important note
The times given on the star charts and in the Monthly Notes are generally given as local times, using the 24-hour clock, the day beginning at midnight. All the dates, and the times of a few events (e.g. eclipses), are given in Greenwich Mean Time (GMT), which is related to local time by the formula

Local Mean Time = GMT − west longitude

In practice, small differences in longitude are ignored, and the observer will use local clock time, which will be the appropriate Standard (or Zone) Time. As the formula indicates, places in west longitude will have a Standard Time slow on GMT, while places in east longitude will have a Standard Time fast on GMT. As examples we have:

Standard Time in

New Zealand	GMT + 12 hours
Victoria; NSW	GMT + 10 hours
Western Australia	GMT + 8 hours
South Africa	GMT + 2 hours
British Isles	GMT
Eastern ST	GMT − 5 hours
Central ST	GMT − 6 hours, etc.

If Summer Time is in use, the clocks will have been advanced by one hour, and this hour must be subtracted from the clock time to give Standard Time.

Part I

Monthly Charts and Astronomical Phenomena

Notes on the Star Charts

The stars, together with the Sun, Moon and planets, seem to be set on the surface of the celestial sphere, which appears to rotate about the Earth from east to west. Since it is impossible to represent a curved surface accurately on a plane, any kind of star map is bound to contain some form of distortion. But it is well known that the eye can endure some kinds of distortion better than others, and it is particularly true that the eye is most sensitive to deviations from the vertical and horizontal. For this reason the star charts given in this volume have been designed to give a true representation of vertical and horizontal lines, whatever may be the resulting distortion in the shape of a constellation figure. It will be found that the amount of distortion is, in general, quite small, and is only obvious in the case of large constellations such as Leo and Pegasus, when these appear at the top of a chart and so are elongated sideways.

The charts show all stars down to the fourth magnitude, together with a number of fainter stars which are necessary to define the shapes of constellations. There is no standard system for representing the outlines of the constellations, and triangles and other simple figures have been used to give outlines which are easy to follow with the naked eye. The names of the constellations are given, together with the proper names of the brighter stars. The apparent magnitudes of the stars are indicated roughly by using four different sizes of dots, the larger dots representing the brighter stars.

The two sets of star charts are similar in design. At each opening there is a group of four charts which give a complete coverage of the sky up to an altitude of 62½°; there are twelve such groups to cover the entire year. In the **Northern Charts** (for 52°N) the upper two charts show the southern sky, south being at the centre and east on the left. The coverage is from 10° north of east (top left) to 10° north of west (top right). The two lower charts show the northern sky from 10° south of west (lower left) to 10° south of east (lower right). There is thus an overlap east and west.

Conversely, in the **Southern Charts** (for 35°S) the upper two charts show the northern sky, with north at the centre and east on the right. The two lower charts show the southern sky, with south at the centre and east on the left. The coverage and overlap is the same on both sets of charts.

Because the sidereal day is shorter than the solar day, the stars appear to rise and set about four minutes earlier each day, and this amounts to two hours in a month. Hence the twelve groups of charts in each set are sufficient to give the appearance of the sky throughout the day at intervals of two hours, or at the same time of night at monthly intervals throughout the year. The actual range of dates and times when the stars on the charts are visible is indicated at the top of each page. Each group is numbered in bold type, and the number to be used for any given month and time may be found from the following table:

Local Time	18h	20h	22h	0h	2h	4h	6h
January	11	12	1	2	3	4	5
February	12	1	2	3	4	5	6
March	1	2	3	4	5	6	7
April	2	3	4	5	6	7	8
May	3	4	5	6	7	8	9
June	4	5	6	7	8	9	10
July	5	6	7	8	9	10	11
August	6	7	8	9	10	11	12
September	7	8	9	10	11	12	1
October	8	9	10	11	12	1	2
November	9	10	11	12	1	2	3
December	10	11	12	1	2	3	4

The charts are drawn to scale, the horizontal measurements, marked at every 10°, giving the azimuths (or true bearings) measured from the north round through east (90°), south (180°) and west (270°). The vertical measurements, similarly marked, give the altitudes of the stars up to 62½°. Estimates of altitude and azimuth made from these charts will necessarily be mere approximations, since no observer will be exactly at the particular latitude, or at the stated time, but they will serve for the identification of stars and planets.

The ecliptic is drawn as a broken line on which longitude is marked every 10°; the positions of the planets are then easily found by reference to the table on p. 74. It will be noticed that on the Southern Charts the *ecliptic* may reach an altitude in excess of 62½° on star charts 5 to 9. The continuations of the broken line will be found on the charts of overhead stars.

There is a curious illusion that stars at an altitude of 60° or more are actually overhead, and beginners may often feel that they are leaning over backwards in trying to see them. These overhead stars are given separately on the pages immediately following the main star charts. The entire year is covered at one opening, each of the four maps showing the overhead stars at times which correspond to those for three of the main star charts. The position of the zenith is indicated by a cross, and this cross marks the centre of a circle which is 35° from the zenith; there is thus a small overlap with the main charts.

The broken line leading from the north (on the Northern Charts) or from the south (on the Southern Charts) is numbered to indicate the corresponding main chart. Thus on p. 40 the N–S line numbered 6 is to be regarded as an extension of the centre (south) line of chart 6 on pp. 26 and 27, and at the top of these pages are printed the dates and times which are appropriate. Similarly, on p. 67 the S–N line numbered 10 connects with the north line of the upper charts on pp. 60 and 61.

The overhead stars are plotted as maps on a conical projection, and the scale is rather smaller than that of the main charts.

1L

October 6 at 5h	October 21 at 4h
November 6 at 3h	November 21 at 2h
December 6 at 1h	December 21 at midnight
January 6 at 23h	January 21 at 22h
February 6 at 21h	February 21 at 20h

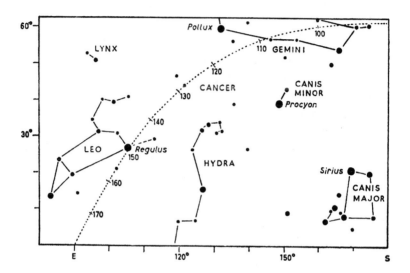

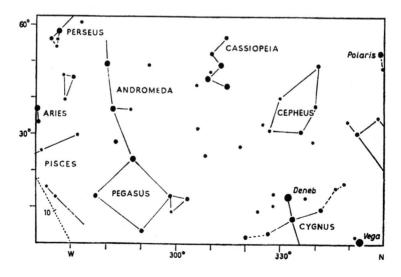

October 6 at 5ʰ	October 21 at 4ʰ
November 6 at 3ʰ	November 21 at 2ʰ
December 6 at 1ʰ	December 21 at midnight
January 6 at 23ʰ	January 21 at 22ʰ
February 6 at 21ʰ	February 21 at 20ʰ

1R

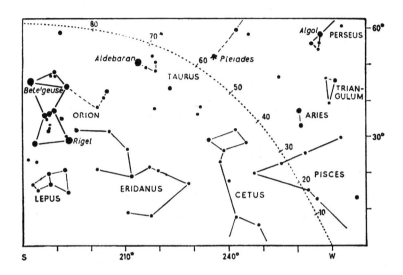

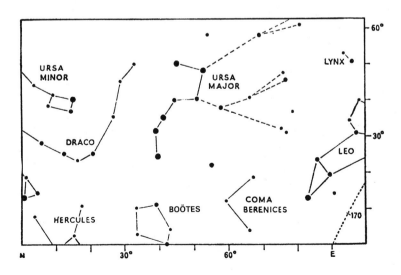

2L

November 6 at 5ʰ	November 21 at 4ʰ
December 6 at 3ʰ	December 21 at 2ʰ
January 6 at 1ʰ	January 21 at midnight
February 6 at 23ʰ	February 21 at 22ʰ
March 6 at 21ʰ	March 21 at 20ʰ

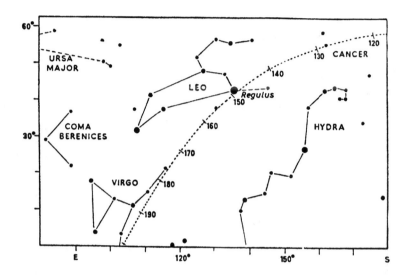

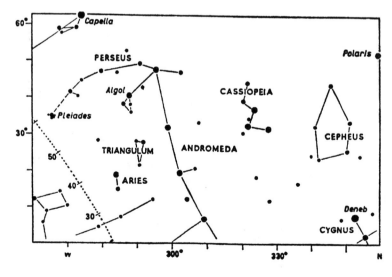

November 6 at 5^h	November 21 at 4^h
December 6 at 3^h	December 21 at 2^h
January 6 at 1^h	January 21 at midnight
February 6 at 23^h	February 21 at 22^h
March 6 at 21^h	March 21 at 20^h

2R

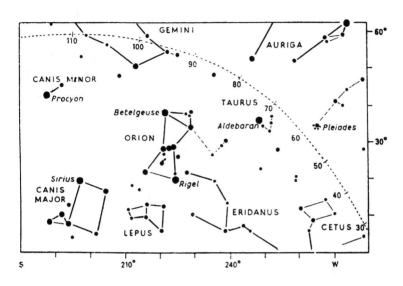

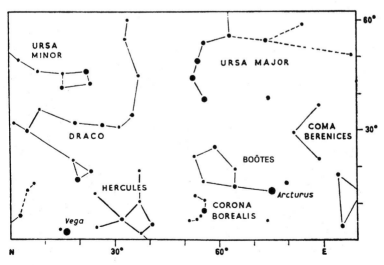

3L

December 6 at 5ʰ	December 21 at 4ʰ
January 6 at 3ʰ	January 21 at 2ʰ
February 6 at 1ʰ	February 21 at midnight
March 6 at 23ʰ	March 21 at 22ʰ
April 6 at 21ʰ	April 21 at 20ʰ

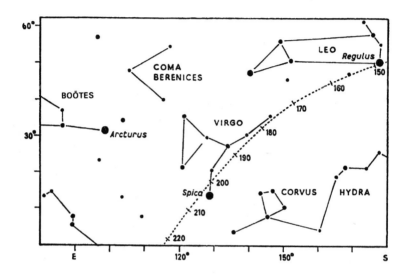

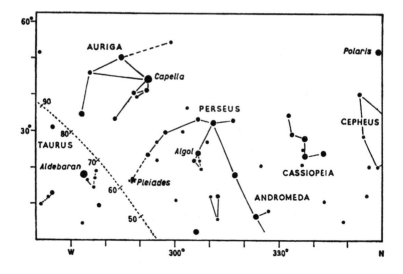

December 6 at 5ʰ
January 6 at 3ʰ
February 6 at 1ʰ
March 6 at 23ʰ
April 6 at 21ʰ

December 21 at 4ʰ
January 21 at 2ʰ
February 21 at midnight
March 21 at 22ʰ
April 21 at 20ʰ

3R

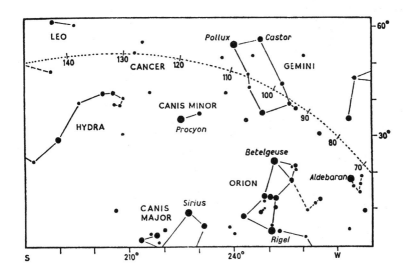

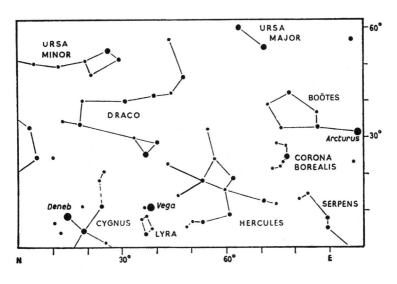

4L

January 6 at 5ʰ	January 21 at 4ʰ
February 6 at 3ʰ	February 21 at 2ʰ
March 6 at 1ʰ	March 21 at midnight
April 6 at 23ʰ	April 21 at 22ʰ
May 6 at 21ʰ	May 21 at 20ʰ

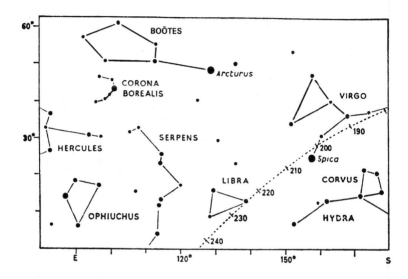

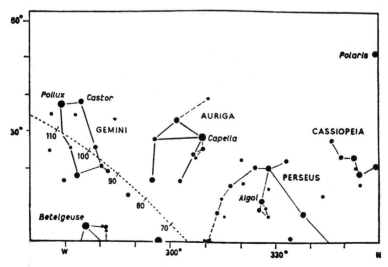

January 6 at 5ʰ	January 21 at 4ʰ
February 6 at 3ʰ	February 21 at 2ʰ
March 6 at 1ʰ	March 21 at midnight
April 6 at 23ʰ	April 21 at 22ʰ
May 6 at 21ʰ	May 21 at 20ʰ

4R

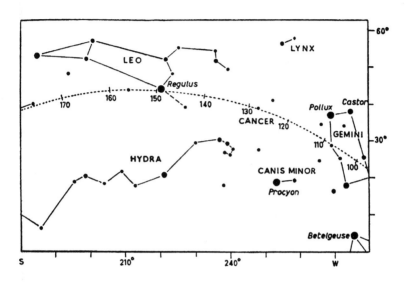

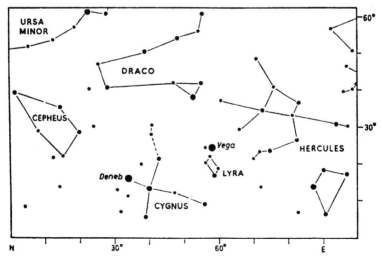

5L

January 6 at 7ʰ	January 21 at 6ʰ
February 6 at 5ʰ	February 21 at 4ʰ
March 6 at 3ʰ	March 21 at 2ʰ
April 6 at 1ʰ	April 21 at midnight
May 6 at 23ʰ	May 21 at 22ʰ

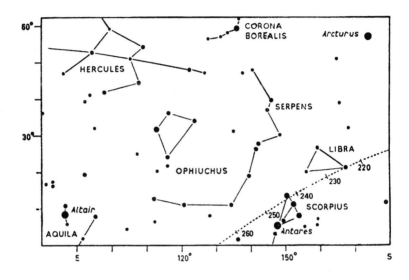

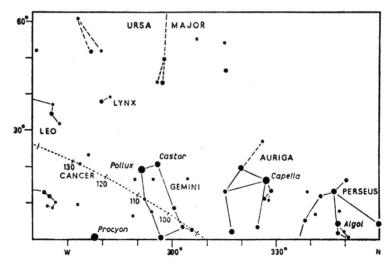

January 6 at 7ʰ	January 21 at 6ʰ
February 6 at 5ʰ	February 21 at 4ʰ
March 6 at 3ʰ	March 21 at 2ʰ
April 6 at 1ʰ	April 21 at midnight
May 6 at 23ʰ	May 21 at 22ʰ

5R

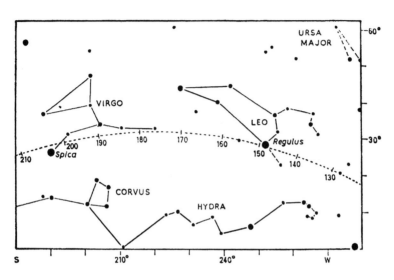

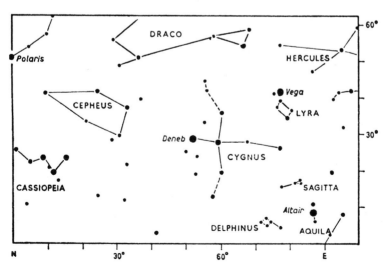

6L

March 6 at 5ʰ	March 21 at 4ʰ
April 6 at 3ʰ	April 21 at 2ʰ
May 6 at 1ʰ	May 21 at midnight
June 6 at 23ʰ	June 21 at 22ʰ
July 6 at 21ʰ	July 21 at 20ʰ

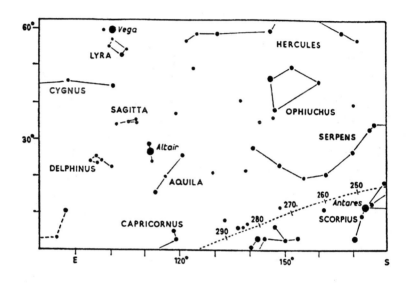

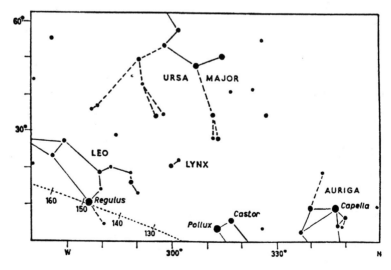

March 6 at 5ʰ	March 21 at 4ʰ
April 6 at 3ʰ	April 21 at 2ʰ
May 6 at 1ʰ	May 21 at midnight
June 6 at 23ʰ	June 21 at 22ʰ
July 6 at 21ʰ	July 21 at 20ʰ

6R

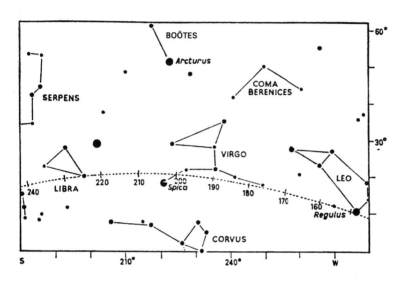

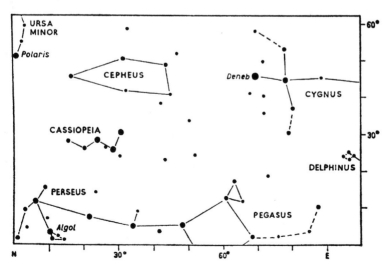

7L

May 6 at 3ʰ	May 21 at 2ʰ
June 6 at 1ʰ	June 21 at midnight
July 6 at 23ʰ	July 21 at 22ʰ
August 6 at 21ʰ	August 21 at 20ʰ
September 6 at 19ʰ	September 21 at 18ʰ

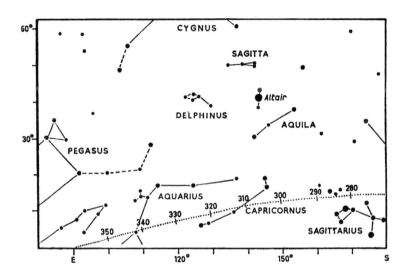

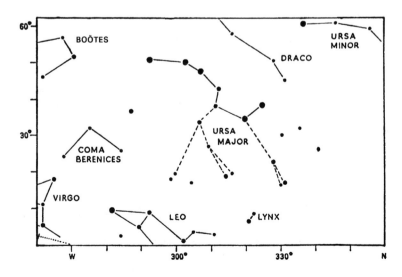

May 6 at 3ʰ	May 21 at 2ʰ
June 6 at 1ʰ	June 21 at midnight
July 6 at 23ʰ	July 21 at 22ʰ
August 6 at 21ʰ	August 21 at 20ʰ
September 6 at 19ʰ	September 21 at 18ʰ

7R

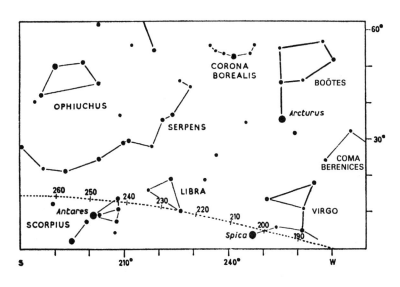

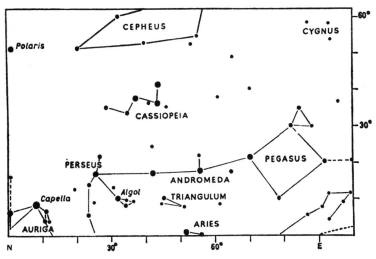

8L

July 6 at 1h	July 21 at midnight
August 6 at 23h	August 21 at 22h
September 6 at 21h	September 21 at 20h
October 6 at 19h	October 21 at 18h
November 6 at 17h	November 21 at 16h

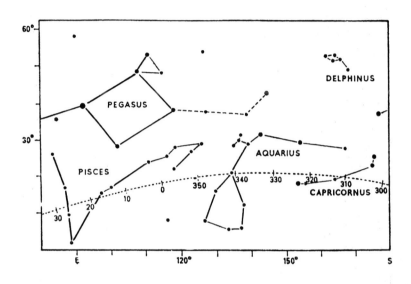

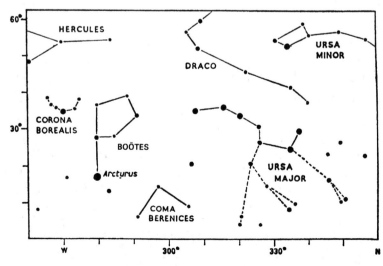

July 6 at 1h	July 21 at midnight
August 6 at 23h	August 21 at 22h
September 6 at 21h	September 21 at 20h
October 6 at 19h	October 21 at 18h
November 6 at 17h	November 21 at 16h

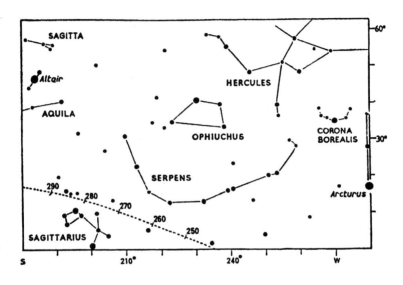

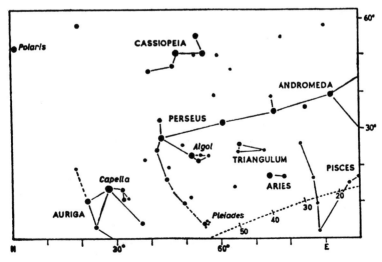

9L

August 6 at 1ʰ	August 21 at midnight
September 6 at 23ʰ	September 21 at 22ʰ
October 6 at 21ʰ	October 21 at 20ʰ
November 6 at 19ʰ	November 21 at 18ʰ
December 6 at 17ʰ	December 21 at 16ʰ

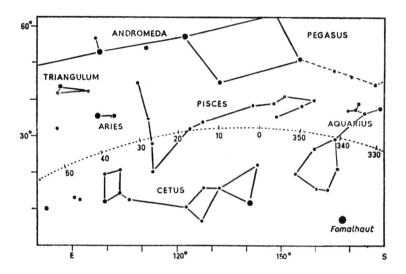

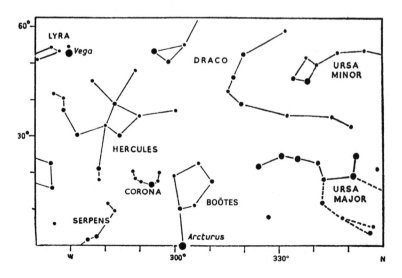

August 6 at 1h	August 21 at midnight
September 6 at 23h	September 21 at 22h
October 6 at 21h	October 21 at 20h
November 6 at 19h	November 21 at 18h
December 6 at 17h	December 21 at 16h

9R

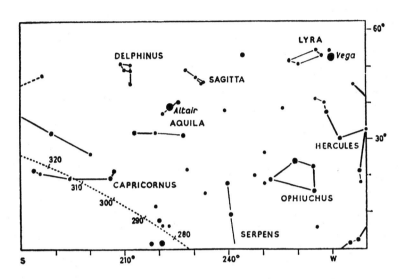

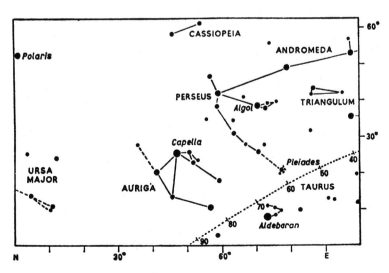

10L

August 6 at 3ʰ	August 21 at 2ʰ
September 6 at 1ʰ	September 21 at midnight
October 6 at 23ʰ	October 21 at 22ʰ
November 6 at 21ʰ	November 21 at 20ʰ
December 6 at 19ʰ	December 21 at 18ʰ

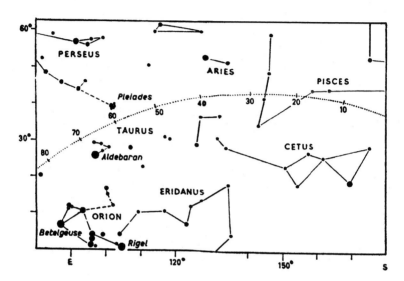

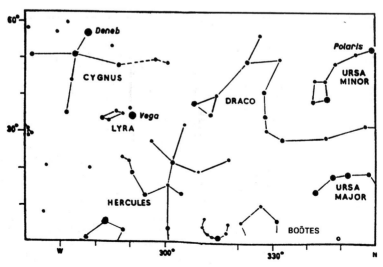

August 6 at 3ʰ	August 21 at 2ʰ	
September 6 at 1ʰ	September 21 at midnight	
October 6 at 23ʰ	October 21 at 22ʰ	
November 6 at 21ʰ	November 21 at 20ʰ	
December 6 at 19ʰ	December 21 at 18ʰ	

10R

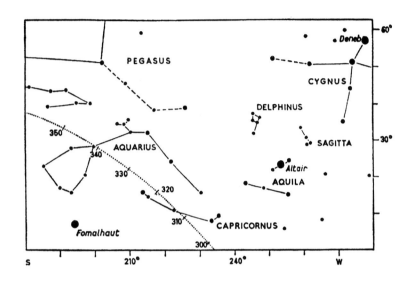

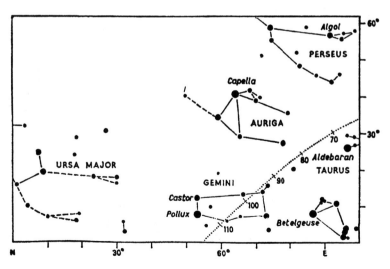

11L

September 6 at 3h	September 21 at 2h
October 6 at 1h	October 21 at midnight
November 6 at 23h	November 21 at 22h
December 6 at 21h	December 21 at 20h
January 6 at 19h	January 21 at 18h

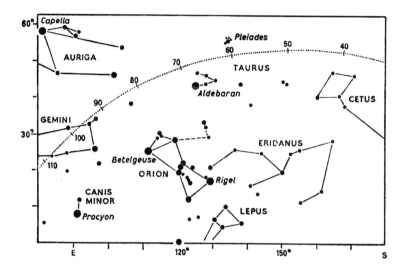

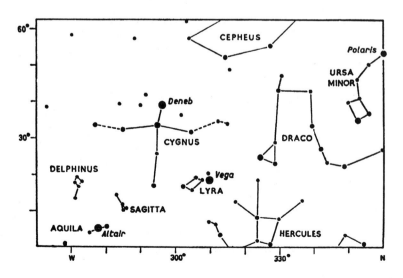

September 6 at 3ʰ	September 21 at 2ʰ
October 6 at 1ʰ	October 21 at midnight
November 6 at 23ʰ	November 21 at 22ʰ
December 6 at 21ʰ	December 21 at 20ʰ
January 6 at 19ʰ	January 21 at 18ʰ

11R

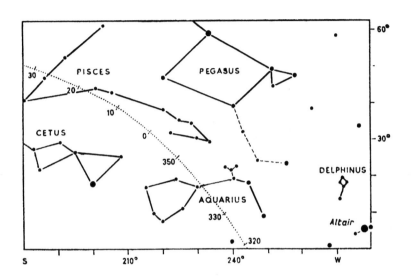

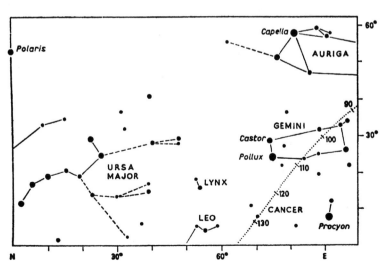

12L

October 6 at	3ʰ	October 21 at	2ʰ
November 6 at	1ʰ	November 21 at midnight	
December 6 at	23ʰ	December 21 at	22ʰ
January 6 at	21ʰ	January 21 at	20ʰ
February 6 at	19ʰ	February 21 at	18ʰ

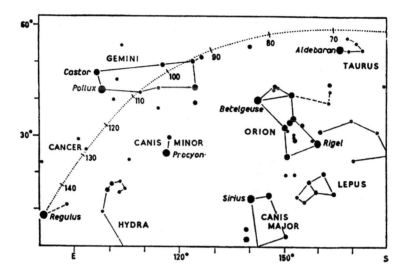

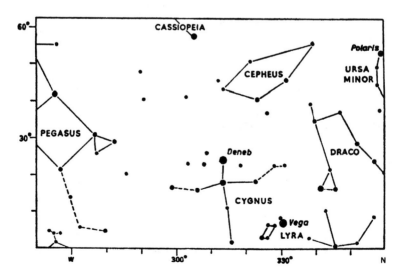

October 6 at 3ʰ	October 21 at 2ʰ
November 6 at 1ʰ	November 21 at midnight
December 6 at 23ʰ	December 21 at 22ʰ
January 6 at 21ʰ	January 21 at 20ʰ
February 6 at 19ʰ	February 21 at 18ʰ

12R

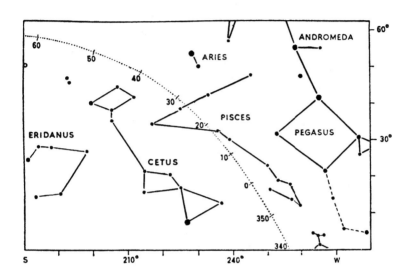

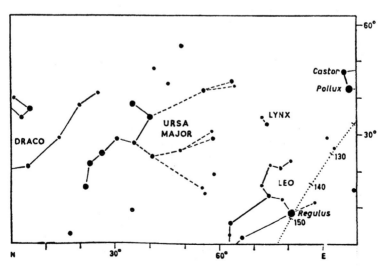

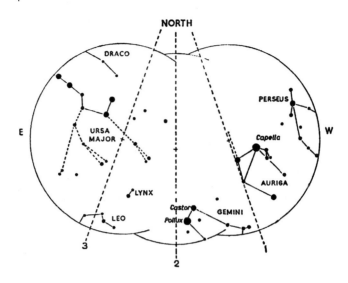

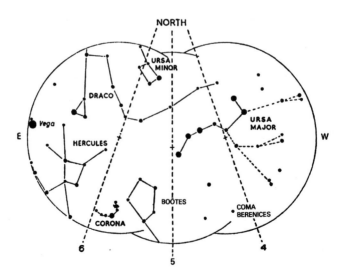

Northern Hemisphere Overhead Stars

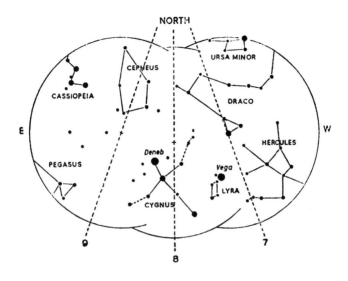

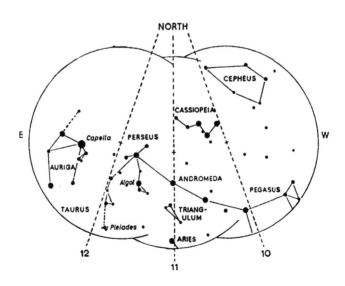

Northern Hemisphere Overhead Stars

1L

October 6 at 5ʰ	October 21 at 4ʰ
November 6 at 3ʰ	November 21 at 2ʰ
December 6 at 1ʰ	December 21 at midnight
January 6 at 23ʰ	January 21 at 22ʰ
February 6 at 21ʰ	February 21 at 20ʰ

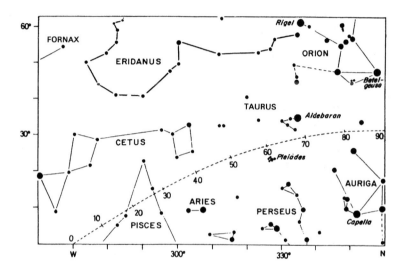

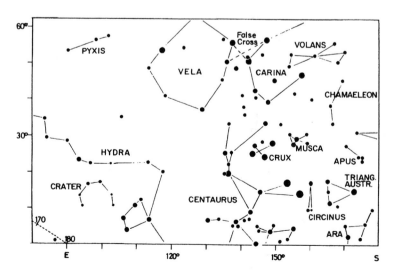

October 6 at	5ʰ	October 21 at	4ʰ
November 6 at	3ʰ	November 21 at	2ʰ
December 6 at	1ʰ	December 21 at midnight
January 6 at	23ʰ	January 21 at	22ʰ
February 6 at	21ʰ	February 21 at	20ʰ

1R

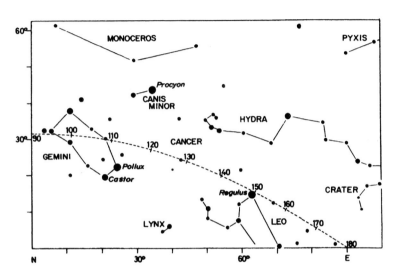

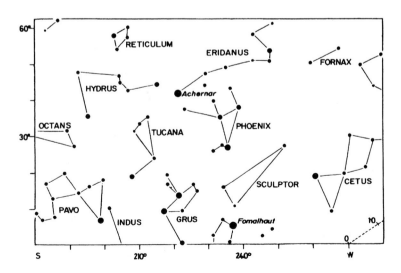

2L

November 6 at 5ʰ	November 21 at 4ʰ
December 6 at 3ʰ	December 21 at 2ʰ
January 6 at 1ʰ	January 21 at midnight
February 6 at 23ʰ	February 21 at 22ʰ
March 6 at 21ʰ	March 21 at 20ʰ

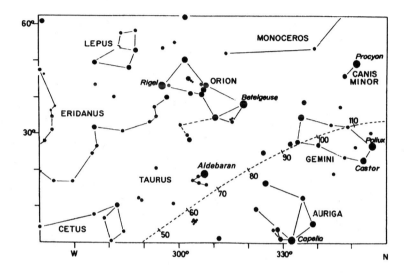

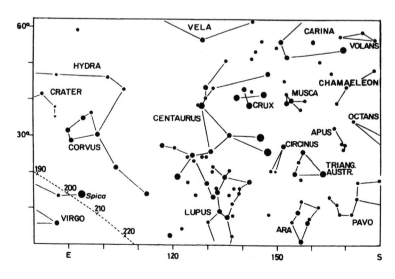

November 6 at	5ʰ	November 21 at	4ʰ
December 6 at	3ʰ	December 21 at	2ʰ
January 6 at	1ʰ	January 21 at midnight
February 6 at	23ʰ	February 21 at	22ʰ
March 6 at	21ʰ	March 21 at	20ʰ

2R

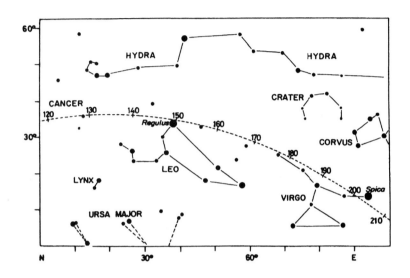

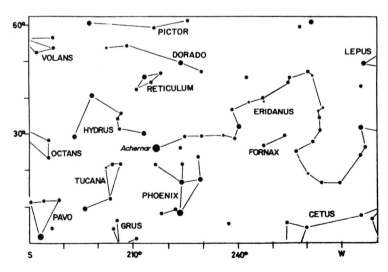

3L

January 6 at 3ʰ   January 21 at 2ʰ
February 6 at 1ʰ   February 21 at midnight
March 6 at 23ʰ   March 21 at 22ʰ
April 6 at 21ʰ   April 21 at 20ʰ
May 6 at 19ʰ   May 21 at 18ʰ

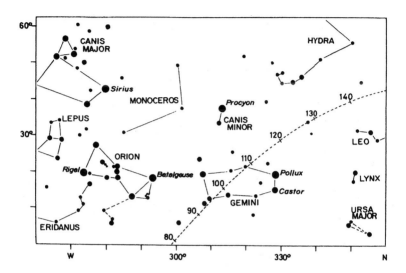

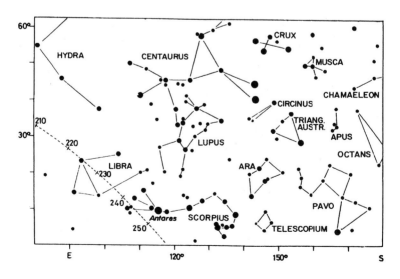

January 6 at 3h	January 21 at 2h
February 6 at 1h	February 21 at midnight
March 6 at 23h	March 21 at 22h
April 6 at 21h	April 21 at 20h
May 6 at 19h	May 21 at 18h

3R

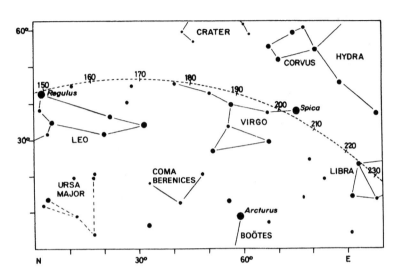

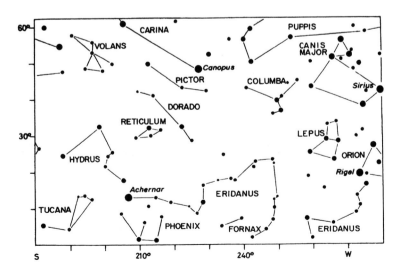

4L

February 6 at 3h	February 21 at 2h
March 6 at 1h	March 21 at midnight
April 6 at 23h	April 21 at 22h
May 6 at 21h	May 21 at 20h
June 6 at 19h	June 21 at 18h

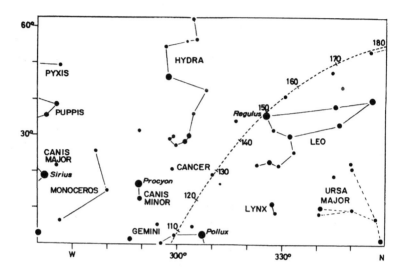

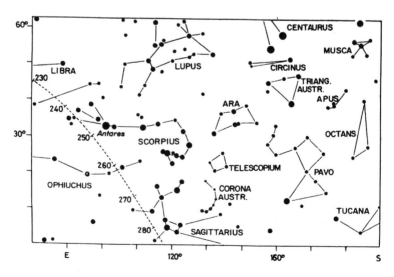

February 6 at 3ʰ	February 21 at 2ʰ
March 6 at 1ʰ	March 21 at midnight
April 6 at 23ʰ	April 21 at 22ʰ
May 6 at 21ʰ	May 21 at 20ʰ
June 6 at 19ʰ	June 21 at 18ʰ

4R

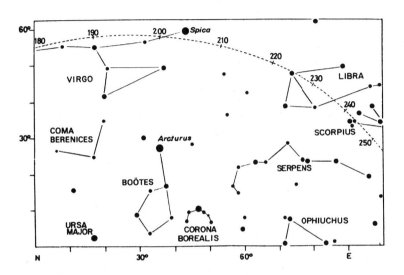

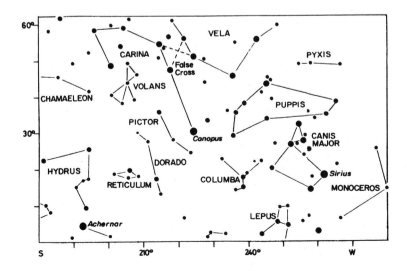

5L

March 6 at 3ʰ	March 21 at 2ʰ
April 6 at 1ʰ	April 21 at midnight
May 6 at 23ʰ	May 21 at 22ʰ
June 6 at 21ʰ	June 21 at 20ʰ
July 6 at 19ʰ	July 21 at 18ʰ

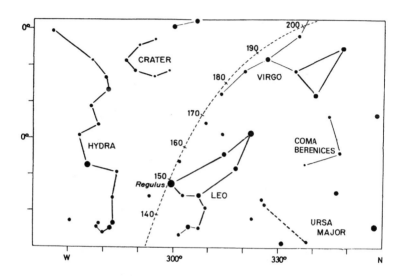

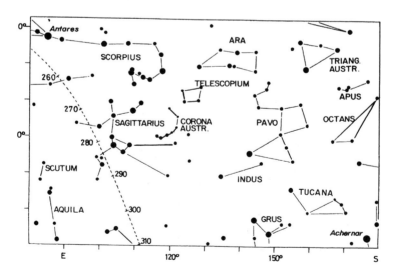

March 6 at 3h	March 21 at 2h
April 6 at 1h	April 21 at midnight
May 6 at 23h	May 21 at 22h
June 6 at 21h	June 21 at 20h
July 6 at 19h	July 21 at 18h

5R

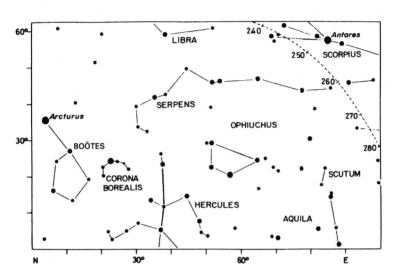

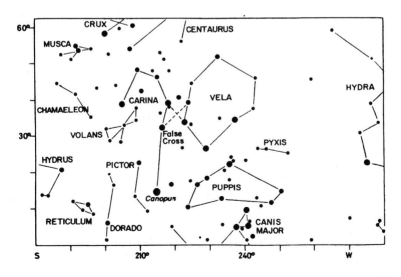

6L

March 6 at 5h	March 21 at 4h
April 6 at 3h	April 21 at 2h
May 6 at 1h	May 21 at midnight
June 6 at 23h	June 21 at 22h
July 6 at 21h	July 21 at 20h

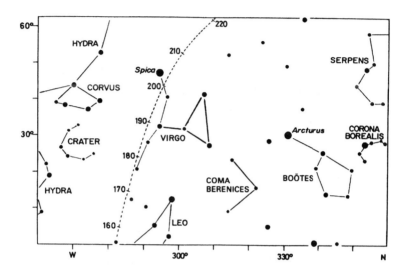

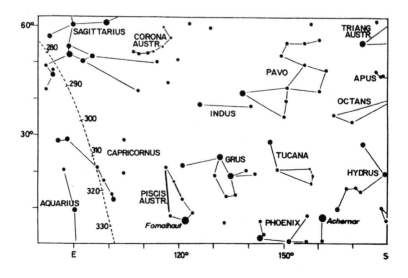

March 6 at	5ʰ	March 21 at	4ʰ
April 6 at	3ʰ	April 21 at	2ʰ
May 6 at	1ʰ	May 21 at midnight	
June 6 at	23ʰ	June 21 at	22ʰ
July 6 at	21ʰ	July 21 at	20ʰ

6R

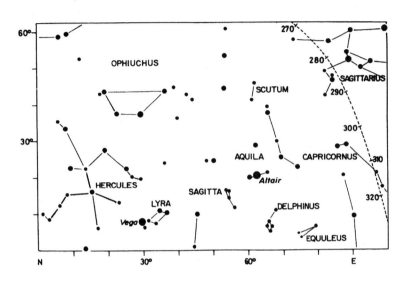

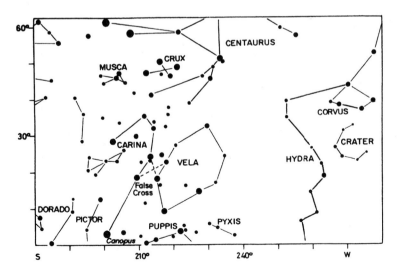

7L

April 6 at 5ʰ	April 21 at 4ʰ
May 6 at 3ʰ	May 21 at 2ʰ
June 6 at 1ʰ	June 21 at midnight
July 6 at 23ʰ	July 21 at 22ʰ
August 6 at 21ʰ	August 21 at 20ʰ

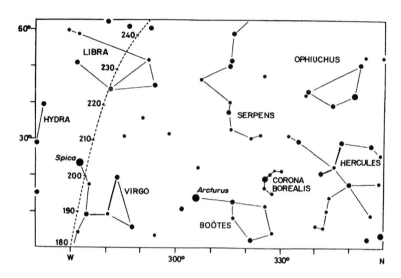

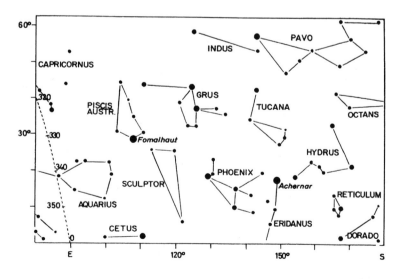

April 6 at 5h	April 21 at 4h
May 6 at 3h	May 21 at 2h
June 6 at 1h	June 21 at midnight
July 6 at 23h	July 21 at 22h
August 6 at 21h	August 21 at 20h

7R

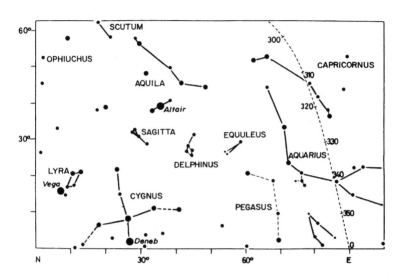

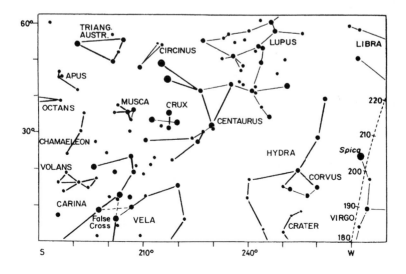

8L

May 6 at 5ʰ   May 21 at 4ʰ
June 6 at 3ʰ   June 21 at 2ʰ
July 6 at 1ʰ   July 21 at midnight
August 6 at 23ʰ   August 21 at 22ʰ
September 6 at 21ʰ   September 21 at 20ʰ

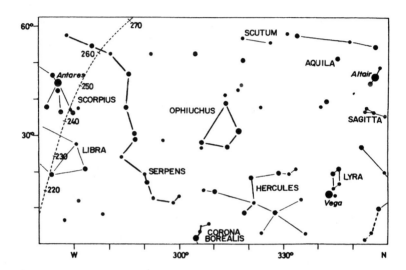

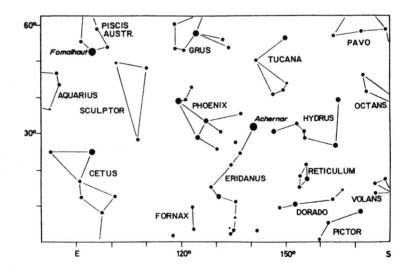

May 6 at   5ʰ   May 21 at   4ʰ
June 6 at   3ʰ   June 21 at   2ʰ
July 6 at   1ʰ   July 21 at midnight
August 6 at 23ʰ   August 21 at   22ʰ
September 6 at 21ʰ   September 21 at 20ʰ

8R

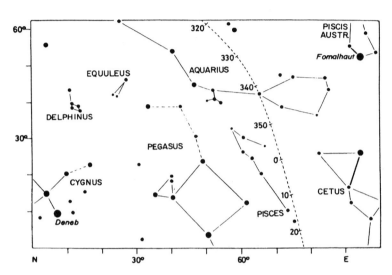

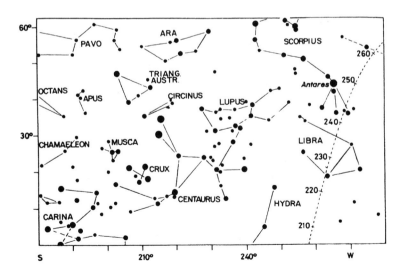

9L

June 6 at 5ʰ	June 21 at 4ʰ
July 6 at 3ʰ	July 21 at 2ʰ
August 6 at 1ʰ	August 21 at midnight
September 6 at 23ʰ	September 21 at 22ʰ
October 6 at 21ʰ	October 21 at 20ʰ

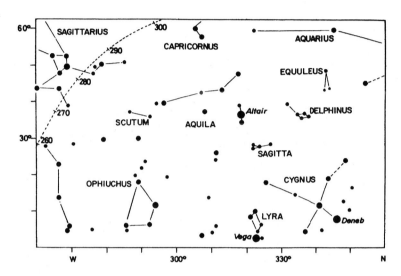

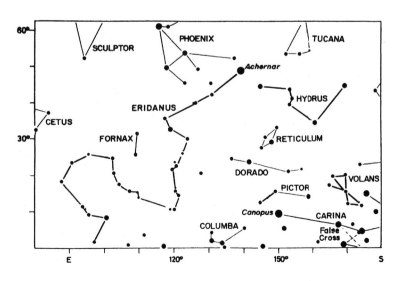

June 6 at 5ʰ	June 21 at 4ʰ
July 6 at 3ʰ	July 21 at 2ʰ
August 6 at 1ʰ	August 21 at midnight
September 6 at 23ʰ	September 21 at 22ʰ
October 6 at 21ʰ	October 21 at 20ʰ

9R

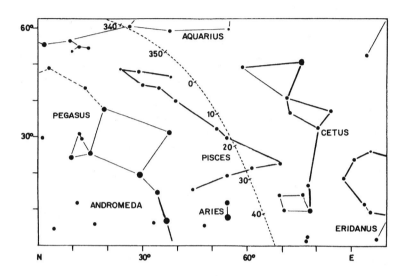

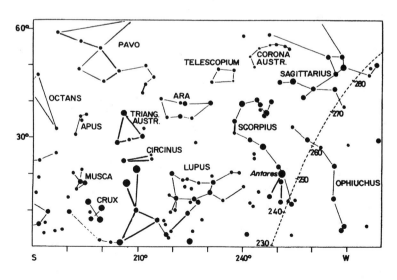

10L

July 6 at 5ʰ	July 21 at 4ʰ
August 6 at 3ʰ	August 21 at 2ʰ
September 6 at 1ʰ	September 21 at midnight
October 6 at 23ʰ	October 21 at 22ʰ
November 6 at 21ʰ	November 21 at 20ʰ

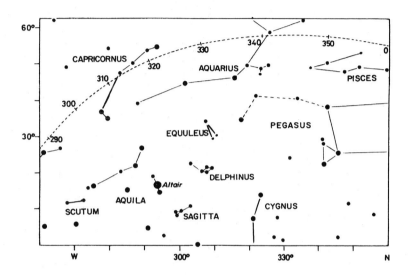

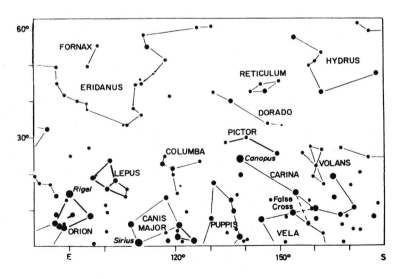

July 6 at	5h	July 21 at	4h
August 6 at	3h	August 21 at	2h
September 6 at	1h	September 21 at midnight	
October 6 at	23h	October 21 at	22h
November 6 at	21h	November 21 at	20h

10R

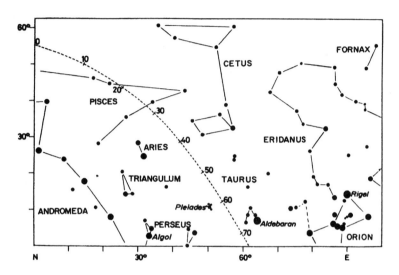

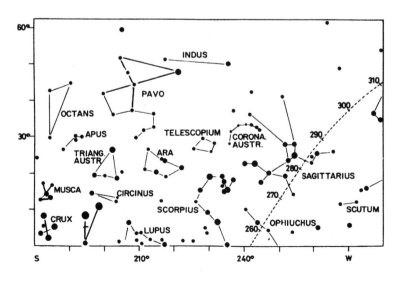

11L

August 6 at	5ʰ	August 21 at	4ʰ
September 6 at	3ʰ	September 21 at	2ʰ
October 6 at	1ʰ	October 21 at midnight	
November 6 at	23ʰ	November 21 at	22ʰ
December 6 at	21ʰ	December 21 at	20ʰ

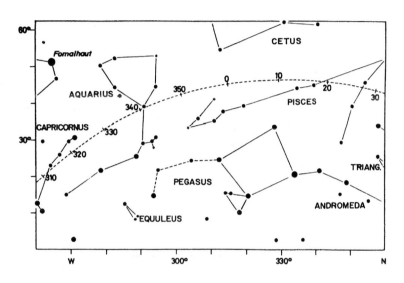

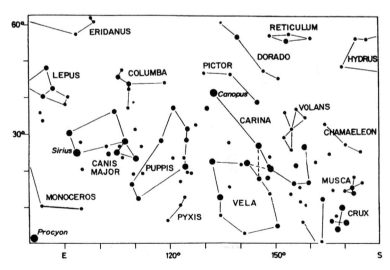

August 6 at 5ʰ	August 21 at	4ʰ
September 6 at 3ʰ	September 21 at	2ʰ
October 6 at 1ʰ	October 21 at midnight	
November 6 at 23ʰ	November 21 at	22ʰ
December 6 at 21ʰ	December 21 at	20ʰ

11R

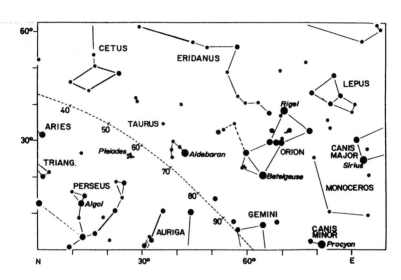

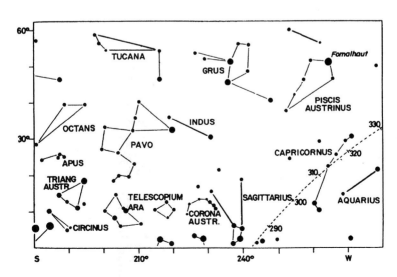

12L

September 6 at 5ʰ	September 21 at 4ʰ
October 6 at 3ʰ	October 21 at 2ʰ
November 6 at 1ʰ	November 21 at midnight
December 6 at 23ʰ	December 21 at 22ʰ
January 6 at 21ʰ	January 21 at 20ʰ

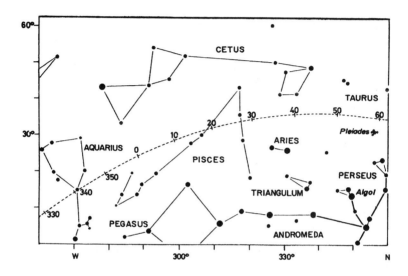

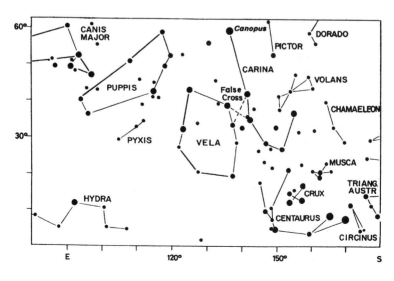

September 6 at 5ʰ   September 21 at   4ʰ

October 6 at 3ʰ   October 21 at   2ʰ

November 6 at 1ʰ   November 21 at midnight

December 6 at 23ʰ   December 21 at   22ʰ

January 6 at 21ʰ   January 21 at   20ʰ

12R

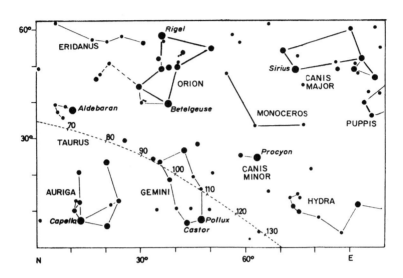

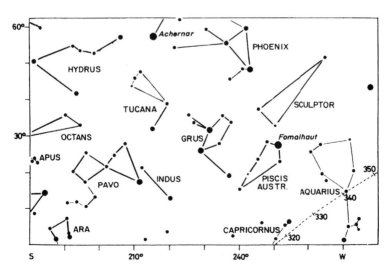

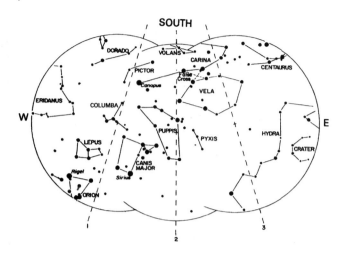

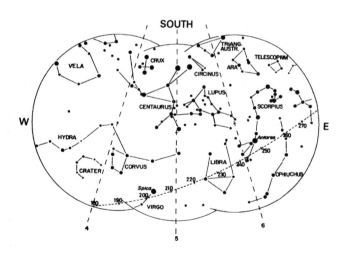

Southern Hemisphere Overhead Stars

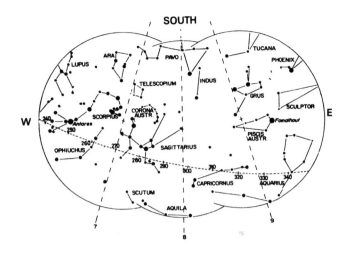

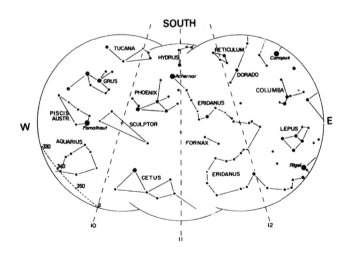

Southern Hemisphere Overhead Stars

The Planets and the Ecliptic

The paths of the planets about the Sun all lie close to the plane of the ecliptic, which is marked for us in the sky by the apparent path of the Sun among the stars, and is shown on the star charts by a broken line. The Moon and naked-eye planets will always be found close to this line, never departing from it by more than about 7°. Thus the planets are most favourably placed for observation when the ecliptic is well displayed, and this means that it should be as high in the sky as possible. This avoids the difficulty of finding a clear horizon, and also overcomes the problem of atmospheric absorption, which greatly reduces the light of the stars. Thus a star at an altitude of 10° suffers a loss of 60 per cent of its light, which corresponds to a whole magnitude; at an altitude of only 4°, the loss may amount to two magnitudes.

The position of the ecliptic in the sky is therefore of great importance, and since it is tilted at about 23½° to the Equator, it is only at certain times of the day or year that it is displayed to the best advantage. It will be realized that the Sun (and therefore the ecliptic) is at its highest in the sky at noon in midsummer, and at its lowest at noon in midwinter. Allowing for the daily motion of the sky, it follows that the ecliptic is highest at midnight in winter, at sunset in the spring, at noon in summer and at sunrise in the autumn. Hence these are the best times to see the planets. Thus, if Venus is an evening object in the western sky after sunset, it will be seen to best advantage if this occurs in the spring, when the ecliptic is high in the sky and slopes down steeply to the horizon. This means that the planet is not only higher in the sky, but will remain for a much longer period above the horizon. For similar reasons, a morning object will be seen at its best on autumn mornings before sunrise, when the ecliptic is high in the east. The outer planets, which can come to opposition (i.e. opposite the Sun), are best seen when opposition occurs in the winter months, when the ecliptic is high in the sky at midnight.

The seasons are reversed in the Southern Hemisphere, spring beginning at the September Equinox, when the Sun crosses the Equator on its way south, summer beginning at the December Solstice, when the

Sun is highest in the southern sky, and so on. Thus, the times when the ecliptic is highest in the sky, and therefore best placed for observing the planets, may be summarized as follows:

	Midnight	Sunrise	Noon	Sunset
Northern lats.	December	September	June	March
Southern lats.	June	March	December	September

In addition to the daily rotation of the celestial sphere from east to west, the planets have a motion of their own among the stars. The apparent movement is generally *direct*, i.e. to the east, in the direction of increasing longitude, but for a certain period (which depends on the distance of the planet) this apparent motion is reversed. With the outer planets this *retrograde* motion occurs about the time of opposition. Owing to the different inclination of the orbits of these planets, the actual effect is to cause the apparent path to form a loop, or sometimes an S-shaped curve. The same effect is present in the motion of the inferior planets, Mercury and Venus, but it is not so obvious, since it always occurs at the time of inferior conjunction.

The *inferior planets*, Mercury and Venus, move in smaller orbits than that of the Earth, and so are always seen near the Sun. They are most obvious at the times of greatest angular distance from the Sun (greatest elongation), which may reach 28° for Mercury, and 47° for Venus. They are seen as evening objects in the western sky after sunset (at eastern elongations) or as morning objects in the eastern sky before sunrise (at western elongations). The succession of phenomena, conjunctions and elongations, always follows the same order, but the intervals between them are not equal. Thus, if either planet is moving round the far side of its orbit its motion will be to the east, in the same direction in which the Sun appears to be moving. It therefore takes much longer for the planet to overtake the Sun – that is, to come to superior conjunction – than it does when moving round to inferior conjunction, between Sun and Earth. The intervals given in the following table are average values; they remain fairly constant in the case of Venus, which travels in an almost circular orbit. In the case of Mercury, however, conditions vary widely because of the great eccentricity and inclination of the planet's orbit.

			Mercury	**Venus**
Inferior Conjunction	to	Elongation West	22 days	72 days
Elongation West	to	Superior Conjunction	36 days	220 days
Superior Conjunction	to	Elongation East	36 days	220 days
Elongation East	to	Inferior Conjunction	22 days	72 days

The greatest brilliancy of Venus always occurs about 36 days before or after inferior conjunction. This will be about a month *after* greatest eastern elongation (as an evening object), or a month *before* greatest western elongation (as a morning object). No such rule can be given for Mercury, because its distance from the Earth and the Sun can vary over a wide range.

Mercury is not likely to be seen unless a clear horizon is available. It is seldom as much as 10° above the horizon in the twilight sky in northern temperate latitudes, but this figure is often exceeded in the Southern Hemisphere. This favourable condition arises because the maximum elongation of 28° can occur only when the planet is at aphelion (farthest from the Sun), and it then lies well south of the Equator. Northern observers must be content with smaller elongations, which may be as little as 18° at perihelion. In general, it may be said that the most favourable times for seeing Mercury as an evening object will be in spring, some days before greatest eastern elongation; in autumn, it may be seen as a morning object some days after greatest western elongation.

Venus is the brightest of the planets and may be seen on occasions in broad daylight. Like Mercury, it is alternately a morning and an evening object, and it will be highest in the sky when it is a morning object in autumn, or an evening object in spring. Venus is to be seen at its best as an evening object in northern latitudes when eastern elongation occurs in June. The planet is then well north of the Sun in the preceding spring months, and is a brilliant object in the evening sky over a long period. In the Southern Hemisphere a November elongation is best. For similar reasons, Venus gives a prolonged display as a morning object in the months following western elongation in October (in northern latitudes) or in June (in the Southern Hemisphere).

The *superior planets*, which travel in orbits larger than that of the Earth, differ from Mercury and Venus in that they can be seen opposite the Sun in the sky. The superior planets are morning objects after conjunction with the Sun, rising earlier each day until they come to opposition. They will then be nearest to the Earth (and therefore at their brightest), and will be on the meridian at midnight, due south in northern latitudes, but due north in the Southern Hemisphere. After opposition they are evening objects, setting earlier each evening until they set in the west with the Sun at the next conjunction. The difference in brightness from one opposition to another is most noticeable in the case of Mars, whose distance from Earth can vary considerably and rapidly. The other superior planets are at such great distances that there is very little change in brightness from one opposition to the next. The effect of altitude is, however, of some importance, for at a December opposition in northern latitudes the planets will be among the stars of Taurus or Gemini, and can then be at an altitude of more than 60° in southern England. At a summer opposition, when the planet is in Sagittarius, it may only rise to about 15° above the southern horizon, and so makes a less impressive appearance. In the Southern Hemisphere the reverse conditions apply, a June opposition being the best, with the planet in Sagittarius at an altitude which can reach 80° above the northern horizon for observers in South Africa.

Mars, whose orbit is appreciably eccentric, comes nearest to the Earth at oppositions at the end of August. It may then be brighter even than Jupiter, but rather low in the sky in Aquarius for northern observers, though very well placed for those in southern latitudes. These favourable oppositions occur every fifteen or seventeen years (1988, 2003, 2018), but in the Northern Hemisphere the planet is probably better seen at oppositions in the autumn or winter months, when it is higher in the sky. Oppositions of Mars occur at an average interval of 780 days, and during this time the planet makes a complete circuit of the sky.

Jupiter is always a bright planet, and comes to opposition a month later each year, having moved, roughly speaking, from one Zodiacal constellation to the next.

Saturn moves much more slowly than Jupiter, and may remain in the same constellation for several years. The brightness of Saturn depends on the aspects of its rings, as well as on the distance from Earth and Sun. The Earth passed through the plane of Saturn's rings in 1995 and 1996, when they appeared edge-on; we shall next see them at maximum opening, and Saturn at its brightest, around 2002. The rings will next appear edge-on in 2009.

Uranus, Neptune and *Pluto* are hardly likely to attract the attention of observers without adequate instruments.

Phases of the Moon, 2000

New Moon				**First Quarter**				**Full Moon**				**Last Quarter**		
	d	h	m		d	h	m		d	h	m		d	h	m
Jan.	6	18	14	Jan.	14	13	34	Jan.	21	04	40	Jan.	28	07	57
Feb.	5	13	03	Feb.	12	23	21	Feb.	19	16	27	Feb.	27	03	53
Mar.	6	05	17	Mar.	13	06	59	Mar.	20	04	44	Mar.	28	00	21
Apr.	4	18	12	Apr.	11	13	30	Apr.	18	17	41	Apr.	26	19	30
May	4	04	12	May	10	20	00	May	18	07	34	May	26	11	55
June	2	12	14	June	9	03	29	June	16	22	27	June	25	01	00
July	1	19	20	July	8	12	53	July	16	13	55	July	24	11	02
July	31	02	25	Aug.	7	01	02	Aug.	15	05	13	Aug.	22	18	51
Aug.	29	10	19	Sept.	5	16	27	Sept.	13	19	37	Sept.	21	01	28
Sept.	27	19	53	Oct.	5	10	59	Oct.	13	08	53	Oct.	20	07	59
Oct.	27	07	58	Nov.	4	07	27	Nov.	11	21	15	Nov.	18	15	24
Nov.	25	23	11	Dec.	4	03	55	Dec.	11	09	03	Dec.	18	00	41
Dec.	25	17	22												

All times are GMT

Longitudes of the Sun, Moon and planets in 2000

		Sun	Moon	Venus	Mars	Jupiter	Saturn
		°	°	°	°	°	°
January	6	285	277	247	331	25	40
	21	300	118	265	343	27	40
February	6	316	322	285	355	29	41
	21	332	169	303	7	31	42
March	6	346	343	321	17	34	43
	21	1	191	339	28	37	44
April	6	16	33	359	40	40	46
	21	31	237	18	51	44	48
May	6	46	71	36	62	47	50
	21	60	270	54	72	51	52
June	6	76	124	74	83	55	54
	21	90	314	93	93	58	56
July	6	104	162	111	103	61	57
	21	119	347	129	113	64	59
August	6	134	212	149	123	67	60
	21	148	36	168	133	69	61
September	6	164	257	187	143	70	61
	21	178	88	206	153	71	61
October	6	193	289	224	162	71	60
	21	208	127	242	171	70	60
November	6	224	332	261	181	69	59
	21	239	179	279	190	67	57
December	6	254	5	297	199	65	56
	21	269	216	315	208	63	55

Longitude of *Uranus* 318°   *Moon*: Longitude of ascending node
           Neptune 305°   Jan. 1: 125°   Dec. 31: 106°

Mercury moves so quickly among the stars that it is not possible to indicate its position on the star charts at convenient intervals. The monthly notes must be consulted for the best times at which the planet may be seen.

The positions of the other planets are given in the table on p. 74. This gives the apparent longitudes on dates which correspond to those of the star charts, and the position of the planet may at once be found near the ecliptic at the given longitude.

EXAMPLE

In the Northern Hemisphere two planets are seen in the eastern morning sky in early August. Identify them.

The Northern Star Chart 10L shows the eastern sky at August 6^d 3^h and shows longitudes 10° to 80°. Reference to the table on p. 74 gives the longitude of Jupiter as 67° and that of Saturn as 60°. Thus these planets are to be found in the eastern sky, and the brighter one is Jupiter.

The positions of the Sun and Moon can be plotted on the star maps in the same manner as for the planets. The average daily motion of the Sun is 1°, and of the Moon 13°. For the Moon an indication of its position relative to the ecliptic may be obtained from a consideration of its longitude relative to that of the ascending node. The latter changes only slowly during the year, as will be seen from the values given on p. 74. Let us denote by d the difference in longitude between the Moon and its ascending node. Then if $d = 0°$, 180° or 360° the Moon is on the ecliptic. If $d = 90°$ the Moon is 5° north of the ecliptic, and if $d = 270°$ the Moon is 5° south of the ecliptic.

On April 6 the Moon's longitude is given as 33°, and the longitude of the node is found by interpolation to be about 120°. Thus $d = 273°$, and the Moon is about 5° south of the ecliptic. Its position may be plotted on Northern Star Charts 1R, 2L, 8R, 9L, 10L, 11L and 12R, and on Southern Star Charts 1L, 9R, 10R, 11R and 12L.

Events in 2000

ECLIPSES

There will be six eclipses, four of the Sun and two of the Moon.

January 21:	total eclipse of the Moon – Asia, Africa, Europe, the Americas.
February 5:	partial eclipse of the Sun – Antarctica.
July 1:	partial eclipse of the Sun – South America.
July 16:	total eclipse of the Moon – the Americas, Australasia, Asia, Africa.
July 31:	partial eclipse of the Sun – Asia, North America, northern Europe.
December 25:	partial eclipse of the Sun – North America.

THE PLANETS

Mercury may be seen more easily from northern latitudes in the evenings about the time of greatest eastern elongation (February 15), and in the mornings around greatest western elongation (November 15). In the Southern Hemisphere the corresponding most favourable dates are around March 28 (mornings) and October 6 (evenings).

Venus is visible in the mornings until April, and in the evenings from August until the end of the year.

Mars does not come to opposition in 2000.

Jupiter is at opposition on November 28.

Saturn is at opposition on November 19.

Uranus is at opposition on August 11.

Neptune is at opposition on July 27.

Pluto is at opposition on June 1.

Monthly Notes 2000

January

EARTH is at perihelion (nearest to the Sun) on January 3 at a distance of 147 million kilometres (91.4 million miles).

MERCURY passes through superior conjunction on January 16 and therefore remains unsuitably placed for observation throughout the month.

VENUS, magnitude −4.0, is a brilliant morning object, completely dominating the south-eastern sky before dawn, though for observers in the latitudes of the British Isles the duration of its period of visibility shortens noticeably during the month.

MARS is visible in the south-western sky in the evenings. Its magnitude is +1.8, and its slightly reddish appearance is an aid to its identification. The path of Mars among the stars for the first three months of the year is shown in Figure 1.

JUPITER is an evening object, visible in the south-western quadrant of the sky shortly after sunset. Jupiter, magnitude −2.4, is in the constellation Pisces; its path among the stars is shown in Figure 7, accompanying the notes for July.

SATURN, magnitude +0.2, is also visible in the south-western quadrant of the sky, roughly 15° east of Jupiter. Saturn reaches its second stationary point in the constellation of Aries on January 12. Its path among the stars is shown in Figure 7, accompanying the notes for July.

Lunar occultations of planets in 2000. Planets, like stars, may be occulted by the Moon, but there is a basic difference in aspect. A star, virtually a point source, snaps out abruptly as the Moon's limb sweeps over it; a planet, which shows a disk, takes time to vanish. Neptune will

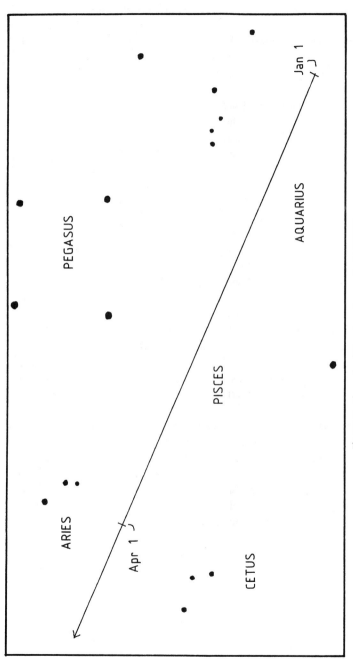

Figure 1. The path of Mars from January to April 2000

be occulted on January 8, but the elongation from the Sun is only 16°, so that the phenomenon will not be too easy to observe. Occultations in 2000, at elongations of more than 15° from the Sun, are as follows:

Date	GMT	Planet	Area of visibility
Jan. 8	6	Neptune	Australia, Indian Ocean
Jan. 9	3	Uranus	Australia, Indian Ocean, New Zealand
Mar. 3	0	Neptune	S. Australia, Indian Ocean, New Zealand
Mar. 4	1	Venus	S. Indian Ocean, Tasmania, New Zealand
Mar. 4	1	Uranus	S. Indian Ocean, New Zealand
Mar. 30	10	Neptune	S. South America, S. Africa, S. Atlantic
Mar. 31	12	Uranus	S. Atlantic
Apr. 26	19	Neptune	S. Pacific
July 29	17	Mercury	N. Pacific, Canada, Iceland, N and W Europe
Aug. 13	17	Neptune	Antarctica
Aug. 28	3	Mars	N and NE Europe, Pacific, Alaska

It is interesting to note that when Venus reaches superior conjunction, on June 11 this year, it will actually be occulted by the Sun, though the phenomenon will of course be completely unobservable.

In 2000, Aldebaran (Alpha Tauri) will be occulted on January 17 (19h) and again on February 4 (3h), though the latter event will be seen only from parts of northern Asia.

Lunar eclipse. The lunar eclipse of January 21 should be well observed. How 'dark' it will be remains to be seen. The Danjon scale ranges from 0 (very dark, Moon almost invisible) to 4 (very bright, coppery or orange-red, with a bluish cast and varied hues). Everything depends upon conditions in the Earth's upper atmosphere, through which all the light from the eclipsed Moon has to pass. Astrophotographers will certainly want to make the most of the eclipse this month.

February

New Moon: February 5   *Full Moon*: February 19

MERCURY is not suitably placed for observers in southern temperate latitudes, but is visible from tropical and northern temperate latitudes after the first week of the month. For observers in the latitudes of the British Isles this will be the most favourable evening apparition of the year. Figure 2 shows, for observers in latitude 52°N, the changes in the azimuth (the true bearing from north through east, south and west) and altitude of Mercury on successive evenings when the Sun is 6° below the horizon. This condition is known as the end of evening civil twilight and in this latitude and at this time of year occurs about 35 minutes after sunset. The changes in the brightness of the planet are

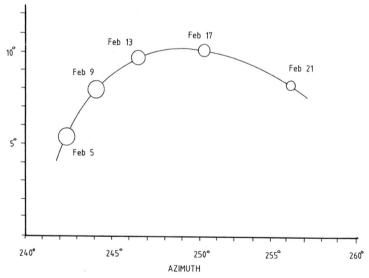

Figure 2. Evening apparition of Mercury, from latitude 52°N.

indicated by the relative sizes of the circles marking Mercury's position at five-day intervals. Mercury is at its brightest before it reaches greatest eastern elongation (18°), on February 15.

VENUS continues to be visible as a brilliant object in the morning skies; magnitude –4.0. As the planet is well south of the equator, observers in the latitudes of the British Isles will only see it low above the south-eastern horizon for a very short period of time, just before sunrise.

MARS continues to be visible as an evening object in the south-western sky, magnitude +1.2. Its rapid eastward motion means that by the end of the month it is less than 20° west of Jupiter.

JUPITER continues to be visible as a prominent object in the south-western sky in the early part of the evening, at magnitude –2.2. During February Jupiter moves from Pisces into Aries.

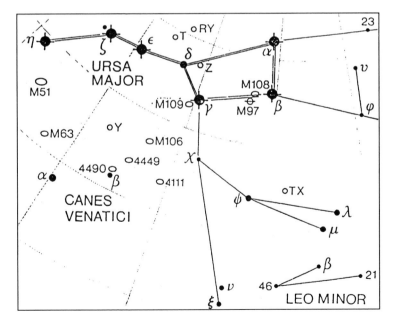

Figure 3. The constellation Leo Minor, below the stars of Ursa Major.

SATURN is still visible in the south-western quadrant of the sky in the evenings. Its magnitude is +0.3.

The little lion. Leo Minor, the Little Lion, lies close to Ursa Major. It was added to the sky by Hevelius, in 1690, but with no apparent reason, since it hardly merits a separate identity. The only star above the fourth magnitude is 46, or Praecipua (mag. 3.8), and there are no objects of particular note. As shown in Figure 3, the three main stars, 46 (3.8), Beta (4.2) and 21 (4.5), form an obscure triangle close to Mu Ursae Majoris (Figure 3). The Mira variable R Leonis Minoris (RA 9 h 45.6 m, dec. +34° 34′) can reach magnitude 6.3 at maximum.

Curiously, the only star in the constellation to have been given a Greek letter is Beta. There is no Alpha Leonis Minoris!

Charles Piazzi Smyth was born in Naples on January 13, 1819; his father was the celebrated astronomer Admiral W. H. Smyth (author of the *Cycle of Celestial Objects*). Piazzi Smyth was assistant Astronomer at the Cape (1835–44), and then became Astronomer Royal for Scotland. He carried out much valuable work, and was among the first to realize the advantages of setting up observatories at high altitude, though unfortunately he became fascinated by the pseudo-science of Pyramidology and largely ruined his reputation. He died on February 21, 1900.

March

New Moon: March 6   *Full Moon*: March 20

Equinox: March 20

Summer Time in Great Britain and Northern Ireland commences on March 26.

MERCURY is not visible from the latitudes of the British Isles in March, but conditions improve further south and for observers in southern latitudes this will be the most favourable morning apparition of the year. Figure 4 shows, for observers in latitude 35°S, the changes in the azimuth (the true bearing from north, through east, south and west) and altitude of Mercury on successive evenings when the Sun is 6° below the horizon. This position of the Sun marks the beginning of morning civil twilight and at this latitude and time of year occurs about 35 minutes before sunrise. The changes in the brightness of the planet are indicated by the relative sizes of the circles, which mark Mercury's position at five-day intervals. Mercury is at its brightest after it reaches greatest western elongation (28°), on March 28. Observers should note the proximity of Mercury to Venus during the second half of the month; the minimum separation (2°) occurs on March 15.

VENUS, magnitude –3.9, continues to be visible as a brilliant morning object in the south-eastern sky. Observers in northern temperate latitudes will find the planet coming to the end of its period of visibility; in particular, those in the British Isles will have lost it in the glare of the rising Sun after the first ten days of the month.

MARS, magnitude +1.4, continues to be visible in the south-western sky in the early evenings. Mars is moving eastwards in the constellation of Pisces. Observers in the Southern Hemisphere will find that Mars is getting more difficult to locate in the gathering twilight, and they are unlikely to be able to detect it after the first three weeks of the month.

JUPITER continues to be visible for a short while in the south-western sky after sunset, at magnitude −2.1.

SATURN, magnitude +0.3, is still an evening object in the western sky, but is moving closer to the Sun and visible only for a short while after sunset. By the end of the month Saturn is only about 6° east of Jupiter, which, although nearer to the Sun, may be used as a guide to locating Saturn, which is over 2 magnitudes fainter.

The zodiacal constellations. Cancer, the Crab, is now well placed for observation. It occupies the area bounded by the large triangle made up by Regulus in Leo, Pollux in Gemini and Procyon in Canis Minor

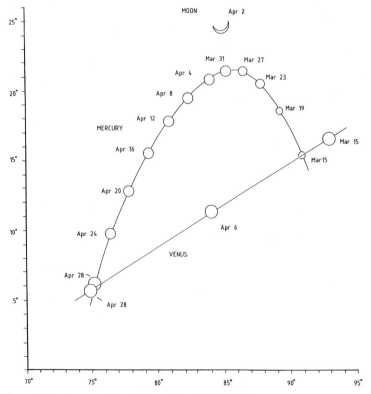

Figure 4. Morning apparition of Mercury, from latitude 35°S.

(Figure 5), but it is decidedly obscure, and contains only two stars above magnitude 4, Beta or Altarf (mag. 3.5) and Delta or Asellus Australis (3.9). It is, however, redeemed by the presence of two splendid open clusters: Praesepe (M.44), which is an easy naked-eye object, and M.67, which is on the fringe of naked-eye visibility. In shape, Cancer rather resembles a dim and ghostly Orion.

It is notable that the zodiacal constellations vary greatly in both area and star density (i.e. the number of stars above fifth magnitude per square degree). The areas, in square degrees, are:

1. Virgo, 1294	5. Sagittarius, 867	9. Cancer, 506
2. Aquarius, 980	6. Taurus, 797	10. Scorpius, 497
3. Leo, 947	7. Libra, 538	11. Aries, 441
4. Pisces, 889	8. Gemini, 514	12. Capricornus, 414

In star density, however, Cancer comes at the foot of the list:

1. Scorpius, 7.6	5. Sagittarius, 3.8	9. Aries, 2.5
2. Taurus, 5.5	6. Aquarius, 3.2	10. Libra, 2.4
3. Gemini, 4.5	7. Leo, 2.8	11. Virgo, 2.0
4. Capricornus, 3.9	8. Pisces, 2.7	12. Cancer, 1.2

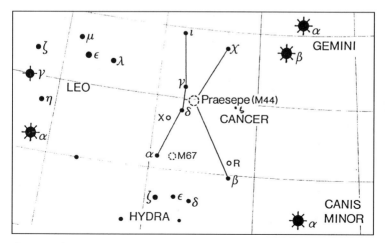

Figure 5. The constellation Cancer.

The very red semi-regular variable X Cancri (RA 8h 55.4 m, dec. +17° 14′) is a fine binocular object. Its magnitude range is from 5.6 to 7.5, and its spectral type is M. There is a very rough period of about 195 days.

April

New Moon: April 4   *Full Moon*: April 18

MERCURY is still unsuitably placed for observation from the latitudes of the British Isles. However, for observers further south it remains visible in the mornings for almost the whole of April. Observers should note the proximity of Mercury to Venus during the month; the minimum separation (0°.3) occurs on April 28.

VENUS, magnitude –3.9, is already too close to the Sun for observation from the British Isles. Even further south it is nearing the end of its period of visibility, though those in southern latitudes will still be able to see it right through the month, low down above the eastern horizon at sunrise.

MARS is no longer visible to observers in southern latitudes. Further north it continues to be visible for a short while, low above the western horizon in the early evenings, magnitude +1.5. After the first three weeks of the month it will be lost in the lengthening evening twilight.

JUPITER, magnitude –2.0, is an evening object, visible for a short while low in the western sky soon after sunset, for the first part of the month. Jupiter passes within 1° of Mars on April 5/6, which is a useful guide to locating the fainter planet. Saturn continues to be in proximity to Jupiter, the separation early in the month being about 6°.

SATURN, magnitude +0.3, is getting lower and lower in the western sky and is unlikely to be seen with the naked eye after the first week of the month. However, it may be possible to detect it with binoculars for some days afterwards as it remains 4° or 5° above and to the left of Jupiter for some time.

Jan Hendrik Oort, unquestionably one of the greatest astronomers of the twentieth century, was born at Franeker, in Holland, on April 23, 1900; his father was a doctor. He graduated from the University of Groningen, under Jacobus Kapteyn, and became deeply interested in the structure of the Galaxy. After a brief period at Yale, in the United States, he came home to join the Leiden Observatory staff. He became Director of the Observatory in 1945, and retained this post until retiring in 1970.

It was mainly Oort's work which showed that the Sun does not lie near the centre of the Galaxy (as Kapteyn had believed), but well out towards the edge; the distance from the galactic centre is now thought to be rather less than 30,000 light-years, and the Sun's revolution period round the centre is 225,000,000 years (one 'cosmic year'). Oort also paid great attention to radio astronomy, and worked with Hendrik van de Hulst in detecting the all-important 21-cm radio emission of neutral hydrogen.

Comets were also very much in his mind. There had been a theory, championed by R. A. Lyttleton and others, that a comet was in effect a 'flying gravel bank'. Oort proposed that a more likely explanation was that a comet was a 'dirty ice-ball', so that the coma and tail (or tails) developed as the comet neared perihelion and was heated. This is now known to be correct. Oort suggested that large comets come from a huge cloud of icy objects, lying far from the Sun at a distance of at least one light-year; if a comet is perturbed for any reason it will leave the cloud and swing inwards, so that we can see it. Though the comets in this cloud cannot be observed at such a distance, it is now generally agreed that the 'Oort Cloud' really exists, though short-period comets are more likely to come from a much closer cloud, named after another Dutch astronomer, Gerard Kuiper.

Oort's work did not end with his official retirement. He continued to be active, and to make major contributions to astronomical science, right up to the time of his death in 1992.

Cecilia Helena Payne-Gaposchkin. May 10 marks the anniversary of the birth of Cecilia Payne-Gaposchkin, one of America's most cele-brated woman astronomers, who was born in 1900. She was British by birth, but spent most of her career in the United States, and married the well-known astronomer Sergei Gaposchkin. She studied under Harlow Shapley, and made major contributions to theories of stellar structure and evolution. In 1938 she was made Phillips Astronomer at Harvard, and in 1956 was offered the Chair of Astronomy there – the first woman to receive such an appointment at Harvard. She was the author of many books, both technical and popular, and became also a leading authority on the subject of variable stars. She died on December 7, 1979.

May

New Moon: May 4   *Full Moon*: May 18

MERCURY passes through superior conjunction on May 9, and therefore is unsuitably placed for most of the month. However, during the last ten days of May observers in northern temperate latitudes will see it as an evening object low above the north-west horizon, at the end of evening civil twilight, though the lengthening twilight at the latitudes of the British Isles will make observation difficult. For the last week of May observers in southern latitudes should also see the planet, low above the north-west horizon in the evenings. During this period its magnitude fades from −0.8 to −0.1.

VENUS is no longer visible from northern temperate latitudes, but can still be seen for the first three weeks of the month from the tropics and southern latitudes, low above the eastern horizon for a short while before sunrise. Its magnitude is −3.9.

MARS is too close to the Sun for observation.

JUPITER passes through conjunction on May 8 and is therefore unsuitably placed for observation throughout the month for observers in northern temperate latitudes. Further south it is possible for the planet to be observed during the last week of the month as it emerges from the morning twilight, low above the east-north-east horizon, about half an hour before sunrise. Jupiter's magnitude is −2.0. In April Jupiter was to the west of Saturn, but when the two planets emerge from the morning twilight next month Jupiter will have passed Saturn and will be further east.

SATURN passes through conjunction on May 10 and thus is unsuitably placed for observation throughout the month by observers in northern temperate latitudes. Further south it may be possible, under very good conditions, to locate Saturn low above the east-north-east horizon during morning twilight on the last few days of the month.

Jean Gambart and comets. The French astromer Jean Félix Adolphe Gambart was born at Cette Hérault in May 1800. In 1819 he became assistant at the Marseilles Observatory, and in 1822 was appointed Director. He specialized in comet-hunting, and made a total of 16 discoveries, one of which was of particular note – and led to a minor controversy.

The comet in question was first detected on February 27, 1826, by the Austrian astronomer Wilhelm von Biela, who was by profession an officer in the Austrian Army but was also a skilled observer. Gambart independently discovered the comet ten days later, from Marseilles. It was found to be of short period, and to be identical with comets previously seen in 1772 and in 1805; on the first occasion it had been discovered by Jacques Montaigne, from Limoges, and on the second by Jean-Louis Pons. When von Biela first saw it in 1826 the magnitude was 6.5, but it brightened to the fringe of naked-eye visibility. Calculations made independently by Biela, Gambart and Thomas Clausen gave the period as 6.5 years. On the basis of these calculations, the comet was successfully recovered on September 24, 1832, by John Herschel.

The controversy arose because the French claimed – wrongly – that only Gambart had worked out the comet's orbit with real accuracy. In his book *The World of Comets*, published in 1877, Amedée Guillemin wrote that 'The comet that astronomers of both hemispheres persist in calling the comet of Biela, ought, therefore, to bear the name of Gambart. It is not the only case of injustice in the history of astronomy.' But in fact Biela's published orbit appeared in the same issue of the periodical *Astronomische Nachrichten*, in March 1826, so that the two sets of elements were made simultaneously, and Biela was in addition the comet's discoverer. The arguments have long since been forgotten – and moreover the comet itself no longer exists. It was missed at the return in 1839, because it was badly placed in the sky, but when it next appeared it split in two. The twins made their final appearance in 1852, and thereafter vanished, though the remnants were seen in the form of meteors; there were bright displays in 1872 and 1885. However, the shower is no longer observable, so that the comet and its débris have passed into history. Jean Gambart died in August 1836.

Centaurus. Almost all of the brilliant constellation Centaurus is too far south to be seen from Britain. However, during May evenings a few of its stars can be glimpsed, very low over the horizon. The northernmost of the bright stars in Centaurus is Theta Centauri (Haratan), magnitude 2.1; its declination is −36° 22′ 12″. Haratan is an orange K-type star, 17 times as luminous as the Sun; at 46 light-years it is one of our nearer stellar neighbours. To have any hope of glimpsing it, however, an observer must travel to a latitude south of 53°N.

June

New Moon: June 2   *Full Moon*: June 16

Solstice: June 21

MERCURY continues to be visible low above the north-west horizon at the end of evening civil twilight for the first half of June, though observers in the latitudes of the British Isles will find it a difficult object to locate in the long evening twilight. During this period of visibility its magnitude fades from 0.0 to +1.0.

VENUS passes through superior conjunction on June 11 and is therefore too close to the Sun for observation. Indeed, for a short while on that date no Earth-based instrument could detect it since it is actually occulted by the Sun.

MARS remains too close to the Sun for observation.

JUPITER, already visible to observers in the Southern Hemisphere, can be seen low above the eastern horizon before sunrise by observers further north, after the middle of the month. Its magnitude is –2.1. Both Jupiter and Saturn are moving eastwards in the western part of Taurus, Jupiter being about 3° further east. It will continue to be a useful guide to locating Saturn, which is over 2 magnitudes fainter.

SATURN, magnitude +0.3, is visible low above the east-north-east horizon in the early mornings before twilight inhibits observation, though not to observers in the latitudes of the British Isles, who are unlikely to see it before the last few days of the month.

The status of Pluto. In 1930 Clyde Tombaugh, at the Lowell Observatory in Arizona, discovered Pluto. It was not due to sheer chance: Tombaugh had been carrying out a systematic search, using a telescope obtained specially for the purpose.

Uranus had been discovered in 1781 by William Herschel, who was undertaking a 'review of the heavens'. Irregularities in its motion led to the realization that it was being perturbed by a more distant planet, and in 1846 Johann Galle and Heinrich d'Arrest, from Berlin, discovered Neptune in almost exactly the position which had been predicted mathematically. However, there were still small discrepancies. Percival Lowell made fresh calculations, and gave a position for yet another planet. Pluto duly turned up very close to the predicted place (Figure 6).

Yet clearly there were problems, because Pluto proved to be very small and lightweight; its diameter is a mere 2302 km (1430 miles) – less than that of our Moon – and its mass is so low that it could not possibly have any measurable effects upon the movements of giants such as Uranus and Neptune. Either Lowell's reasonably correct prediction was sheer luck, or else the real 'Planet X' awaits discovery.

Meanwhile, there have been discussions about the status of Pluto itself. Its orbit is much more eccentric than those of any of the other planets, and for part of its 248-year period it is actually closer to the Sun than Neptune can ever be; this was so between 1979 and 1999, and only in the early part of 1999 did Pluto pass beyond the path of Neptune.

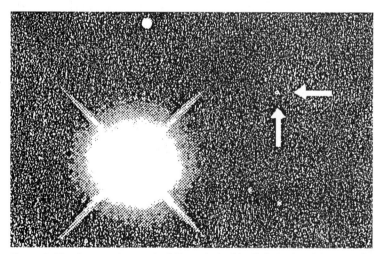

Figure 6. The discovery photograph of Pluto, obtained by Clyde Tombaugh in 1930. The bright, overexposed star is Delta Geminorum.

(There is no fear of collision, because Pluto's orbit is inclined at an angle of 17°, and at the present epoch no close approaches to Neptune are possible.)

Pluto is undoubtedly too small to be ranked as a bona-fide planet. On the other hand it is much too big to be classed as asteroidal, quite apart from the fact that it has a companion, Charon, which is itself larger than any known asteroid. In recent years various small bodies have been found orbiting the Sun in these remote parts of the Solar System, and are said to make up the Kuiper Belt, named after Gerard Kuiper, who first suggested its existence. Very probably Pluto will in the end have to be officially ranked as the senior member of the Kuiper Belt. Meanwhile, it is still, officially, classed as a planet.

Pluto's opposition magnitude is only 14, and in average telescopes it appears as a starlike point. The Hubble Space Telescope can show a certain amount of surface detail, but as yet our knowledge of the nature of the surface is very sketchy indeed, and we are not likely to learn a great deal more until a space probe passes by and sends back information from close range.

July

EARTH is at aphelion (farthest from the Sun) on July 4, at a distance of 152 million kilometres (94.5 million miles).

MERCURY passes through inferior conjunction on July 6, and is thus unsuitably placed for observation for most of the month. However, for the last week of the month it may be glimpsed as a difficult morning object, low above the east-north-east horizon at the beginning of morning civil twilight. During this period its magnitude brightens from +0.6 to −0.3.

VENUS, magnitude −3.9, is unsuitably placed for observation from the latitudes of the British Isles for most of July. However, during the last week of the month observers there may see it for a short while after sunset, low above the west-north-west horizon, but it will not be an easy object to locate in the bright twilight. Further south, from the tropics and southern latitudes, Venus becomes visible in the evenings after the first week of the month.

MARS passes through conjunction on the first day of the month and in the evenings thus too close to the Sun for observation.

JUPITER, magnitude −2.1, continues to be visible as a morning object in the south-eastern sky. It is moving eastwards between the Pleiades and the Hyades; its path among the stars is shown in Figure 7.

SATURN is visible in the eastern sky well before dawn, though the long duration of twilight means that it is still not an easy object to detect by observers in the latitudes of the British Isles. It is rising earlier and earlier each night, and by the end of the month it may be detected low above the eastern horizon shortly after midnight. Its magnitude is +0.3.

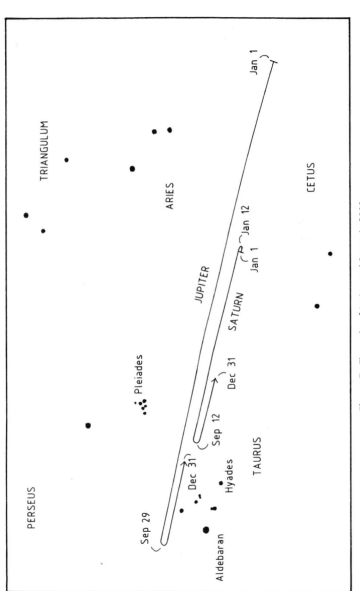

Figure 7. The paths of Jupiter and Saturn in 2000.

Saturn is in the constellation Taurus; its path among the stars is shown in Figure 7.

NEPTUNE is at opposition on July 27, in the constellation of Capricornus. It is not visible to the naked eye since its magnitude is +7.8. At opposition the planet is 4353 million kilometres (2705 million miles) from the Earth.

Harp in the sky. As seen from Britain, the brilliant blue star Vega is almost overhead during summer evenings – a position occupied during winter evenings by Capella. Vega is a star of spectral type A0, 25 times as luminous as the Sun and 52 light-years away; its diameter is about 3.7 million kilometres (2.3 million miles), more than twice that of the Sun. Its apparent magnitude is 0.03, so that it is surpassed by only four stars: Sirius, Canopus and Alpha Centauri in the Southern Hemisphere, and Arcturus in the Northern.

Lyra is a small constellation (Figure 8), covering less than 300 square degrees of the sky, but it contains a wealth of interesting objects. One is the eclipsing binary Beta Lyrae (Sheliak), which has a magnitude range of 3.3 to 4.3; the period is 12.9 days, and there are alternate deep and shallow mimima, so that the two components are not nearly so unequal as in Algol, for example. Gamma Lyrae, magnitude 3.2, is a convenient comparison star. Another variable in the same constellation is R Lyrae, a red semi-regular with a rough period of about 46 days and a magnitude range of 3.9 to 5.0. The fluctuations can easily be followed with

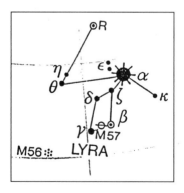

Figure 8. The constellation Lyra.

binoculars; Eta and Theta Lyrae (each mag. 4.4) are available for comparison.

Epsilon Lyrae, close to Vega, is a naked-eye double with almost equal components (mags 4.7 and 5.1). A small telescope will show that each component is again double, so that we have a quadruple star. Another star lies between the two pairs, but this is not connected with the system, and is much farther away. Zeta Lyrae is also double, wide enough to be 'split' with almost any telescope; the separation is almost 44 arcseconds. Yet another double is Delta Lyrae, with a separation of over 10 arcminutes. The brighter member (mag. 4.5) is of type M, and its obvious redness makes a good contrast with the companion (5.5), which is white. Binoculars will give good views of this pair.

Between Beta and Gamma lies the famous Ring Nebula, M.57 – the most celebrated of all planetary nebulae. It can be seen with a small telescope, and gives the impression of a tiny, luminous bicycle tyre; the central star is decidedly elusive. Binoculars will show the globular cluster M.56, which appears as a faint patch of light.

Lyra is indeed a rich constellation. Mythologically, it represents the harp or lyre which Apollo gave to the great musician Orpheus.

August

MERCURY continues to be visible as a morning object during the first few days of the month, very low above the east-north-east horizon at the beginning of morning civil twilight. During this period its magnitude increases from −0.4 to −1.1. For the rest of the month it is too close to the Sun for observation, superior conjunction occurring on August 22.

VENUS, magnitude −3.9, is moving slowly out from the Sun and is visible low above the western horizon in the evenings after sunset. It is still a difficult object for observers in the latitudes of the British Isles, who will be able to see it only for a very short while after sunset, extremely low above the western horizon.

MARS is unsuitably placed for observation by those in the Southern Hemisphere, but further north it gradually becomes visible as a difficult morning object towards the end of the month, when it may be seen low above the east-north-eastern horizon, about an hour before sunrise. Its magnitude is +1.8.

JUPITER is still a splendid morning object in the south-eastern sky, magnitude −2.3. For observers in the latitudes of the British Isles, it starts to become visible before midnight early in the month.

SATURN, magnitude +0.2, continues to be visible as a morning object, though now rising before midnight and visible in the south-eastern sky for the rest of the night.

URANUS is at opposition on August 11. It is barely visible to the naked eye as its magnitude is +5.7, but it is readily located with modest optical aid. At opposition the planet is 2832 million kilometres from the Earth. Uranus is in the constellation Capricornus.

Otto Rosenberger and Halley's Comet. The first predicted return of Halley's Comet was that of 1759. The orbit had been worked out by Edmond Halley, who had predicted a return for 1758; the comet was discovered on Christmas Night of that year by Johann Palitzsch, and perihelion took place in 1759.

The return of 1835 was accurately predicted by several astronomers. Among them was Otto August Rosenberger, a Latvian of German descent, who was born at Tukkim on August 10, 1800. He became an assistant astronomer at Königsberg Observatory, and later Professor of Astronomy at Halle. His main work was associated with cometary orbits; he died on January 23, 1890. Since then the comet has been back in 1910 and 1986.

Comets are associated with meteor streams, and Halley's is no exception – it is the parent of two annual showers. Known cometary associations include:

Meteor shower	Maximum	Comet
Lyrids	Apr. 21	Thatcher (1861)
Eta Aquarids	May 5	Halley
Perseids	Aug. 12	Swift–Tuttle
Orionids	Oct. 26	Halley
Draconids	Oct. 21	Giacobini–Zinner
Taurids	Nov. 3	Encke
Leonids	Nov. 17	Tempel–Tuttle
Andromedids	Nov. 20	Biela
Geminids	Dec. 13	(Phaethon)
Ursids	Dec. 23	Tuttle

The Andromedids are now almost undetectable. Phaethon is an asteroid, not a comet, but there are unconfirmed theories that it may be an ex-comet which has lost all its volatiles; certainly its orbit is strikingly similar to that of the Geminid meteor stream. Thatcher's Comet has an estimated period of 415 years; all the others listed here have periods of less than 150 years. Biela's Comet has certainly disintegrated (see p. 93).

Encke's Comet, discovered in 1785, has a period of 3.3 years (the shortest known) and has been seen at every return since 1822 apart from that of 1945, when it was very badly placed and many astronomers had other things on their mind. It has occasionally reached naked-eye visibility, and can sometimes show a tail (as much as 3° in 1805, before its periodicity was established). Modern instruments enable it to be followed throughout its orbit; even at aphelion it remains much closer in than the path of Jupiter. It is named in honour of Johann Encke, who was the first to establish its periodicity following the return of 1822.

Perihelion is due on September 9, 2000, but the comet is not likely to be a conspicuous object.

The summer triangle. During August evenings the night sky is dominated by the Summer Triangle, consisting of three bright stars: Vega, Altair and Deneb. The nickname is unofficial, and was introduced by the Editor of this *Yearbook* in a television programme many years ago, but it has become widely used. It is interesting to remember that Deneb, which appears the faintest of the three stars, is actually much the most luminous, and could equal 70,000 Suns, as against 25 Suns for Vega and only 10 for Altair. In other words, Deneb is the equal of 2800 Vegas or 7000 Altairs. Appearances can be highly deceptive.

September

New Moon: September 27   *Full Moon*: September 13

Equinox: September 22

MERCURY, for observers at the latitudes of the British Isles, is unsuitably placed for observation throughout the month. Further south Mercury becomes an evening object after the first few days of the month, low above the western horizon at the end of civil twilight. During this period its magnitude fades slowly from –0.7 to 0.0. See Figure 10, given with the notes for October.

VENUS, magnitude –3.9, continues to be visible as an evening object for a short while after sunset, above the western horizon. Although it is farther from the Sun at the end of the month than at the beginning, its rapid southward motion in declination compensates for this increase in elongation, so that the time available for observation by those in the latitudes of the British Isles remains almost exactly the same throughout the month.

MARS, magnitude +1.8, though already visible to observers in the Northern Hemisphere, does not become visible to those in the Southern Hemisphere until the very end of the month. Mars is a difficult morning object in the constellation of Leo, passing 1° north of Regulus on September 16.

JUPITER, magnitude –2.5, continues to be visible as a splendid object in the southern half of the sky, from late evening and through the night. Jupiter commences its retrograde motion after reaching its first stationary point on September 29, in the constellation of Taurus. The four Galilean satellites of Jupiter can easily be detected with a good pair of binoculars, provided they are steadily supported. All of them have magnitudes between +5 and +6, and the main difficulty in observing them with small apertures is the overpowering brightness of Jupiter itself.

SATURN continues to be visible as a morning object, magnitude 0.0, some 10° west of Jupiter. Saturn commences its retrograde motion after reaching its first stationary point on September 12, in the constellation of Taurus.

September anniversaries. Two celebrated astronomers have their anniversaries this month. Abraham Gotthelf Kästner was born in Leipzig on September 27, 1719, and was Professor of Mathematics at Göttingen for over half a century; his pupils included Johann Schröter and Heinrich Olbers. He wrote a major history of mathematics, and carried out investigations of the Sun, Moon and eclipses. He died at Göttingen on June 20, 1800.

James Edward Keeler was born at La Salle, Illinois, on November 10, 1857. He became assistant at Allegheny Observatory in 1881, and after a period at the Lick Observatory returned to Allegheny as Director in 1891. He was a pioneer spectroscopist, and it was he who first proved that Saturn's rings are made up of swarms of orbiting particles. He was appointed Director of the Lick Observatory in 1898, and continued his photographic surveys, which resulted in the discovery of 120,000 new nebulae, half of them spiral in form. He was an exceptionally able and popular director, but sadly his career was cut short by his sudden and quite unexpected death at San Francisco on August 12, 1900.

The Southern Fish. During September evenings, the bright star Fomalhaut may be seen from most of Britain, very low over the southern horizon. Its declination is –29° 37', so that from the north of Scotland it is always very elusive.

Fomalhaut is the only bright star in the constellation Piscis Australis, the Southern Fish. To find it, use two of the stars in the Square of Pegasus as guides (Figure 9). Do not confuse Fomalhaut with Diphda (Beta Ceti), which is a magnitude fainter, and from Britain is always higher up. Fomalhaut is one of our closer neighbours: it is 22 light-years away, and 13 times as luminous as the Sun, with an A3-type spectrum. It is one of the stars known to be associated with cool, possibly planet-forming material.

The rest of Piscis Australis is very undistinguished. There are no other stars above magnitude 4, and there is no particular pattern. Neither are there any objects of special interest, though Beta (Fum el Samakah) is double; the components are of magnitudes 4.4 and 7.9, separated by 30 arcseconds. This is, however, an optical double, not a binary system.

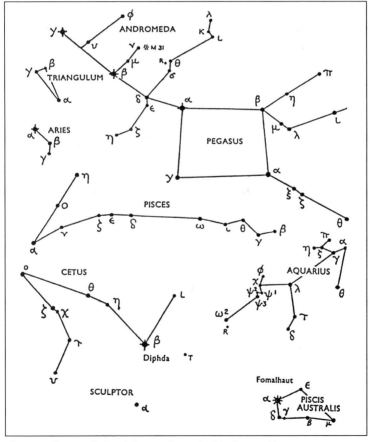

Figure 9. The constellation Piscis Australis, south of the Square of Pegasus.

October

New Moon: October 27   *Full Moon*: October 13

Summer Time in Great Britain and Northern Ireland ends on October 29

MERCURY is not suitably placed for observation from the latitudes of the British Isles. However, for observers in tropical and southern latitudes this will be the most favourable evening apparition of the year. Figure 10 shows, for observers in latitude 35°S, the changes in the azimuth (the true bearing from north through east, south and west) and altitude of Mercury on successive evenings when the Sun is 6° below the horizon. This position of the Sun marks the end of evening civil twilight, which for this latitude and time of year occurs about 30 minutes after sunset. The changes in the brightness of the planet are

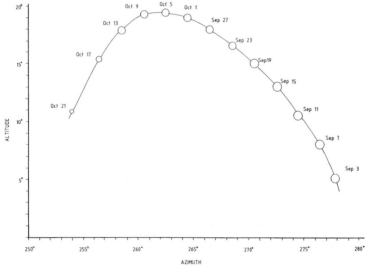

Figure 10. Evening apparition of Mercury, from latitude 35°S.

indicated by the relative sizes of the circles marking Mercury's position at five-day intervals. Mercury is at its brightest before it reaches greatest eastern elongation (26°), on October 6.

VENUS, magnitude –4.0, is a brilliant object in the early evenings in the south-western sky. By the end of the month it is still visible only for about half an hour after sunset for observers in the latitudes of the British Isles.

MARS continues to be visible in the pre-dawn sky, low above the eastern horizon, until the morning twilight inhibits observation. It is not a conspicuous object, its magnitude being only +1.8. The path of Mars among the stars for the rest of the year is shown in Figure 11.

JUPITER is a prominent object in Taurus, magnitude –2.7, about 5° north of Aldebaran. It is becoming visible for the greater part of the night, as it moves towards opposition next month.

SATURN, magnitude –0.2, is now visible for the greater part of the night as it approaches opposition next month. The rings of Saturn present a beautiful spectacle to the observer with a small telescope. The Earth passed through the ring plane twice in 1995, since when the rings have been slowly opening up: the diameter of the minor axis is now 19 arcseconds, marginally greater than the polar diameter of the planet itself. The rings will not be at their maximum opening for another couple of years.

The far side of the Moon. It is now over thirty years since the first images of the Moon's far side were obtained. They were sent back in October 1959 by the Russian spacecraft Lunik (or Luna) 3, which had been sent on a 'round trip'. Previously only two vehicles had been successfully dispatched to the Moon: Lunik 1, which flew past on January 2, 1959, and Lunik 2, which impacted the surface on September 13, 1959, though without sending back any data.

The Moon's orbital period is the same as its axial rotation period: 27.32 days. There is no mystery about this. Tidal action over the ages has been responsible, and the effect is to keep the same face of the Moon turned towards us all the time. The lunar orbit is not circular, so that its speed of motion varies, and the Moon seems to rock very slowly

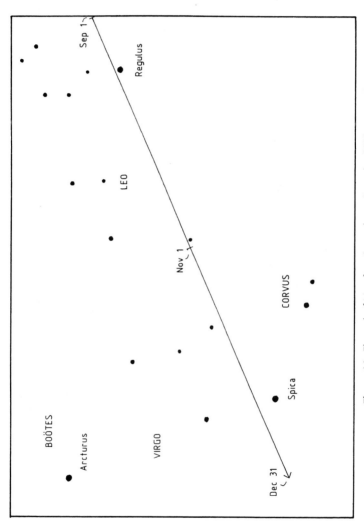

Figure 11. The path of Mars from September to December 2000.

to and fro; this is termed libration in longitude. All in all, it is possible to examine a total of 59 per cent of the total surface, though of course never more than 50 per cent at any one moment.

The 'edges' or libration zones are always very foreshortened, and are difficult to map from Earth, but various points were well established; none of the major seas (maria) crossed the limb to the averted areas, and it was suspected that the far side might have many fewer of the maria than the side we have always known. This did indeed prove to be the case. There is one major sea, the Mare Orientale, which extends over the limb, but only a small part of its border can be seen from Earth (it was in fact first reported, long before Lunik 3, by the Editor of this *Yearbook*).

Lunik 3 passed beyond the Moon, and then swung back to Earth; the images were received on 26 October. They were of poor quality by modern standards, but were good enough to show that the Moon's far side is just as cratered and barren as the known side. One feature was taken to be a huge range of peaks, and was named the Soviet Mountain range; however, it proved to be nothing more than a bright ray, and the name was tactfully deleted from later maps.

By now the whole of the Moon has been mapped in great detail, but it is true that only 27 men have had direct views of the far side – the crews of Apollos 8 and 10 to 17.

November

New Moon: November 25   *Full Moon*: November 11

MERCURY For observers in northern temperate latitudes this will be the most favourable morning apparition of the year. Figure 12 shows, for observers in latitude 52°N, the changes in the azimuth (the true bearing from north through east, south and west) and altitude of Mercury on successive mornings when the Sun is 6° below the horizon. This position of the Sun marks the beginning of morning civil twilight, which for this latitude and time of year occurs about 35 minutes before sunrise. The changes in the brightness of the planet are indicated by the relative sizes of the circles marking Mercury's position at five-day intervals. Mercury is at its brightest after it reaches greatest western elongation (19°), on November 15. Mercury is not suitably placed for observation from the southern hemisphere.

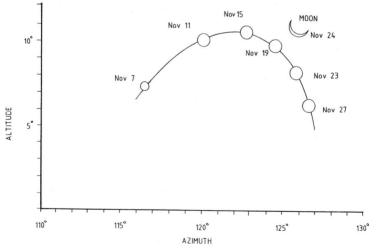

Figure 12. Morning apparition of Mercury, from latitude 52°N.

VENUS, magnitude –4.1, continues to be visible as a brilliant object after sunset, above the west-south-west horizon.

MARS, at magnitude +1.7, continues to be visible as a morning object, moving steadily eastwards in the constellation of Virgo.

JUPITER, magnitude –2.9, reaches opposition on November 28 and is therefore visible throughout the hours of darkness. At opposition, Jupiter is 606 million kilometres (377 million miles) from the Earth.

SATURN reaches opposition on November 19 and is thus visible throughout the hours of darkness. Its magnitude is –0.4. At opposition it is 1217 million kilometres (756 million miles) from the Earth.

Saturn and Jupiter. Both the giant planets come to opposition this month. Jupiter is much the more brilliant of the two, partly because it is much larger than Saturn and partly because it is much closer. Indeed, at the moment Saturn is almost exactly twice as remote as Jupiter. If you could go there by spacecraft, travelling by the most direct route, the halfway point to Saturn would be found at the orbit of Jupiter.

The ring system is now well displayed. In 1995 the rings were edgewise-on to the Earth, and small telescopes would not show them at all, so that Saturn was temporarily shorn of its beauty. They have now opened out, and are at their very best; they will again be edgewise-on in 2009 (Figure 13 over the page).

The rings may look solid, but in fact no solid or liquid ring could exist; it would be torn to pieces by Saturn's powerful gravity. The rings are made up of vast numbers of icy particles, all orbiting the planet in the manner of dwarf moons. Spacecraft pictures have shown that there are many hundreds of ringlets and narrow divisions, so that the whole system has been found to be unexpectedly complex.

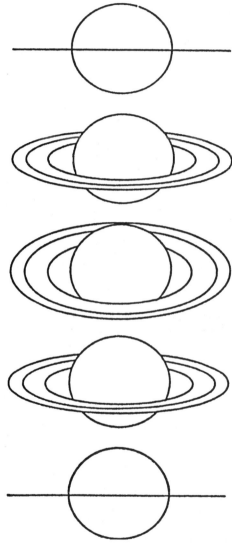

Figure 13. The changing aspect of Saturn's rings.

December

New Moon: December 25   *Full Moon*: December 11

Solstice: December 21

MERCURY passes through superior conjunction on December 25, and therefore remains too close to the Sun for observation throughout the month.

VENUS, magnitude –4.2, is a magnificent object in the early evenings, completely dominating the south-western sky. As Venus moves northward in declination, observers in the latitudes of the British Isles obtain a longer period of observation – by the end of the year this extends to over three hours after sunset.

MARS, magnitude +1.5, continues to be visible low in the east-south-eastern sky in the early mornings. Mars continues its relatively rapid eastward motion in the constellation Virgo, passing 4° north of Spica on December 11.

JUPITER is only just past opposition, so that it is effectively visible throughout the hours of darkness until morning twilight begins. Its magnitude is –2.8. Jupiter is retrograding slowly in Taurus, between the Pleiades and the Hyades.

SATURN, magnitude –0.2, continues to be visible as an evening object, from the end of evening twilight until the early hours of the morning.

The end of the millennium. December 31, 2000, marks the end of a millennium. The first day of the new millennium is January 1, 2001.

Why is this so, when so many people believe that the new millennium began on January 1, 2000? The answer is quite straightforward. There was no year 0: the zero did not come into the reckoning until much later. Therefore the first day of the first Christian millennium was the first day of the year we call AD 1.

In any case, it is all rather meaningless. Jesus Christ was certainly born several years before 'Year 1', so that on this reckoning the new millennium has been in progress for some time. Moreover, the reckoning depends entirely upon the Christian religion, and there are many other religions on the face of the Earth.

However, by any method of calculating, the new millennium is about to begin. We have come a long way since the year 1001. What will the situation be in AD 3001? Only time will tell.

Eclipses in 2000

There will be six eclipses, four of the Sun and two of the Moon.

1. *A total eclipse of the Moon on January 21* is visible from northern and western Asia, Asia Minor, Africa, Europe, the Atlantic Ocean, Iceland, Greenland, the Arctic Ocean, the Americas and the Pacific Ocean (except the western part). The eclipse begins at 03h 01m and ends at 06h 26m. Totality lasts from 04h 04m to 05h 22m.

2. *A partial eclipse of the Sun on February 5* is visible from the southern Indian Ocean and Antarctica. The eclipse begins at 10h 56m and ends at 14h 43m. At maximum eclipse, 58 per cent of the Sun is obscured.

3. *A partial eclipse of the Sun on July 1* is visible from the south Pacific Ocean and southern South America (roughly south of latitude 40°S). The eclipse begins at 18h 07m and ends at 20h 58m. At maximum eclipse, 48 per cent of the Sun is obscured.

4. *A total eclipse of the Moon on July 16* is visible from southern South America, western North America, the Pacific Ocean, Antarctica, Australasia, Asia (except the extreme northern regions), the Indian Ocean, south and east Africa, and the Middle East. The eclipse begins at 11h 57m and ends at 15h 54m. Totality lasts from 13h 02m to 14h 49m.

5. *A partial eclipse of the Sun on July 31* is visible from northern Scandinavia, Finland, northern Asia, the Arctic Ocean, Greenland (except the southern part), Alaska, northern and western Canada, north-western U.S.A. and the north Pacific Ocean. The eclipse begins at 00h 37m and ends at 03h 49m. At maximum, 60 per cent of the Sun is obscured.

6. *A partial eclipse of the Sun on December 25* is visible from the north-eastern part of the Pacific Ocean, North America (except the extreme north-west), Central America, the extreme south of Greenland, the Caribbean and the north Atlantic Ocean, including the Azores. The eclipse begins at 15h 27m and ends at 19h 43m. At maximum, 72 per cent of the Sun is obscured.

Occultations in 2000

In the course of its journey round the sky each month, the Moon passes in front of all the stars in its path, and the timing of these occultations is useful in fixing the position and motion of the Moon. The Moon's orbit is tilted at more than 5° to the ecliptic, but it is not fixed in space. It twists steadily westwards at a rate of about 20° a year, a complete revolution taking 18.6 years, during which time all the stars that lie within about 6½° of the ecliptic will be occulted. The occultations of any one star continue month after month until the Moon's path has twisted away from the star, but only a few of these occultations will be visible from any one place in hours of darkness.

There are five occultations of bright planets in 2000: one of Mercury, two of Venus and one of Mars.

Only four first-magnitude stars are near enough to the ecliptic to be occulted by the Moon: Aldebaran, Regulus, Spica and Antares. Aldebaran undergoes occultation twice in 2000.

Predictions of these occultations are made on a worldwide basis for all stars down to magnitude 7.5, and sometimes even fainter. The British Astronomical Association has produced a complete lunar occultation prediction package for personal computer users.

Occultations of stars by planets (including minor planets) and satellites have aroused considerable attention.

The exact timing of such events gives valuable information about positions, sizes, orbits, atmospheres and sometimes of the presence of satellites. The discovery of the rings of Uranus in 1977 was the unexpected result of the observations made of a predicted occultation of a faint star by Uranus. The duration of an occultation by a satellite or minor planet is quite small (usually of the order of a minute or less). If observations are made from a number of stations it is possible to deduce the size of the planet.

The observations need to be made either photoelectrically or visually. The high accuracy of the method can readily be appreciated when one realizes that even a stopwatch timing accurate to a tenth of a second is, on average, equivalent to an accuracy of about 1 kilometre in the chord measured across the minor planet.

Comets in 2000

The appearance of a bright comet is a rare event which can never be predicted in advance, because this class of object travels round the Sun in enormous orbits with periods which may well be many thousands of years. There are therefore no records of the previous appearances of these bodies, and we are unable to follow their wanderings through space.

Comets of short period, on the other hand, return at regular intervals, and attract a good deal of attention from astronomers. Unfortunately they are all faint objects, and are recovered and followed by photographic methods using large telescopes. Most of these short-period comets travel in orbits of small inclination which reach out to the orbit of Jupiter, and it is this planet which is mainly responsible for the severe perturbations which many of these comets undergo. Unlike the planets, comets may be seen in any part of the sky, but since their distances from the Earth are similar to those of the planets their apparent movements in the sky are also somewhat similar, and some of them may be followed for long periods of time.

The following periodic comets are expected to return to perihelion in 1999, and to be brighter than magnitude +15:

Comet	Year of discovery	Period (years)	Predicted date of perihelion
9P/Tempel 1	1867	5.5	Jan. 2
108P/Ciffréo	1985	7.3	Apr. 18
76P/West–Kohoutek–Ikemura	1974	6.5	June 1
2P/Encke	1785	3.3	Sep. 9
71P/Clark	1973	5.5	Dec. 1

Minor Planets in 2000

Although many thousands of minor planets (asteroids) are known to exist, only a few thousand of them have well-determined orbits and are listed in the catalogues. Most of these orbits lie entirely between the orbits of Mars and Jupiter. All these bodies are quite small, and even the largest, Ceres, is only 913 km (567 miles) in diameter. Thus, they are necessarily faint objects, and although a number of them are within the reach of a small telescope few of them ever attain any considerable brightness. The first four that were discovered are named Ceres, Pallas, Juno and Vesta. Actually the largest four minor planets are Ceres, Pallas, Vesta and Hygeia. Vesta can occasionally be seen with the naked eye, and this is most likely to happen when an opposition occurs near June, since Vesta would then be at perihelion. Ephemerides for these four brightest minor planets in 2000 are given below.

1 Ceres

					Geo-centric distance	Helio-centric distance	Phase angle	Visual magni-tude	Elonga-tion
		RA 2000.0		Dec.					
		h	m	°	′	AU	AU	°		°
Jan.	7	12	40.07	+9	02.2	2.188	2.552	22.3	8.2	100.2W
	17	12	47.30	+9	08.4	2.065	2.553	21.4	8.0	108.4W
	27	12	52.36	+9	30.6	1.950	2.555	20.0	7.9	117.2W
Feb.	6	12	54.95	+10	08.6	1.845	2.557	18.1	7.7	126.5W
	16	12	54.83	+11	00.4	1.754	2.559	15.5	7.5	136.1W
	26	12	51.99	+12	02.0	1.682	2.562	12.5	7.3	145.9W
Mar.	7	12	46.60	+13	07.2	1.630	2.565	9.3	7.1	155.2W
	17	12	39.22	+14	07.7	1.604	2.569	6.9	6.9	162.0W
	27	12	30.75	+14	55.3	1.604	2.572	6.7	6.9	162.4W
Apr.	6	12	22.23	+15	23.3	1.629	2.576	9.0	7.1	156.1E
	16	12	14.74	+15	27.9	1.680	2.581	12.2	7.3	147.2E
	26	12	09.08	+15	09.1	1.751	2.585	15.2	7.5	137.7E

1 Ceres (cont)

		RA		Dec.		Geo-centric distance	Helio-centric distance	Phase angle	Visual magni-tude	Elonga-tion
		h	m	°	′	AU	AU	°		°
May	6	12	05.72	+14	28.9	1.841	2.590	17.8	7.7	128.3E
	16	12	04.85	+13	30.7	1.945	2.596	19.8	7.9	119.4E
	26	12	06.37	+12	18.1	2.061	2.601	21.3	8.1	111.0E

2 Pallas

		RA		Dec.		Geo-centric distance	Helio-centric distance	Phase angle	Visual magni-tude	Elonga-tion
		h	m	°	′	AU	AU	°		°
Jan.	7	8	4.84	−29	30.9	1.407	2.141	21.7	7.6	126.3W
	17	7	57.05	−28	25.5	1.363	2.138	20.4	7.5	130.6W
	27	7	49.01	−26	21.1	1.335	2.136	19.5	7.4	133.6E
Feb.	6	7	42.04	−23	21.9	1.325	2.136	19.2	7.4	134.5E
	16	7	37.33	−19	39.5	1.336	2.137	19.7	7.5	133.1E
	26	7	35.61	−15	31.5	1.369	2.139	20.9	7.5	129.5E
Mar.	7	7	37.13	−11	15.8	1.422	2.144	22.5	7.7	124.3E
	17	7	41.84	−7	08.6	1.494	2.149	24.1	7.8	118.0E
	27	7	49.41	−3	21.4	1.582	2.156	25.5	8.0	111.4E
Apr.	6	7	59.46	−0	00.9	1.684	2.164	26.6	8.2	104.6E
	16	8	11.58	+2	49.8	1.796	2.174	27.2	8.4	97.8E
	26	8	25.35	+5	10.6	1.917	2.185	27.4	8.5	91.3E
May	6	8	40.42	+7	02.8	2.043	2.197	27.2	8.7	84.9E
	16	8	56.51	+8	28.4	2.172	2.211	26.7	8.8	78.8E
	26	9	13.33	+9	30.2	2.302	2.225	25.8	8.9	72.9E

3 Juno

		2000.0			Geo-centric distance	Helio-centric distance	Phase angle	Visual magni-tude	Elonga-tion
		RA		Dec.					
	h	m	°	′	AU	AU	°		°
Aug. 4	21	22.58	−3	29.2	1.624	2.617	5.8	8.8	165.0W
14	21	14.30	−4	46.7	1.587	2.589	4.2	8.7	169.1E
24	21	06.10	−6	15.7	1.578	2.561	6.7	8.8	162.9E
Sept. 3	20	58.98	−7	49.2	1.594	2.533	10.5	8.9	152.7E
13	20	53.84	−9	19.7	1.634	2.505	14.3	9.0	142.0E

4 Vesta

		2000.0			Geo-centric distance	Helio-centric distance	Phase angle	Visual magni-tude	Elonga-tion
		RA		Dec.					
	h	m	°	′	AU	AU	°		°
Jan. 7	16	31.20	−17	37.0	2.858	2.161	16.0	7.8	37.4W
17	16	52.47	−18	23.3	2.780	2.157	17.9	7.8	42.4W
27	17	13.57	−18	58.7	2.694	2.155	19.7	7.8	47.5W
Feb. 6	17	34.37	−19	23.5	2.603	2.152	21.4	7.8	52.7W
16	17	54.72	−19	38.3	2.505	2.151	22.9	7.7	57.9W
26	18	14.45	−19	44.0	2.403	2.150	24.3	7.7	63.3W
Mar. 7	18	33.41	−19	41.8	2.297	2.149	25.5	7.6	68.9W
17	18	51.41	−19	33.2	2.187	2.149	26.5	7.5	74.6W
27	19	8.27	−19	20.2	2.075	2.150	27.3	7.4	80.5W
Apr. 6	19	23.77	−19	05.0	1.962	2.151	27.7	7.3	86.7W
16	19	37.67	−18	50.1	1.848	2.153	27.7	7.2	93.2W
26	19	49.73	−18	38.4	1.736	2.155	27.4	7.1	100.1W
May 6	19	59.64	−18	32.8	1.628	2.158	26.5	6.9	107.5W
16	20	07.07	−18	36.5	1.524	2.161	25.0	6.7	115.5W
26	20	11.70	−18	52.4	1.428	2.165	22.8	6.5	124.1W
June 5	20	13.19	−19	22.8	1.343	2.170	19.8	6.3	133.4W
15	20	11.39	−20	08.3	1.272	2.175	16.1	6.1	143.6W
25	20	06.40	−21	07.2	1.218	2.180	11.6	5.9	154.5W
July 5	19	58.66	−22	15.3	1.186	2.186	6.5	5.7	165.9W
15	19	49.21	−23	25.6	1.177	2.192	1.4	5.4	176.9W
25	19	39.42	−24	30.9	1.192	2.199	4.7	5.6	169.7E

4 Vesta (cont)

					Geo-centric distance	Helio-centric distance	Phase angle	Visual magni-tude	Elonga-tion
		2000.0 RA		Dec.					
		h	m	° ′	AU	AU	°		°
Aug.	4	19	30.75	−25 25.5	1.232	2.206	9.8	5.9	158.2E
	14	19	24.48	−26 06.6	1.293	2.214	14.4	6.1	147.2E
	24	19	21.34	−26 34.0	1.374	2.222	18.1	6.4	136.9E
Sept.	3	19	21.60	−26 48.8	1.470	2.230	21.1	6.6	127.2E
	13	19	25.18	−26 52.4	1.578	2.238	23.3	6.8	118.4E
	23	19	31.75	−26 45.9	1.695	2.247	24.8	7.0	110.1E
Oct.	3	19	40.89	−26 29.7	1.819	2.256	25.7	7.2	102.4E
	13	19	52.21	−26 04.2	1.947	2.266	26.0	7.4	95.1E
	23	20	05.26	−25 29.5	2.077	2.275	25.9	7.5	88.2E
Nov.	2	20	19.71	−24 45.6	2.207	2.285	25.4	7.7	81.6E
	12	20	35.25	−23 52.6	2.337	2.294	24.7	7.8	75.3E
	22	20	51.60	−22 50.8	2.463	2.304	23.6	7.9	69.1E
Dec.	2	21	08.56	−21 40.4	2.586	2.314	22.3	7.9	63.1E
	12	21	25.94	−20 22.0	2.703	2.324	20.9	8.0	57.3E
	22	21	43.59	−18 56.2	2.815	2.334	19.3	8.1	51.6E
	32	22	01.41	−17 23.7	2.919	2.344	17.5	8.1	45.9E

A vigorous campaign for observing the occultations of stars by minor planets has produced improved values for the dimensions of some of them, as well as the suggestion that some of these planets may be accompanied by satellites. Many of these observations have been made photoelectrically. However, amateur observers have found renewed interest in the minor planets since it has been shown that their visual timings of an occultation of a star by a minor planet are accurate enough to lead to reliable determinations of diameter. As a consequence many groups of observers all over the world are now organizing themselves for expeditions should the predicted track of such an occultation cross their country.

Meteors in 2000

Meteors ('shooting stars') may be seen on any clear moonless night, but on certain nights of the year their number increases noticeably. This occurs when the Earth chances to intersect a concentration of meteoric dust moving in an orbit around the Sun. If the dust is well spread out in space, the resulting shower of meteors may last for several days. The word 'shower' must not be misinterpreted – only on very rare occasions have the meteors been so numerous as to resemble snowflakes falling.

If the meteor tracks are marked on a star map and traced backwards, a number of them will be found to intersect in a point (or a small area of the sky) which marks the radiant of the shower. This gives the direction from which the meteors have come.

The following table gives some of the more easily observed showers with their radiants; interference by moonlight is shown by the letter M.

Limiting dates	Shower	Maximum	RA		Dec.	
			h	m	°	
Jan. 1–4	Quadrantids	Jan. 3	15	28	+50	
Apr. 20–22	Lyrids	Apr. 22	18	08	+32	M
May 1–8	Eta Aquarids	May 4	22	20	−01	
June 17–26	Ophiuchids	June 19	17	20	−20	M
July 15–Aug. 15	Delta Aquarids	July 29	22	36	−17	
July 15–Aug. 20	Piscis Australids	July 31	22	40	−30	
July 15–Aug. 25	Capricornids	Aug. 2	20	36	−10	
July 27–Aug. 17	Perseids	Aug. 12	3	04	+58	M
Oct. 15–25	Orionids	Oct. 21	6	24	+15	
Oct. 26–Nov. 16	Taurids	Nov. 3	3	44	+14	
Nov. 15–19	Leonids	Nov. 17	10	08	+22	M
Dec. 9–14	Geminids	Dec. 13	7	28	+32	M
Dec. 17–24	Ursids	Dec. 23	14	28	+78	

Some Events in 2001

ECLIPSES

There will be four eclipses, two of the Sun and two of the Moon.

January 9:	total eclipse of the Moon – Australia, Africa, Europe, eastern part of the Americas.
June 21:	total eclipse of the Sun – South America, Africa.
July 5:	partial eclipse of the Moon – Australasia, Asia, Africa.
December 14:	annular eclipse of the Sun – the Americas.

THE PLANETS

Mercury may be seen more easily from northern latitudes in the evenings about the time of greatest eastern elongation (May 22) and in the mornings around greatest western elongation (October 29). In the Southern Hemisphere the corresponding most favourable dates are around March 11 (mornings) and September 18 (evenings).

Venus is visible in the evenings until the last week of March, and in the mornings from mid-April to early December.

Mars is at opposition on June 21.

Jupiter does not come to opposition in 2001.

Saturn is at opposition on December 3.

Uranus is at opposition on August 15.

Neptune is at opposition on July 30.

Pluto is at opposition on June 4.

Part II

Article Section

Oh, Be A Fine Girl: Astronomical Colour

CHRIS LINTOTT

Whenever there is a special occasion to mark, my friends and family seem to scour all the shops in town to find the one greetings card which may possibly be said to have an astronomical theme (they know my passion all too well!). At Christmas, of course, their task is made easier by the availability of cards featuring the Star of Bethlehem. I've lost count of the times I have received one of these with the message, 'Well, what is it then?' Last year, however, one slightly more original card found its way under the tree. It featured several Stars of Bethlehem, in many different colours: red, green, yellow, blue and the traditional white. The sender, who is responsible for this essay on the colours of stars, felt the need to apologize with the comment, 'Yes, I *know* stars are white, but I liked the card.'

Go outside on any clear night, look up, and you will be able to see in an instant the source of my friend's puzzlement, for at first glance the stars do appear colourless to the naked eye. But look closer at certain stars, for example Arcturus (in the constellation of Boötes, the central star of the instantly recognizable 'Y' shape). Stare at it long and hard and try to see what colour it is, for it is indeed coloured. To me it appears a slightly orange shade, but others have described it as anything from golden yellow or topaz (Robert Burnham, in his *Celestial Handbook*) through to reddish (W. H. Smyth, in the *Cycle of Celestial Objects*). Other prominent stars that display colour are Aldebaran (in Taurus, a definite red colour), Betelgeuse (in Orion, also red), Capella (in Auriga, yellow) and many more. Others, such as Vega, one of the brightest stars in the sky, are lauded for their 'pure white' hues. So it appears that, at least in bright stars, we can see colour. But this cannot be down to some difference in the structure of bright stars – after all, many of the stars that appear to be bright are just faint stars that happen to be close to us. In fact, it is merely an artefact of the way our eyes sense light. There are two kinds of light-sensitive cells within the human eye: cones, situated at the centre of the eye, and rods, situated at the edges of the eye. The cones are the cells which are sensitive to colour, but they need a relatively high intensity of light to trigger them. The rods are more sensitive to faint light, but cannot detect colour. (Incidentally, this is why the deep-sky observer's trick of averted vision – looking slightly to one side of the object being viewed. This brings the rods directly in line with the incoming light, and thus increases sensitivity.) Thus, bright stars are able to trigger the cones, while faint stars don't and so can't be seen to have colour.

This suggests an obvious experiment. In order to see colour in the fainter stars, all you have to do is increase the amount of light reaching the eye. Astronomers have a wide variety of equipment to perform this most essential task, but for spotting star colours binoculars are unrivalled. Try scanning slowly along the Milky Way, or looking at a cluster like the Pleiades (which are definitely blue), and you will realize that much of the beauty in the sky is in the subtle shades revealed to the observer who takes more than a passing glance. Double-star observers, in particular, treasure the colours of the gems they study. Take Albireo, for example, the bottom-most of the bright stars that make up the body of Cygnus, the Swan. This is a double star, consisting of a golden-coloured primary and a blue secondary. It was the first object I ever viewed through a telescope, and therefore holds a special place in my catalogue of favourite sights.

The description of Albireo's colours is my personal one. Colour is a very subjective thing. Just consider how many different words we have for the same shade; blue, for example, may be navy blue, royal blue, ultramarine, and many, many others. There is no guarantee that one observer will agree with another on how to describe the hue of a particular star. You might imagine, therefore, that colour would be the very last area to be studied by serious astronomers, amateur and professional. In fact, it would be no exaggeration to say that the majority of what we know about the heavens is derived from the observation of colours. Colour, after all, is one way of perceiving the wavelength of light. What we call visible light is only a small portion of the full spectrum of radiation we can detect. It is, for example, the same kind of radiation as radio waves, and your car stereo can be tuned to different wavelengths!

So why is this so important? Well, as we have seen it is possible to detect the colour of a star, which provides us with a measure of the wavelength at which the star is emitting radiation most prominently. (All stars emit light over the full range of colours.) We can also relate wavelength to energy, and temperature is merely a measure of energy. Just think of how we describe things as 'red hot', or 'white hot', or how a light bulb changes colour as the current through it increases (the filament will glow red, then yellow, and finally white). Thus by observing the colour of a star, we can deduce its temperature. This discovery, together with increased use of the spectrograph (see below), during the course of the nineteenth century, allowed stars to be systematically classified for the first time. The system we use today is based on one drawn up at Harvard where each type of star has a letter assigned to it according to its colour and therefore its temperature. The sequence was originally alphabetical, but many changes since have produced the well-known sequence of O, B, A, F, G, K, M, and the traditional mnemonic, 'Oh, Be A Fine Girl, Kiss Me!'. In this sequence of spectral types, as they are called, O-types are the hottest white or blue stars, and S-types are the coolest red stars (see Table 1). These two types are relatively rare, and the majority of stars lie in the range from B to M. Our Sun, for example, is a standard G star. Other types have come and gone: W for extremely hot stars, and R and N for particular types of cool star. R and N have given way to C stars (C is for carbon), and recently a new class of small, cool L stars was introduced. (I can't resist mentioning the football team of the Department of Physics and Astronomy at University College, London, which goes under the name of the OBAFGKMRNS Stars, to the puzzlement of less astronomically knowledgeable opposition!)

Type	Colour	Typical temperature (K)
O	Very blue	40,000
B	Blue	28,000
A	Blue-white	9900
F	White	7400
G	Yellow	6000
K	Orange	4900
M	Orange-red	3500
S	Red	3000

Table 1. Stellar classification.

The next great conceptual leap came in 1910 when Henry Norris Russell plotted luminosities of stars (the luminosity of a star is a measure of the intensity of the light it gives off) against their spectral class. The resulting diagram, honouring its creators in its name, the Hertzsprung–Russell or HR diagram (the Danish astronomer Ejnar Hertzsprung had independently plotted it a few years before), is perhaps the most important single creation in modern astrophysics. Perhaps we might have expected a random distribution with points scattered freely all over the grid. In fact, nothing could be further from the truth.

As shown in Figure 1, the immediately striking feature is that most stars fall in a band running from top left (white, high-temperature stars which are also very luminous) to bottom right (red, low-temperature and low-luminosity stars). In addition, there is an extra group of red stars on the right side of the diagram, which have much higher luminosity (and therefore greater mass). These are the red giants and supergiants. The other main grouping is the white dwarfs, stars with exceptionally low luminosity. When this general picture first emerged, astronomers became enamoured with the possibility of an evolutionary sequence: when a star first condensed out of a collapsing cloud of gas and dust, it would necessarily be large, cool and therefore red (top right of the HR diagram). As gravity exerted its powerful influence, it would become slowly hotter and move to the left along the top of the HR diagram, before sliding down the main sequence as fuel was used up, ending up as a red dwarf.

Sadly, this simple and appealing picture is completely wrong. Once it was realized that the stars shine by using hydrogen as a fuel for nuclear fusion, the picture collapsed. The critical factor is not the star's size or gravity but the amount of available fuel. In the new picture, a star collapsing out of one of the numerous nebulae which abound in our Universe is initially a variable, flickering object, known as a T Tauri star, which continues to condense as it moves towards the main sequence, where it will spend most of its life. Instead of sliding up or down the sequence, the star will spend most of its life at a particular point on it, depending on its mass. The greater the mass, the closer the star will be to the top left of the main sequence. Eventually, the star grows old as all things must (even teenagers like myself!) and its fuel begins to run out. Through a complex series of nuclear reactions, it is able to change to burning the helium by-product of its first, hydrogen-burning stage, and produce carbon. At this point the star leaves the main sequence and moves into the realm of the giants and super-giants to the top right of the diagram. There it stays until eventually the outer layers are blown away completely, producing a planetary nebula, and leaving behind a white dwarf (at least for stars of the Sun's mass; a more exotic fate awaits those stars which are substantially more massive).

This is emphatically not the end of the story for the uses of the information hidden in the light we receive from the stars. I mentioned above that the most useful instrument in the astronomer's toolkit is

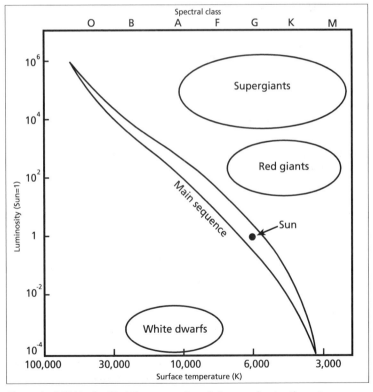

Figure 1. A highly simplified Hertzsprung–Russell diagram, showing the main sequence, giants, supergiants and white dwarfs.

the spectrograph. The principle on which this instrument works is simplicity itself (at least in theory). Isaac Newton was without doubt one of the greatest scientists produced by this country, and has the reputation of being the closest thing British science has to a god. That doesn't mean he was always right, of course. I vividly remember attending a public event at a university in which we were invited to be right where Newton was wrong; many of his ideas about optics were not only later shown to be wrong, but disagreed with results of experiments he himself carried out. It is perhaps a mark of his genius that even here he managed to carry out one of the best-known experiments in the field.

I refer, of course, to his splitting of 'white' sunlight into the full rainbow by a prism, thus demonstrating that white light is nothing more than the combination of the full spectrum. This occurs when light entering the glass from the air bends, or is refracted, to a degree which depends on its wavelength, so that red light bends more than violet light. It is this spectrum which is viewed, either by eye or electronically, in all spectrographs. (A similar effect can be observed by looking for reflection off a CD held up to sunlight, should you want to observe the Sun's spectrum for yourself without waiting for the next rainbow.)

Early in the nineteenth century, the English physicist William Wollaston became the first to pass light through a slit and then a prism. The spectrum was once again observed, except this time thin, dark lines were observed. These were later to be catalogued by the German physicist Joseph von Fraunhofer, whose name they bear still. It was around this time that the French philosopher August Comte wrote in his *Cours de philosophie positive* that we 'shall never be able to study, by any method, the stars' chemical composition or their mineralogical structure'. But these lines are nothing less than the signature of the elements that make up the Sun. This incredible result was found by Gustav Kirchhoff and Robert Bunsen in 1859. In fact, the latter's burner was produced to enable more accurate laboratory readings of the spectra of different elements to be taken. The method is simple: a glowing gas, liquid or solid sample of an element at low pressure will produce a spectrum made of up of a series of thin bright lines which form a unique fingerprint of that element. But the Sun's spectrum is made up of a series of dark, not bright lines. The answer tells us something about the structure of the Sun. A continuous spectrum is produced by the high-pressure gas in the photosphere. (Remember that low pressure is necessary for the fingerprint to be visible.) Above the photosphere is the low-pressure gas of the chromosphere, which we would expect to produce a spectrum of bright lines as a result of absorption by its constituent elements. However, when we observe the Sun's spectrum, instead of bright lines we see dark lines silhouetted against a brighter continuous spectrum. The dark lines appear where light of certain wavelengths is being absorbed by the elements present in the chromosphere and then re-emitted. Light of other wavelengths, which is not absorbed by the elements in the chromosphere, passes straight through with undiminished intensity. The spectrum we see is therefore a bright background crossed by dark lines, whose positions we can map to determine the Sun's composition as described above.

It is therefore possible to deduce the composition of the Sun simply by comparing the Fraunhofer lines with those produced in laboratory conditions here on Earth. When this was done, by Devon physicist Norman Lockyer, among many others, one set of lines remained unexplained. Rather than put this down to 'experimental error', it was realized that this was the signature of an element not yet identified on Earth. It was named helium (from the Greek *helios*, which means 'Sun'), but it was to be many years before this elusive substance was found closer to home, in certain minerals. Today, we have a complete picture of the Sun's composition, as shown in Table 2.

Element	Relative number of atoms
Hydrogen	1,000,000
Helium	63,000
Oxygen	690
Carbon	420
Nitrogen	87
Silicon	45
Magnesium	40
Neon	37
Iron	32
Sulphur	16
All others	below 5

Source: Patrick Moore, *Atlas of the Universe*, London, George Philip, 1997, p. 156.

Table 2. Composition of the Sun.

The same technique can be applied to the stars, as long as the amount of light reaching the instrument is sufficient. Applying this most incisive of techniques to objects beyond our own Galaxy therefore had to wait for larger telescopes, capable of collecting more light from the faintest sources. When this happened, spectroscopy again was the source of a huge leap in our understanding of the Universe and our position in it. The Lowell Observatory is probably best known for its original purpose – to search for the canals of Mars, which its founder believed existed – or for its fame as the site of Clyde Tombaugh's discovery of Pluto (whether it be planet or asteroid!). But it was also where Vesto Slipher discovered that the spectral lines of all the galaxies he observed (with the exception of a few, like the Andromeda Galaxy, which are now known to be the closest to us and to make up the Local Group) did not match those observed in laboratories, but were shifted towards the red end of the spectrum.

This is a manifestation of the Doppler effect, in which light from a rapidly receding source appears to change in wavelength. The same effect happens with sound. Think of an ambulance's siren approaching, passing and then receding: it changes in pitch, as we perceive the wavelength of the sound to increase, then decrease. The implication of this remarkable result was that the entire Universe appeared to be rushing away from us at terrific speed! This came as quite a shock to a scientific community which still viewed the Universe as essentially static and unchanging. Meanwhile, working at Mount Wilson, another of the great American observatories, was Edwin Hubble. He used what was then the most powerful telescope in the world to detect a class of variable star, the Cepheids, in distant galaxies. The luminosity of a Cepheid can be found by observing the period of the oscillations in the star's brightness, and then the distance can be calculated by comparing the actual luminosity with the observed brightness. Using this information, and the redshift values for the galaxies under study, Hubble was able to calibrate the relationship between redshift and distance. He found that the greater the redshift, the faster the galaxy is receding and the farther away it is. (This is the view held by the vast majority of modern astrophysicists; a few, such as Fred Hoyle and Halton Arp, still hold reservations.) From this foundation, modern cosmology was born and for the first time we beheld a picture of the Universe born in what is now known as the Big Bang.

I started this essay with a Christmas card from a friend, and we have travelled from there to the very foundations of our Universe, simply by looking at the information encoded in the starlight that every human being has noticed at some time or another. I wonder what it will reveal to us next? I, for one, can't wait to find out!

ACKNOWLEDGEMENTS

Thanks to Catherine Burgess, Ali Braden, Trevor Linney and Nicky Farrer for help and advice.

Water: A Cosmic History

PAUL MURDIN

Water in a glass has an almost magical appearance. It is transparent, yet reflections from its surface and the distortion of what lies beyond both show where the water is. Water naturally adapts to the shape of its container – under gravity, it is both mobile and settled. Of course, water's significance to us is more profound than its appearance. It is the fluid that enables our bodies to work, the solvent in which amazing biochemicals can get together and carry out the innumerable processes that make our life possible.

This article is about where this interesting and important substance, water, originates. The chemical formula for water is H_2O, a water molecule being made of two hydrogen atoms with an oxygen atom between them. I shall trace water from its origin as matter in the Big Bang, show how hydrogen and oxygen are made and brought together in interstellar space to make water molecules, and look at how water is distributed around the Solar System, including to our own Earth.

CREATION OF MATTER, AS HYDROGEN

Some 12 to 15 billion years ago, the Universe was born in the Big Bang, an enormous, explosive, energetic event. In the first 4 minutes, matter was created. This matter was in the form of hydrogen (75%) and helium (25%), with traces of lithium, beryllium and boron. Because of the density of the radiation of the Big Bang, the hydrogen and helium atoms were ionized, separated into their nuclei (protons and alpha particles) and electrons. The nuclei and electrons, having opposite electric charge, attracted each other and recombined as atoms. At first, every time an electron was captured by a hydrogen or helium nucleus, and an atom was formed, a photon of radiation immediately passed by and ionized the atom again. But as time went on the Universe expanded, and the matter and radiation grew less dense. Nuclei and electrons still attracted each other and recombined, but ionizing encounters between photons and atoms became rarer.

After about 300,000 years the Universe had grown to such a size that encounters between the photons of radiation and any atoms that had formed were very infrequent. From this time on, the hydrogen that recombined into atoms remained as atoms. The epoch of the Universe at which this happened is called the recombination epoch. The atoms of hydrogen in a glass of water have nearly all survived from that time – if it were possible to put a marker on one of the hydrogen atoms in the glass, the atom could probably be traced back, unchanged for billions of years, to the recombination epoch.

From that time too, the radiation that was wandering in space between the atoms also remained unaltered by interaction with matter. The expansion of the Universe after the recombination epoch increased the wavelength of the radiation, and at the same time decreased its energy and its temperature. The temperature of the radiation is now 3 degrees kelvin. The radiation is perceived as the cosmic microwave background, a bath of microwave radiation 'visible' to radio astronomers wherever they look in the sky.

Because the cosmic microwave background has been unaltered since it was created, the radiation provides radio astronomers with an image of the Universe as it was at the age of 300,000 years. The image is not entirely uniform, but has preserved details which represent some of the features of the Universe at the recombination epoch. The first measurements of the size of the details was made by the COBE (Cosmic Background Explorer) satellite after its first year of operation. The first feature identified in the cosmic microwave background was a 'bump' which was imaged by the Tenerife Microwave Background Experiment, initiated by Jodrell Bank radio astronomers.

COBE lasted four years, and careful analysis of all the data has produced a map of several identified features, distributed over the whole sky. COBE's resolution was 10°, and a map with finer resolution (but of a small patch, rather than of the whole sky) has been made by the Cosmic Anisotropy Telescope, Cambridge. The cosmic microwave background is astonishingly uniform, much more uniform in shade than the purest white paper. The details on the images have a contrast only of 1 part in 100,000, or 0.001%.

The features on maps of the cosmic microwave background represent regions of the Universe that were hotter and/or denser than average. They are blobs of (mostly) hydrogen that evolved into the largest structures known in the Universe. The blobs on the Cambridge map, for example, evolved into groups of galaxies spanning some 150 million light-years. The feature known as the Great Wall of galaxies, which stretches across the sky at a distance of some 500 million light-years from us, is one such feature.

The details on the maps of the cosmic microwave background thus represent the earliest traceable images of part of the matter (hydrogen) in the Universe that became water.

CREATION OF OXYGEN

No oxygen was created in the Big Bang. The oxygen in the water molecules in the glass of water has been made in stars, principally by the nuclear fusion processes that generate stars' energy. This chain of nuclear reactions fuses hydrogen to helium, and then helium to carbon and oxygen, going on to make silicon and heavier atoms. The centres of stars, particularly the centres of the more massive stars, thus became huge accumulations of what astronomers call 'heavy elements' – all those whose atoms are heavier than helium.

Heavy elements, including oxygen, were distributed from massive stars into interstellar space in two ways. A star's stellar wind dredges up material from interior and carries it out into the surrounding region of space. And if a star becomes a supernova, the explosion blasts processed stellar material into space at high speeds.

The gaseous atoms of heavy elements cool in space, where they wander, mostly single and alone. But some might stick together, first as small and then large molecules, and eventually as solid particles called interstellar grains. Astronomical observations show that the grains are small (less than 0.01 to 10 micrometres in size). The grains are either carbon grains (pure graphite, or hydrogenated amorphous carbon grains), or amorphous grains of oxygen-bearing silicate material, particularly olivine, which includes a larger proportion of oxygen than most other silicaceous minerals. Olivine shows as a distinctive feature in the infrared spectra of dusty places in the Universe as examined by ESA's Infrared Space Observatory, ISO.

Interstellar grains can be collected from interplanetary space. As the Solar System moves through the Galaxy, the grains stream like rain between the planets, and can be collected by sticky pads on high-flying planes and satellites. Among the interplanetary dust of cometary and asteroidal origin which such experiments collect are particles which show evidence of long exposure to high-radiation cosmic rays in space. This suggests that the particles are interstellar grains.

Laboratory studies of the grains show that most are silicate or carbonaceous grains. From an analysis of their compositions, astronomers conjecture that silicate grains form from a mixture of material from a star where there is more oxygen than carbon, and carbonaceous grains from when the carbon content exceeds that of oxygen. Most of the interstellar grains analysed have formed around carbon-rich stars.

There is evidence that interstellar grains were first formed very early on in the life of the Universe. This indicates that very early on there was oxygen in space, mixing with interstellar hydrogen and, as we shall see, producing water. For instance, ISO examined an area of the sky imaged earlier by the Hubble Space Telescope and known as the Hubble Deep Field (HDF). The ISOCAM instrument on ISO, working with large ground-based telescopes, identified in the HDF five sources emitting infrared radiation at a wavelength of 15 micrometres. They are dust-shrouded 'starburst' galaxies. Such galaxies are making stars at a formation rate of 10–1000 solar masses per year (compared with the current rate of star formation in our Galaxy of 1 solar mass per year). The newly forming stars include massive stars which have strong stellar winds; many explode as supernovae. They are thus distributing heavy elements into space and making dust grains in abundance, which, heated by the radiation of the remaining stars, glow warmly and emit the infrared radiation detected by ISO.

Observations made by, among others, ISO, the Hubble Space Telescope, the William Herschel Telescope and the Anglo-Australian Telescope, show that dust, and thus oxygen, was made in abundance in the early Universe. In fact, it was during the first 10% of the life of the Universe that most of the stars that have ever been made were formed. This was the main epoch of the manufacture of large amounts of solid dust and oxygen. Very early on, there were the ingredients in galaxies to make water – and provide the start for life.

HYDROGEN AND OXYGEN MAKE WATER IN SPACE

During its three-year operational lifetime, ISO examined numerous nebulae, including an object called GL2591. This object consists of a cloud wrapped around a newly formed massive star, and includes silicate grains, dry ice (carbon dioxide) and water ice. ISO also mapped the Orion Nebula and detected water vapour there. In fact, ISO discovered that water was common, both as gaseous vapour and, in cold places, in solid form as ice.

Water vapour in the Orion Molecular Cloud was created by shock waves propagating through the mixture of hydrogen and oxygen. The shock waves were generated from the violent early stages of starbirth in Orion, a process which both causes the cloud material to contract to make a star and ejects some of the starbirth material back into space in jets. The collisions of the jets with the surrounding cloud make shock waves, and when the temperature of the cloud material reaches over 100°C, chemical reactions convert hydrogen and oxygen into water. In the Orion Molecular Cloud, the production rate of water is one oceanful every few minutes.

Water molecules are unstable when exposed to the ultraviolet light emitted by newly forming stars. This means that the water produced in the Orion Molecular Cloud would first be produced and then destroyed by the star-forming process, unless there were a protection mechanism. There is such a mechanism, acting as a kind of parasol, shading the water from the new stars. The parasol is the dust in the cloud, which shades the water from destructive UV light.

FORMATION OF PLANETS

As a star contracts from a giant molecular cloud like Orion's, some of its material spins off, orbiting the star in its equatorial plane. Such material has been imaged by the Hubble Space Telescope in Orion's stars; it is visible as dust disks around some of the young stars. This is the raw material for the stars' planetary systems. Water shielded in the dust, as vapour or condensed as ice on the dust grains in the more distant regions of the disk, thus finds its way into planetary systems.

The Orion dust disks are about a million years old. Older disks have recently been imaged by a new camera installed on the James Clerk Maxwell Telescope in Hawaii. SCUBA is the name of the camera (Submillimetre Common-User Bolometric Array), and it is sensitive to long-wavelength infrared radiation emitted by warm dust. Around two nearby stars, SCUBA has imaged dusty disks. Around Fomalhaut, SCUBA has seen a 200-million-year-old dusty disk, edge on.

Around Epsilon Eridani, SCUBA has seen a ring of dust of 60 AU radius. The disk is estimated to be a billion years old. The disk is empty in the centre – the dust in this system has presumably been rolled into large lumps which have already formed planets. The remaining dust is at the position occupied by the Kuiper Belt in our own Solar System – a circle of dust and icy material in the cold regions near and beyond the outer planets.

WATER IN OUR SOLAR SYSTEM

The dust in the inner part of our Solar System is mostly dry. We have samples of it in large chunks in the form of chondritic meteorites. They have a crumbly, granular structure of lightly compacted material (not fused by melting), and were formed in our Solar System about 4.55 billion years ago. This is the same material that merged into larger lumps and built up the terrestrial planets – Mercury, Venus, Earth, Mars and the asteroids. The material is dry because the heat of the Sun, both at the time the Sun formed, and during its lifetime since as its heat output doubled, has melted, vaporized, dissociated and driven away the water molecules. Beyond the asteroids, in the outer zone of the Solar System, it is colder. Lighter gases can survive, including water as vapour and as solid ice. The gas giant planets – Jupiter, Saturn, Uranus and Neptune – are made of this material.

Orbiting through and around the outer reaches of the Solar System are comets, which are made of the icy material left over from the formation period of the Solar System – the icy, watery counterparts of the dry chondritic meteorites. The only comet whose nucleus has been inspected at close quarters is Halley's Comet, viewed by the ESA probe Giotto from a distance of 20,000 km. The nucleus was an irregular ellipsoid measuring $9 \times 9 \times 15$ km, consisting of 75 per cent water ice contained within a dark crust, like chocolate-coated ice cream. The crust is organic and silicate material, the solid components of the Solar

System material that were originally embedded in the ice and are left on the surface of the nucleus as its outer parts melt in the heat of the Sun.

Comets, and therefore aboriginal ice from the epoch of formation of the Solar System, are distributed in two zones: the Oort Cloud and the Kuiper Belt. The Oort Cloud surrounds the Solar System, and is conjectured to be the source of the long-period comets. These comets have periods in excess of 200 years. Their orbits are very large (up to 50,000 AU), but there is surprisingly little spread in the sizes of the orbits. This suggests that all the long-period comets started out from the same distance, as would be the case if they fell in towards the Sun from a thin spherical shell, rather than from a range of large distances from the Sun. Half the long-period comets have retrograde orbits – travelling round the Solar System the 'wrong way' – and the inclinations of their orbits can be high. Both these properties are what you would expect if the comets originally had an isotropic distribution. All this suggests that the Oort Cloud is in the form of a hollow sphere of radius about 50,000 AU.

By contrast, the Kuiper Belt also surrounds the Solar System, but in the form of a disk whose inner rim lies just beyond the orbit of Neptune. The Kuiper Belt is the main source of the short-period comets. The orbits of most of these comets are *direct* – they move around the Solar System in the same direction as the planets – and most are in orbits which have fairly low inclinations. These comets 'remember' their origin in the Kuiper Belt.

As well as in the comets, aboriginal water remains in the planets of the outer Solar System. Some has sunk out of sight below the cloud tops of the atmospheres of the giant planets (as on Jupiter), but elsewhere it has evaporated (as in the volcanic heat of Io), or escaped from the low gravitational pull of its parent body (as from some of the dry small moons).

Water is common on the larger moons of the outer planets. The Galileo spacecraft has shown that Jupiter's satellite Europa has a completely spherical, nearly smooth surface, which however shows a grooved structure. The interpretation of this appearance is that Europa is covered with icy plains, the grooves being evidence of the cracking of the ice floes. The floes are mobile because they float on subsurface fluid water. The ice layer of Europa is perhaps as much as a kilometre thick, and it is the pressure of the floating ice, and the small radioactive and tidal heating of Europa's interior, which liquidizes the water below.

Water has recently been discovered on Saturn's moon Titan. The surface of Titan has never been seen, since it is covered in an atmosphere, principally of nitrogen, but also containing opaque hydrocarbon compounds, mostly methane and ethane. Titan's atmosphere is reminiscent of the proto-atmosphere of the Earth, which accounts for its strong scientific interest. This is why ESA sent the Huygens probe, carried by the Cassini spacecraft, to land on Titan. An even greater impetus to the Huygens mission was given by the discovery by ISO of water in Titan's atmosphere.

The outermost planet, Pluto, and its moon, Charon, are two Solar System objects which may well be covered with water ice. They orbit the Sun in a highly inclined, rather eccentric orbit which lies at the inner edge of the Kuiper Belt. Some astronomers regard them as Kuiper Belt objects, rather than as a planet and its moon. From ground-based observations it is clear that Pluto has an atmosphere, but there has never been a close inspection of Pluto by a spacecraft to elucidate its nature in detail. The incredible resolution of the Hubble Space Telescope has made it possible to produce the first crude maps of Pluto and Charon, and the features of their surfaces seem to be variable. An explanation could be that there is indeed frost on the surface of both these objects.

WATER TRANSPORTATION IN THE SOLAR SYSTEM

As well as aboriginal water in the outer Solar System, water can be added to any of the moons and planets by cometary impacts. Such impacts inject new supplies of water into the atmospheres of the planets and onto the surfaces of the moons. The most dramatic example of such an event in history was the recent impact on Jupiter of Comet Shoemaker–Levy 9. This was a short-period comet which was first broken up and then captured by a near encounter with Jupiter, after which it impacted on Jupiter in July 1994. The frictional melting of the ice during the comet's plunge into Jupiter's atmosphere added water vapour to the upper regions of the atmosphere, even though aboriginal water had sunk out of sight below the cloud tops. ISO detected some water vapour in Jupiter's atmosphere, in fact in the atmospheres of all the gas giant planets, and this water is believed to have been transported to the planets by the impacts of comets throughout recent times (the last few million years).

Jupiter's satellites Ganymede and Callisto show evidence of past cometary impacts. The Galileo probe has imaged on each a row of what appear to be impact craters which form a straight line. Each crater chain could have been formed by the successive impacts of the fragments of a comet onto the surface of each moon. The peaks of the crater chain of Callisto are white with frost.

If comets impact on the distant planets and moons of the Solar System, then they impact on the nearer bodies too. The SOHO solar probe has imaged several 'sungrazer' comets in the vicinity of the Sun, including one which approached the Sun but was not seen to leave – evidently it impacted on the Sun. Is there evidence that comets have impacted on the Earth or the Moon?

WATER ON THE MOON

Conventionally our own Moon is regarded as a dry place, made hot enough during the 14-day long lunar 'days' to evaporate water, and with a low surface gravity, so that the water vapour escapes. This expectation was confirmed by the Apollo astronauts, who found during their sunlit exploration of the Moon's equatorial regions that it was indeed a dry, dusty place.

However, not all of the Moon is sunlit, and in particular the Moon's south polar region is marked by a depression called the Aitken Basin, whose centre is perpetually in shadow, although the mountains and high crater walls which populate it can be sunlit. In fact, the south pole of the Moon lies within an unnamed small crater, whose walls are 'peaks of perpetual sunlight' – no matter what the time of day or season, the mountain tops are in view of the Sun. This is an extraterrestrial phenomenon which is impossible on Earth, because of the inclination of the Earth's axis of rotation to the plane of the ecliptic and therefore to the direction of the Sun. In this respect the Moon is unlike the Earth – a mountain at the south pole in Antarctica could not be so high that in winter it would reach above the shadow cast by the body of the Earth within the Antarctic Circle. It appears from calculations that the Moon's axis has been at this angle, perpendicular to the ecliptic, for more than a billion years.

The first satellite to orbit the Moon over its poles was Clementine, in 1994, and it provided the first indications that, within the perpetually shadowed, cold regions of the south polar crater, was ice. The clue came in its radio transmissions as it approached the Earth over the crater. Reflections of the radio beam indicated that the floor of the crater was icy.

Further evidence came from Lunar Prospector, a satellite which entered lunar polar orbit in 1998, with an instrument designed to map the composition of the surface of the Moon. The detector used neutron spectroscopy at three energies, and it detected hydrogen nuclei. As the detector scanned the Moon's surface, it found dips in the numbers of medium-energy neutrons at both lunar poles – this has been interpreted as a signature for water, although it is not unequivocal. If water ice is present, the material is distributed in lumps over the polar surface, within the ground soil layer, in the cold shadows of both the north and south poles.

The origin of this water is conjectured to be the impact and melting of a comet or comets on the Moon at some time in the last millions or billions of years. Temporarily the Moon would have had an atmosphere of water vapour, which condensed at the cold polar regions. Of course it would have condensed on the night side of the Moon too, but would then have been evaporated on subsequent sunrises, and lost into space.

The discovery of water on the Moon means that a resource is available for establishing a lunar colony. It will be not only drinking water for the astronauts, but also something that can be separated by electrolysis into hydrogen and oxygen to manufacture fuels for the return journey. The Peak of Perpetual Light at the south polar crater has been identified as a good place for a colony. Not only is there water nearby, but it is also a good location, in perpetual sunlight, for a solar array with which to generate power. Solar electric power from the Peak of Perpetual Light would be used, not only for the electrolysis but also for all the needs of the colony, obviating the need to carry batteries which would have to last the fortnight's darkness of a lunar night, or a nuclear reactor whose use might be problematical.

WATER ON MARS

In recent astronomical history Mars has been alternately regarded as dry, and as watery. Its dark markings were at first identified as oceans, and thought to be linked by *canali*, channels, which in popular culture became visualized as irrigation systems constructed by an advanced civilization to counter the drying out of the planet. Its white polar caps were thought to be icy caps like the Antarctic and Arctic regions of the Earth.

The first impressions from close surveys were a complete contrast to this picture. Orbiting spacecraft showed that there were no bodies of water on Mars – it was a place of deserts and dust storms. Only at the north pole was there a region of permanent water – an ice cap, covered by carbon dioxide 'snow' most of the time, but exposed when the dry ice evaporates during the northern Martian summer. According to measurements by Mars Global Surveyor released in the summer of 1999, Mars has ice deposits about the same size as the ice covering Greenland. The Viking landers looked out from their landing sites near the Martian equator over rocky and dusty plains. However, close inspection of the geological evidence showed that although Mars was now dry, it once had rivers, lakes and floods of water.

Viking Orbiter mapped dry rivers, forming dendritic systems of merging streams, in the pattern of tree branches (hence the term 'dendritic'). These drainage systems showed evidence of water shaping the landscape over long periods of time, and in some cases the absence in the dendritic pattern of small-scale streams suggested that the dry beds had been carved by groundwater flowing beneath a protective cover of ice rather than by the run-off of rain. Mars Global Surveyor, in orbit around Mars at the present time, has confirmed the presence of dry rivers and crusty, dried-up lake beds. Its high-resolution images identified stepped cliffs on the interior walls of craters, which appear to be wave-cut platforms, formed at different levels of the water which once filled the craters.

A startling discovery by the Viking orbiters was of crater-crowned 'islands', standing proud above a dry plain at Ares Vallis in the Chryse Planitia region of Mars. Their lozenge shapes suggested that they were made by a flood which formed streamlined islands around 8–10 km craters. The height of the scarps surrounding the islands is 400–600 metres. The flood that carved these cliffs must have been of catastrophic proportions. Mars Pathfinder landed in a similar flood valley, observing the varied rocks and rounded boulders brought to its location by another flood.

Where is this Martian water now? It could be under the surface, perhaps as a permafrost many kilometres deep. Some recent craters, like the one known as Yuty, are surrounded by outflowing lobes which look like the petals of a flower. Such patterns are not found on the Moon or on Mercury. Craters like Yuty are known as 'splosh' craters, and the lobate pattern is described as a 'fluidized impact surface pattern', as if formed by a projectile impacting in mud. This indeed suggests that the subsurface of Mars is ice, and that it was melted by the impact, flowing outwards and then refreezing.

What happened to Mars to turn it from a planet with water to a dry desert? Mars has an orbit whose eccentricity is exceeded only by Mercury and Pluto. The amount of sunlight Mars receives therefore changes a lot, as its orbit takes it far from and near to the Sun. Mars also has a high axial inclination, so the intensity of sunlight varies as the Martian surface presents differing angles to the Sun. These factors mean that Mars's seasonal weather cycle is exaggerated, with profound differences between summer and winter. Moreover, both the eccentricity and the axial inclination vary a lot as the Martian orbit evolves on timescales of millions of years. The eccentricity changes between zero and 0.1; the axial inclination changes between 13° and 42°, and may occasionally have been as low as zero or as high as 60°. Changes like these may have subjected Mars to a periodic drying-out process.

An alternative theory is that Mars became dry after a major impact that changed its global climate. Mars Global Surveyor has measured the largest crater in the Solar System on Mars – it is called Hellas, and is 2400km wide and 10km deep (deeper than Mt Everest is tall). Unlike the Earth after the asteroid impact of 65 million years ago, which changed the climate, triggered the change from the Tertiary geological epoch to the Cretaceous, and is credited with the extinction of the dinosaurs, Mars may never have recovered from its large impact, most of its water having evaporated into space during a period of intense global warming.

WATER ON THE EARTH

The only place in the Universe which we know for sure has liquid water is the Earth. Table 1 shows how water is distributed on the Earth. The vast majority of the water is in the oceans which, covering two-thirds of the Earth's surface at an average depth of nearly 4 km, contain a mass which is millions of times more than the mass of a comet like Halley. By coincidence, the amount of water held in the biomass of terrestrial life (including you and me) is roughly equal to the mass of a comet.

There are two theories about the origin of terrestrial water. The geological theory of its origin points to the water content of the rocks from which the Earth was assembled, consisting of minerals which would have taken up water. As the Earth's material was heated by volcanic processes, the minerals were dried out again and the water expelled from volcanoes as steam. No doubt this process did occur, but astronomers point to an alternative explanation, and it is not settled which of the two alternatives is dominant.

	Depth (m)	Area (km²)	Mass (tonnes)
Oceans	3800	350×10^6	1400×10^{15}
Fresh water			
Ice sheets	1000	14×10^6	10×10^{15}
Glaciers	100	1×10^6	1×10^{14}
Snow/ice	1	80×10^6	1×10^{14}
Sea ice	$1-100$	30×10^6	5×10^{14}
Lakes/rivers	100	2×10^6	2×10^{14}
Biomass	20 mm	510×10^6	1×10^{12}
Halley's Comet	$15 \times$	9×9 km	1×10^{12}

Table 1. Water on the Earth.

Astronomers point out that the terrestrial planets were formed close to the Sun from dry, dusty material, so water must have been transported to the Earth after it was formed. Moreover, there is a growing belief among astronomers that the Earth was subjected to a major heating event up to a billion years after it was first formed. This was the event that formed the Moon, and it explains not only why the Moon is so dry but also why the Moon is made of the same stuff as the surface rocks of the Earth, as analysis of the 300 kg of lunar rocks brought back by the Apollo astronauts has shown.

The idea is that the proto-Earth and a Mars-sized body collided about a billion years after the Solar System formed. The Moon subsequently condensed from dry material splashed into orbit after the two bodies merged. The impact scrambled all the geology of the Earth prior to 3.5 billion years ago (which is why older rocks are so rare), and it sterilized and dried the Moon and the Earth.

This must mean that the water of the oceans came from somewhere else, and astronomers identify extraterrestrial impacts of asteroids, and particularly comets, as the source. Such impacts were common in the first couple of billion years of the history of the Solar System, and made the craters of Mercury, the Moon and Mars. The Earth was not spared a bombardment, although it has been protected from impacts of smaller bodies by its atmosphere, and the craters produced by larger bodies have mostly been weathered away by geological processes – only some 150 terrestrial impact craters are known to survive.

The impacts altered the Earth's environment and shaped its evolution. They also delivered extraterrestrial material to the Earth: iridium, the materials of organic chemistry, and water.

DEUTERIUM

The key to understanding the origin of the water on the Earth will be the abundance of deuterium. Deuterium is 'heavy hydrogen', and is made of hydrogen atoms with nuclei consisting of a proton and a neutron, rather than the single proton of ordinary hydrogen. The abundance of deuterium in water alters as water is evaporated and subjected to other processes. Astronomers are now concentrating on determining deuterium abundances in order to identify the various processes that produced and transported it, and determine the history of the bodies in which it is found.

The Big Bang produced deuterium, which is found in intergalactic clouds at very low abundance. There are two deuterium atoms for every 10,000 ordinary hydrogen atoms. The abundance of deuterium in the interstellar medium is increased by stellar nucleosynthesis, but depleted because deuterated ice preferentially forms on interstellar grains. Comets which form from solid interstellar material are enriched by deuterated material, and Comets Hale–Bopp, Halley and Hyakutake all show a high deuterium abundance. It is highly suggestive that the deuterium abundance in the Earth's ocean water is similar to the value in these comets.

COMET IMPACTS ON EARTH

If water was indeed delivered by comets early in history of the Earth, there must have been about a million comet impacts over (say) a billion years to deliver the amount of water that exists here today. This corresponds to one cometary impact per millennium. The number of comets that impacted the Earth can only have been a small fraction of the comets that passed close by, so bright comets would have been common.

Thus, a glass of water does indeed contain a magical substance. Although transparent, water nevertheless calls to mind, as we gaze into it, a picture of the Earth in its early history with a night sky permanently ablaze with great comets, some of them crashing onto the Earth and melting to form the oceans, and the rain.

Meteoritics at the Millennium

JOE MCCALL

The approach of the millennium is a suitable time to consider the re-volution in meteoritics that has occurred in the last quarter of the twentieth century. Since the studies of the 'Pallas' meteorite, found at Kranojarsk in 1749, by E. F. Chladni, and the Wold Cottage stone, observed to fall in Yorkshire in 1795, meteorites have been acknow-ledged by science as 'gifts that fall from the sky' (Krinov 1960, p. 10). Meteorites have been called the 'poor man's space probe' or 'nature's space probes' (Hutchison 1995), and since those early discoveries they have supplied the basis for much geological, geochemical and planeto-logical research, and theorizing. However, meteorites fall only sporadi-cally, recoveries from observed bolides are extremely rare, and finds were made equally sporadically over the years. So, despite their acknowledged scientific importance, for many decades meteoritics was 'a nice peaceful area of study by museum curators and a few academics' (McCall 1998b), because new material came in but slowly. With a full teaching load at the University of Western Australia, I was able during the 1960s to rescue and curate the quite large but neglected collections of the Western Australian Museum (McCall and de Laeter 1965, 1968, 1972), and describe new finds and falls there, by allocating one after-noon per week, unpaid, quite unaware that a revolution was at hand and one in which I was to play a small part.

The prime mover in this revolution was the onset of the space age, with Sputnik in 1957 and the first manned flights in the early 1960s. Space research became a major scientific employer in the 1960s. Once manned travel to the Moon was proposed, meteorites grew in impor-tance because of their role in formulating theories about the possible nature of the individual bodies in the Solar System, and specifically the cratered surface on which a lunar landing had to be made; this extended to the study of meteorite impact processes which might have formed the craters. There was no suggestion that any meteorites found on Earth could be lunar in origin, with the exception of *tektites*, for which many scientists favoured a lunar origin. We now know that meteorites from the Moon have landed on Earth, but are unlike other meteorites except in their physical form (e.g. fusion crust), and that tektites are *not* of lunar origin.

Two other quite fortuitous events also contributed to the revolution. In December 1969, a Japanese expedition found nine meteorites on a small area of bare ice in the Yamato Mountains, Antarctica. This 5 × 10 km area subsequently yielded a thousand meteorites (Marvin and Mason 1980). Zolensky (1998) reports that over 15,000 meteorites (including those from paired falls) have now been recovered from Antarctica. The second fortuitous event was that a rabbit trapper, John Carlisle, kept bringing in meteorites from the Nullarbor limestone desert in Western Australia. It was realized that here was a quite extraordinarily prolific region covering 240,000 km2 where meteorites not only were preserved for long periods of time on the surface due to the extreme climatic aridity, but also showed up dark in contrast to the ubiquitous Miocene limestone. (Prophetically, I wrote in 1967 that 'the Nullarbor Plain must be littered with meteorites of all types' (McCall 1967).) Thousands of recoveries have since been made on the Nullarbor Plain, representing about 260 distinct meteorites (Bevan *et al.* 1998), and systematic gridding and recovery there is by no means completed.

Other desert areas attracted attention. The Libyan and Algerian Sahara is the prime desert recovery region at the present time, with 1238 recoveries in 14 years up to 1998. It can be confidently predicted that other prime, multiple-recovery desert regions will emerge in the course of the next decades. The Gobi Desert is reportedly disappointing, but there are many desert areas elsewhere in Asia, for example, which have not been searched.

I recently attended the 61st Meeting of the Meteoritical Society in Dublin (Sears 1998a), attended by some 300 meteoriticists, and it was apparent that this flood of new material becoming available has resulted in an escalation of research, both in quantity and direction. What was astonishing was the degree of detail achieved. When I was describing new meteorites in Australia in the 1960s, it was enough to describe the physical characteristics of the mass, and the petrology and mineralogy. Nowadays, entire presentations are devoted to single ultramicroscopic mineral grains and the isotopes in them. Many presentations were based on 'maps' of individual chondrules or microscopic areas of interstitial glass.

In the remainder of this article, I highlight some developments in meteoritics which I regard as highly significant at this 'benchmark' time of the new millennium.

RESEARCH ON METEORITES

The flood of new material has not resulted in the erection of radical new major divisions of the classification system, which was devised for a much smaller known total number. The most significant discovery was of meteorites which match the lunar rocks recovered by Apollo and Luna missions. However, the divisions within the classification system have been stretched with the addition of new classes, and the system is now creaking at the seams. It is likely that an international conference of meteoriticists will in the near future have to be solely devoted to ironing out the problems of classification. Naming has been another problem: in neither Antarctica nor the deserts are there local names to attach to finds, so a number and grid or area system has been adopted: examples are Hughes 030, from the Nullarbor; Dar-al Ghani 400, from the Sahara; and ALH 84001, from the Antarctic. This problem was much easier to resolve than the problems of classification.

Research on meteorite masses has many strands. The complexities of chondrules and their history continue to engage researchers, and there is also much research into refractory inclusions rich in calcium, aluminium and titanium (known as CAIs), probably the oldest surviving material that was processed within the Solar System (Hutchison 1995). There is also great interest in possible pre-solar grains in chondrites, which have been recycled and so may contain such relict grains. Carbonaceous chondrites are particularly important in such studies, and the Antarctic recoveries include many of them. Most Antarctic meteorites are small, and because carbonaceous chondrites are generally small, more are recovered from the Antarctic than from anywhere else. Also, these primitive meteorites are very easily altered by terrestrial weathering processes, whereas those from the Antarctic ice may be almost pristine. The comparative lack of terrestrial weathering of Antarctic meteorites generally has been an important bonus for researchers. Research on presolar grains provides input into models of the early development of the Solar System.

There have been a number of studies of the flux of meteorites to Antarctica, the Nullarbor Plain and other regions. The aim of these is to show whether the total flux and the proportions of the classes have been constant or variable, to the Earth as a whole and to the various optimum recovery regions. These studies are complicated by the differences between Antarctica and other terrains – in Antarctica meteorites landed on a 'conveyor belt' of ice, were buried in ice, were transported in it and resurfaced when the flow of the ice was arrested by a nunatak (an isolated protrusion of rock amid the ice), as shown in Figure 1. There may also be complications of recycling and of new falls on the surface of arrestment. In the Nullarbor, in contrast, the meteorites land on a stable surface and stay there. To be meaningful, such studies must rigorously eliminate possible pairings (finds of two or more meteorites which fell to Earth together), something not always easy to achieve. There may be differences in collection methods, introducing human bias. The weathering rates and patterns, the subject of complex oxidation studies, are quite different, Antarctic meteorites weathering much more slowly (Bland *et al.* 1998). Fragile and easily weathered meteorites like carbonaceous chondrites and small irons are preserved preferentially in the Antarctic. All these factors have to be taken into account. The time of arrival on Earth can be measured by various isotopic methods (^{36}Cl, ^{81}Kr, ^{10}Be, ^{14}C or ^{26}Al abundances). The statistical pattern of ages of arrival derived for different recovery areas in the Antarctic (Allan Hills, Yamato, etc.) varies widely (Zolensky 1998). A few meteorites fell on the Antarctic ice as long as 1–3 million years ago. Similar studies of the Nullarbor (Bevan *et al.* 1998) indicate that most came in less than 35,000 years ago, but the Mundrabilla iron meteorite shower (McCall 1998a) happened about a million years ago. Meteorites are preserved less well in desert terrains than in Antarctica.

Such studies do reveal disparities in the proportion of classes, but this disparity may be due to causes other than variations in flux. There is some evidence from Antarctica that certain types of H and L chondrites differ in character according to their time of arrival, which may indicate that the flux has changed over time. Small, unusual iron and carbonaceous chondrite populations not found outside Antarctica are recognized, but this may be due to lack of rapid oxidation and weathering under Antarctic conditions. However, in general the

Figure 1. A meteorite in its flagged position, as found on blue ice arrested in its flow against an impediment such as a nunatak, or buried rock mass, on the Antarctic ice sheet.

relative populations of the Antarctic types seem to agree with that of modern falls, with only minor differences (Zolensky 1998).

This work will undoubtedly be refined in the future, particularly with the better constraint of variables related to ice flow, meteorite catchment areas, weathering, removal rates and pairings in the Antarctic.

LARGE-SCALE IMPACT STRUCTURES AND PROCESSES

When I compiled two sets of readings from the literature on meteorite craters, cryptoexplosion structures and astroblemes twenty years ago (McCall 1977, 1979) there were two schools of thought: those who believed these structures to be endogenous (cryptovolcanic) and those who invoked extraterrestrial agencies. There now remains little doubt about the extraterrestrial origin of such large structures, ranging from less than a kilometre to 180 km in diameter (Chicxulub) and perhaps 350 km (Sudbury shock effects: Spray 1998). Only the smallest (Wolfe Creek, Meteor Crater) have meteoritic material associated with them, and the inference of an impact origin was based on the scale of the explosive process indicated by the presence of the polymorphs of silica (coesite, stishovite), which require extremely high shock pressures for their formation, and shatter cones coupled with shock-induced lamellations in quartz. These were proposed as the indicators of impact explosion. More recently, four allotropes of carbon, including diamond, have been added to the list of indicators (Gilmour 1998).

No fewer than 156 such structures were listed by Grieve (1998). The global distribution (Figure 2) shows heavy concentrations in Canada, the USA, Scandinavia and Australia – these surely cannot be solely due to the enthusiasm of searchers there. There is a paucity in South America, Central Africa and Asia (notably China). This distributional unevenness is interesting, as one would expect the globe to be evenly struck. It is possible that geological factors such as the age and type of the target rocks, the nature of the rocks now exposed at the surface and obliteration by geological processes may cause the uneven distribution, but it will be interesting to see whether new finds in the near future even out the pattern.

An example of a heavy concentration of structures in a small area

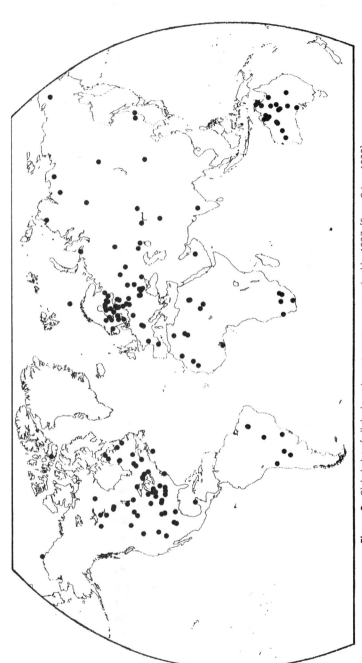

Figure 2. Global plot of all the large impact structures recognized by 1997. [From Grieve 1998]

has been given by Grieve *et al.* (1998), reporting the recognition of three new structures in the Williston Basin, straddling North Dakota, Montana and Saskatchewan: Elbow (8 km), Maple Creek (6 km) and Viewfield (2.4 km) (Figure 3). The first two have central uplifts and associated breccias: the last is a simple crater. Samples from all three sites show planar deformation features in quartz grains. With Newporte and Red Wing, this brings the count of structures in the basin up to five, of which three (Newporte, Red Wing, Viewfield) are hydrocarbon producers, as is the Heidt structure, a possible sixth. Such concentrations can provide the basis for estimating the flux of large impacting objects to Earth, provided the geological ages of formations are known and the size of the impactor can be modelled.

Researchers have used the distribution and age range of meteorites in Australia and Canada to calculate the flux of large impacting bodies to the Earth. However, the constancy of the flux is uncertain, and the databases used were numerically small, so much more research will be needed to obtain really meaningful figures for the flux of such large impactors. Hughes (1998) suggested a flux of one 500-tonne mass every 400 years. Shoemaker (1997) suggested that, late in geological time, comets have produced half the craters more than 20 km in diameter

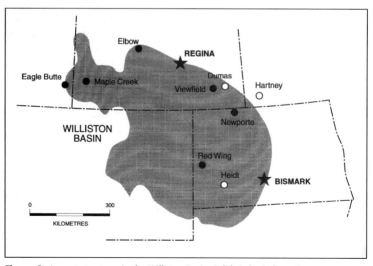

Figure 3. Impact structures in the Williston Basin. Solid circles indicate impact structures; open circles indicate structures of uncertain origin. [From Grieve *et al.* 1998].

and nearly all those greater than 100 km in diameter. Hildebrand *et al.* (1998) inferred, on the basis of the scale of the iridium anomaly, that a comet produced the 180-km diameter Chicxulub structure; direct evidence for this has come from chromium isotope studies, which show that it was either a carbonaceous chondrite (unlikely, since they are all small) or a cometary mass (Shukolyukov *et al.* 1998).

The question of the role of the Chicxulub event at the K/T boundary in causing the mass extinction at that time remains uncertain. The extreme model of a sudden 'frying of the dinosaurs' is not tenable on the palaeontological evidence (Macleod *et al.* 1997, Macleod 1998, Milner 1998, Hallam 1998). The extreme comparisons with a 'nuclear winter' are difficult to equate with the record of survival patterns. There are three possibilities: the straight impact scenario, one involving flood basalts (as at Deccan), and progressive sea-level and climatic changes at the end of the Cretaceous. As Hallam (1998) observed, a compound scenario involving gradual extinctions and a *coup de grâce* delivered by the impact is attractive, yet he suspects that even without an impact there would have been a mass extinction at the end of the Cretaceous anyway.

Perhaps the most important development recently has been the discovery of a late Pliocene impact structure on the floor of the Southern Ocean (Figure 4) (Kyte and Brownlee 1985, Gersonde *et al.* 1997, Kyte *et al.* 1998). Discovered in the 1960s by the USNS *Eltanin*, the so-called Eltanin structure has been extensively cored. It is a 25-km diameter structure (Figure 5) in which chaotic relict sediment and an ejecta layer have been recognized. Actual meteorite fragments have been recovered, apparently of a mesosiderite with howardite inclusions, in which the metal component has largely decomposed (Figure 6). This discovery is important, not only because there are identifiable meteorite fragments in association with a large structure, but also because it is the first such structure discovered in the deep ocean, as had been predicted by several scientists (Kyte and Brownlee 1985). It is estimated that the impactor was a 1-km diameter asteroid. A possible second such structure may exist in the Tore Seamount off Portugal (Monteiro *et al.* 1998).

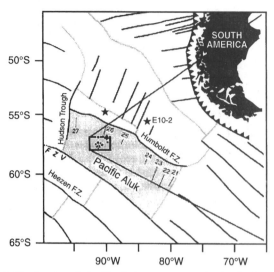

Figure 4. The location of the Eltanin impact structure in the Southern Ocean. [From Gersonde *et al.* 1997]

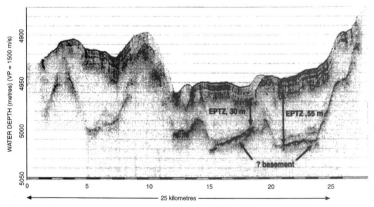

Figure 5. Parasound echo-sounding cross-section of the sediments in the Eltanin structure. [From Gersonde *et al.* 1997]

Figure 6. A scanning electron microscope image of a small fragment of Eltanin meteoritic material, a howardite achondrite enclave within a mesosiderite host; the short scale bar represents 100 micrometres. [From Kyte *et al.* 1998]

LUNAR METEORITES

Since the discovery of the first lunar meteorite in Antarctica (Figure 7), a number of others have been recovered there. Both maria basalts and highland anorthosites have been found. The first non-Antarctic recovery of a lunar meteorite was made at Calcalong Creek, in the central part of Western Australia (Hill *et al.* 1991), during a search for further specimens of the Millbillillie achondrite fall of 1960. It is a breccia of highland anorthosite, low-titanium basalt, KREEP and Sc–Cr–V components. Since then two more recoveries have been made in the Sahara (Dar-al Ghani 262, Dar-al Ghani 400) (Bischoff and Weber 1997, Scherer *et al.* 1998, Zipfel *et al.* 1998). Dar-al Ghani 400, which takes the total count to 14 (Table 1), is the largest lunar meteorite mass recovered, weighing 1.425 kg. This mass was covered with a brownish fusion crust, and is an anorthosite breccia. The noble gas composition does not support a pairing with Dar al Ghani 262. The finding of two meteorites ejected into space by impacts on the Moon and not paired within a distance of about 50 km (Figure 8) on the surface of the Sahara is extraordinary, and suggests that the Earth has been peppered with lunar meteorites through quite recent geological time. Indeed, it makes it strange that no lunar meteorite was

Figure 7. ALH 81005: the first lunar meteorite discovered at Allan Hills, Antarctica, in 1981; the cube measures 1 centimetre.

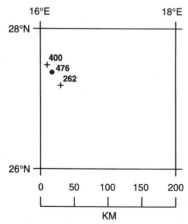

Figure 8. Sketch of the relative locations of the two lunar and single Martian meteorites found in the Dar-al Ghani area of Libya.

Designation	Discovery location	Discovered	Mass (g)
ALH 81005	Allan Hills	1981	31.4
Y 791197	Yamato Mountains	1979	52.4
Y 793169	Yamato Mountains	1979	6.1
Y 793274	Yamato Mountains	1979	8.7
Y 82192	Yamato Mountains	1982	36.7
EET 87521	Elephant Moraine	1987	30.7
EET 96008	Elephant Moraine	1996	53
Asuka 881757	Nansen Ice Field	1988	442.1
MAC 88105	MacAlpine Hills	1988	662.5
QUE 93069	Queen Alexandra Range	1993	21.4
QUE 94281	Queen Alexandra Range	1994	23.4
Calcalong Creek	Western Australia	1960	19
Dar al Ghani 262	Al Jufrah, Libya	1997	513
Dar al Ghani 400	Al Jufrah, Libya	1998	1425

Source: Natural History Museum, London, and Beatty et al. (1998), p. 356 (used with the permission of Sky Publishing Inc.)

Table 1. The 14 meteorites believed to have come from the Moon; all were found in Antarctica, except where indicated. (Where there are two or more individual meteorites in the same fall, only the largest mass is listed.)

found before the existence of the Antarctic recovery province was known.

It is also perhaps surprising that all the lunar meteorites recovered match the known lunar surface rock types – the lunar craters are so large that they must have thrown out material from deep below the lunar surface, material that should be unfamiliar to us. If, as it is widely believed, immense impacts produced vast crater structures on the Moon more than 3500 million years ago, why has not some of the material so ejected been preserved? It may have all been swept up by the Sun, the greatest space waste-disposal agent, but one would expect that, as numerous collisions of asteroidal meteorites forming heterogeneous breccias during the long time span since the impact ejections are known to have occurred, there would have been collisions between lunar and asteroidal material, and lunar material would be mixed with asteroidal material in breccias. Where is such material?

'MARTIAN' METEORITES

The original suggestion by John Ashworth that the igneous Nakhla meteorite (Figures 9 and 10), which contains iddingsite, a mineral produced by hydrous alteration, could be from Mars was supported by chemical and isotopic information from Viking missions which revealed the present atmospheric composition of Mars. Entrapped trace volatiles within the achondrite shergottite, nakhlite and chassignite (SNC) meteorites – and in particular the shock-melted glass in Antarctic meteorite EET A79001 – were found to be of similar composition. Studies of carbonates and sulphates in such SNC meteorites also revealed evidence of the activity of liquid water. Now 13 SNC meteorites are known (Table 2). These meteorites have ages of formation ranging up to 180 million and 1.3 billion years, rather than the 4.5-billion-year age of asteroidal meteorites, and share the same oxygen isotope signatures, indicating that they originated on the same differ-

Figure 9. One of the 40 stones that fell at Nakhla, Egypt, in 1911.

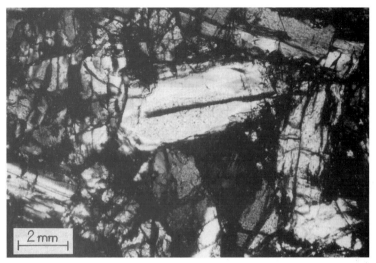

Figure 10. Photomicrograph of the microtexture of the Nakhla meteorite, showing a quite coarse aggregate of elongate clinopyroxenes and olivine. This texture is very similar to that of clinopyroxenites in igneous intrusions on Earth, formed for example in subvolcanic magma chambers.

entiated planet. The shergottites resemble basalts and lherzolites among igneous rocks on Earth, the nakhlites clinopyroxenites, and the single chassignite a dunite (Lodders 1998). This neat grouping was upset by the discovery of ALH 84001 in Antarctica, an orthopyroxenite, which does not appear to have such a close genetic relationship as the SNC meteorites, but does contain the same trapped gases. This meteorite has received star billing because of the discovery of possible microbial life forms within it. Suffice it to say here that at the recent meeting of the Meteoritical Society in Dublin, no less than a dozen papers were presented on it, but the controversy remained unresolved. This meteorite has had an extraordinarily complicated history, on Mars, after ejection from Mars (if indeed it comes from Mars) and after landing on the Earth.

The atmosphere recorded by Viking is similar to the *present* Martian atmosphere. All these meteorites have spent long periods in space before fortuitously hitting the Earth, and it is a long time (many millions of years?) since they were part of Mars. Isotopic studies reveal a very great age of formation for ALH 84001: 4.445 billion years.

Discovery location / designation	Discovered	Mass	Main mineral components
Shergottites			
(a) Basalts			
Shergotty*, India	1865	5 kg	Pigeonite, augite, maskelynite
EET 79001, Antarctica	1979	7.94 kg	Pigeonite, augite, maskelynite
QUE 94201, Antarctica	1994	12 g	Pigeonite, augite, maskelynite
Zagami*, Nigeria	1962	23 kg	Pigeonite, augite, maskelynite
Dar-al Ghani 476, Libya	1998	2.015 kg	Olivine, pigeonite, augite, feldspathic glass
(b) Lherzolite and harzburgite			
ALH 77055, Antarctica	1977	480 g	Cumulate olivine, chromite, pigeonite, augite
LEW 88516, Antarctica	1988	13 g	Cumulate olivine, chromite, pigeonite, augite
Y 793605, Antarctica	1979	18 g	Cumulate olivine, chromite, pigeonite, augite
Nakhlites			
(c) Cliopyroxenites and wehrlites			
Governador Valdares, Brazil	1958	160 g	Cumulate augite, olivine
Lafayette, USA	1931	600 g	Cumulate augite, olivine
Nakhla*, Egypt	1911	40 kg	Cumulate augite, olivine
Chassignite			
(d) Dunite			
Chassigny*, France	1815	3.4 kg	Cumulate olivine
Unique orthopyroxenite			
ALH 84001, Antarctica	1984	3.4 kg	Orthopyroxene

Source: Data from Lodders (1998) and Grossman (1999).

Table 2. The 13 meteorites believed to have come from Mars. Those asterisked are falls; the remainder are finds.

Comparable determinations for nakhlites give a figure of 1.3 billion years, for shergottites 180 million years. The trapped volatiles must relate to processes on Mars long ago, not the present atmosphere. The Earth's atmosphere has changed through geological time, and change is surely the expectation for Mars. For example, the shergottites must record an atmosphere not more than 180 million years old, but not the present composition. Studies of such changes are an exciting prospect and such a study has been commenced on ALH 84001 by Grady *et al.* (1998a), and has identified a possible two-stage process of trapping.

The evidence for the SNCs and ALH 84001 coming from Mars seems very sound, but space exploration, like geological exploration, is full of surprises, and it could be that future direct exploration of Mars will not support this attribution. One reason for doubt is posed by the following question. The Moon has a very simple surface composition-ally, of brecciated basalts and anorthosites, but Mars has a much more complicated surface, shaped by volcanism, erosive processes (aeolian and possibly by stream action) and ice at the poles. So why should only this very limited suite of SNC meteorites (a genetically related suite of igneous rocks) have been spalled off by impacts from the surface and landed here on Earth, and *no others that we know of except the solitary Allan Hills oddball*? If, as it is believed, Mars has suffered deposition in water in the past, we might even expect sedimentary meteorites – but possibly we do not know how to recognize them. This would seem to be a major and unexplained anomaly.

TEKTITES

I covered tektites in a previous review (McCall 1997). We have to some extent solved the riddle of tektites. Thought by Charters Darwin to be a form of volcanic bomb, they were for many decades accepted as a strange form of meteorite. Before the Apollo 11 mission a lunar origin was strongly favoured, but the basaltic/anorthositic chemistry of the lunar surface rocks and the quite different contents of rare-earth element virtually excluded a lunar source as a possibility, though a few diehards clung to this explanation. The rare-earth contents favour a terrestrial source, and we now know that this must be the answer. The four strewnfields have been well plotted, based on contributions from on-land recoveries and micrometeorites recovered by deep-sea drilling (and a single whole meteorite find from the Indian Ocean, as well as some tektite fragments from DSDP Hole 612 off the New Jersey coast and sediments on land in Barbados). They are, with radiometrically determined age of fall: North American (34–35 million years, in the Eocene), Central European (14–15 million years, Miocene), Ivory Coast (about 1 million years, Pleistocene) and Australasian (0.7–0.8 million years, Pleistocene). Recently, microtektite finds have been reported in a core from the Weddell Sea off Antarctica (B.P. Glass, personal communication), and this evidence extends the North American strewnfield to 4 times its size. Melosh (1998) has demolished the last objection of lunar diehards to the terrestrial theory of tektites, based on the difficulty in removing water from glass in glass technology, by showing that the shock pressures and temperatures (over 50,000 K) involved in an impact explosion producing tektites are in no way similar to the lower levels associated with glass manufacture.

We now have identified three impact explosion structures, the Rieskessel in Germany (diameter 22–24 km), Bosumtwi Crater in Ashanti (8 km) and the Chesapeake Structure (about 90 km) in the USA, which correspond in radiometrically determined age and location to the tektite strewnfields. The Australian source structure remains an enigma. Various localities in Indochina have been suggested. Of those on land the structure forming the great Tonle Sap lake in Cambodia looked promising, but reconnaissance on the ground yielded no evidence of impact; the area is, however, difficult for field study on account of insurgent activity. A geophysical anomaly offshore from Vietnam also looks possible. A source in China, obscured by the loess deposits which span the age of the tektite arrival, was suggested (McCall 1997), though tektites cannot stem from loess itself. The Chesapeake structure, related confidently to the North American strewnfield, has a diameter of about 90 km so surely the source structure of the much more extensive Australasian strewnfield is larger: how could it remain hidden when it formed only 0.7–0.8 million years ago?

We have established the terrestrial origin of tektites and have now some understanding of the impact processes that produced them, but two major problems remain. The first is the unknown source of the Australasian strewnfield. The second is the lack of any explanation for the layered and irregular-shaped Muong Nong tektites which occur in Indochina over a distance of 600 km – and possibly 2000 km if the report of Muong Nong forms in the Philippines is correct. They are less homogenized than other Australasian tektites, but cannot be proximal to the source except by comparison with Australian finds. The mass and dimensions are astonishing – up to at least 12.8 kg and 20 cm in diameter (Figure 11).

The story of tektites is extraordinary, and it is difficult to believe that it is true, yet true it is. As Glass (1997), has observed. 'one-tenth of the Earth's surface was showered with glass about 0.7 million years ago, and we know no source'. A major area for future exploration is the search for microtektites and even whole tektites in older rock formations. Glimmerings of such developments are appearing, and there is little doubt that rigorous geological exploration will uncover more.

DIRECT STUDY OF ASTEROIDS

Hitherto, though all meteorites other than lunar and (possibly) Martian ones are believed to come from asteroids, correlation has been restricted mainly to reflectance of light and spectrometry to determine composition. Reflectance correlations may be misleading as the

Figure 11. A layered and irregular-shaped Muong Nong tektite weighing 12.8 kg from Amphoe Khemerat, Thailand. [From Barnes and Barnes 1973]

asteroid may have a surface regolith which will not match the surface of the freshly cut interior of a meteorite. Recently the Near Earth Asteroid Rendezvous (NEAR) and Galileo spacecraft have imaged three asteroids: Mathilde, Ida and Gaspra (Figure 12). All three are irregular, cratered chunks of rock resembling closely the Martian moon Phobos (which may itself be a captured asteroid). NEAR also obtained lower-quality views of Eros (33 × 13 × 13 km, S type) at its first encounter in 1998; the craft should later orbit around the asteroid in 2000 for closer study. Spectrometry suggests that Eros is composed of silicate rocks, and many favour a basaltic achondrite composition such as that of a eucrite meteorite, but it could equally be chondritic.

The story of asteroids has lately been complicated by the suggestion by Bailey and Emel'yanenko (1998) that there are 'dark' unobserved Halley-type comets – extinct or inert cometary nuclei, moving on less elliptical Halley-type orbits – and now forming a population of dark cometary asteroids. These they believe dominate the flux of potential large impactors.

CONCLUSION

Meteoritic research will run and run. These gifts that fall from the sky allow continuing research *at a reasonable cost*. Even the cost of searching the Antarctic or the Nullarbor systematically is minute compared with that of space probes. There was a recent meeting at Los Angeles, in which bringing space travel to the general public was the theme: it seems that media hype has lost touch with financial reality. It is entirely praiseworthy that we should consider direct exploration of the asteroid

---

Figure 12 (see opposite). Images of the asteroids Mathilde (57 × 53 × 50 km), Gaspra (18 × 11 × 9 km) and Ida (55 × 24 × 20 km) taken from the NEAR and Galileo spacecraft. Mathilde has at least five craters larger than 20 km in diameter, and it is difficult to see how impacts could have caused them without fragmenting the asteroid. Of C type, in the inner main belt, its reflectance is actually darker than that of the other two. Gaspra is an unusually red member of the S type, believed to be olivine-rich, and is at the inner edge of the main asteroid belt. Ida is an S-type asteroid believed from its albedo to be composed of olivine and pyroxene silicates. Ida has a moonlet, Dactyl, the first asteroidal satellite to be discovered. [NASA images supplied by Patrick Moore]

Eros and further direct exploration of Mars by unmanned probes, but these projects each cost many millions of dollars. And the cold truth is that each mission will perform only what a single geologist could achieve in two or three days in the field, transported on Earth by road vehicle or helicopter. Sears (1998b) admits that all that will be attempted on Eros will be a grab sample! The cost of buying the floppy disk on which this article was composed has been reduced by a quarter during the past decade, but there will surely be no comparable reduction by market forces in the costs of space exploration – even though each mission does feed into and lessen the cost of the next. Direct exploration of other bodies in the Solar System requires immense financial outlay and will always do so. We must be thankful indeed for our 'gifts that fall from the sky'! They may even include treasures such as part of the core of an ancient planetesimal that no longer exists, and could never be explored directly.

ACKNOWLEDGEMENTS

I am indebted to Monica Grady for stimulating discussions and supplying Figures 1, 7, 8 and 9; and to R. A. F. Grieve, F. T. Kyte, Patrick Moore and A. M. Therriault for supplying illustrative material.

REFERENCES

Bailey, M. E. and Emel'yanenko, V. V. 1998. 'Cometary capture and the nature of the impactors.' In Grady *et al.* (1998b), 11–17.

Barnes, V. E. and Barnes, M. 1973. *Tektites*. Dowden, Hutchinson and Ross, Stroudsburg, Pennsylvania, 445pp.

Beatty, J. K., Petersen, C. C. and Chaikin, A. (eds) 1998. *The New Solar System*, 4th edn. Sky Publishing Corp., Cambridge, Mass., and Cambridge University Press.

Bevan, A. W. R., Bland, P. A. and Jull, A. J. T. 1998. 'Meteorite flux on the Nullarbor region, Australia'. In Grady *et al.* (1998b), 59–73.

Bischoff, A. and Weber, D. 1997. 'Dar-al Ghani 262. The first lunar meteorite from the Sahara'. *Meteoritics and Planetary Science*, 32 (supplement), A13–14.

Bland, P. A., Conway, A., Smith, T. B., Berry, F. J., Swabey, S. E. J. and Pillinger, C. T. 1998. 'Calculating flux from meteorite decay rates: A discussion of the problems encountered in deciphering 10^5–10^6 year integrated meteorite flux at Allan Hills and a new approach to pairing'. In Grady *et al.* (1998b), 4–58.

Gersonde, R., Kyte, F. T., Bleil, U., Diekmann, B., Flores, J. A., Gohl, K., Hagen, R., Kuhn, G., Sierro, F. J., Volker, D., Abelmann, A. and Bostwick, J. A. 1997. 'Geological record and reconstruction of the Late Pliocene impact of the Eltanin asteroid in the southern ocean'. *Nature*, **390**, 357–63.

Gilmour, I. 1998. 'Carbon chemistry in terrestrial impact processes'. In Grady *et al.* (1998b), 205–16.

Glass, B. P. 1997. 'Tektites'. In Shirley, J. H. and Fairbridge, R. W. (eds), *International Encyclopedia of Planetary Sciences*. Chapman & Hall, London, 802–5.

Grady, M. M., Hutchison, R., McCall, G. J. H. and Rothery, D. (eds) 1998b. *Meteorites: Flux with Time and Impact Effects*. Geological Society Special Publication No. 140, 278pp.

Grady, M. M., Wright, I. P. and Pillinger, C. T. 1998a. 'A nitrogen and argon stable isotope study of Allan Hills 84001: Implications for the evolution of the Martian atmosphere'. *Meteoritics and Planetary Science*, **33**, 795–802.

Grieve, R. A. F. 1998. 'Extraterrestrial impacts on Earth: The evidence and the consequences'. In Grady *et al.* (1998b), 105–31.

Grieve, R. A. F., Kreis, K. and Therriault, A. M. 1998. 'Impact structures in the Williston Basin'. In Sears (1998a), A63–4.

Hallam, A. 1998. 'Mass extinctions in Phanerozoic time'. In Grady *et al.* (1998b), 259–74.

Grossman, L., 1999. 'The Meteoritical Bulletin, No. 83, 1999 July'. *Meteoritics and Planetary Science*, **34**.

Hildebrand, A. R., Pilkington, M., Ortiz-Aleman, C., Chavez, R. E., Urrutia-Fucugauchi, J., Connors, M., Graniel-Castro, E., Camara-Zi, A, Halfpenny, J. F. and Niehaus, D., 1998. 'Mapping Chicxulub crater structure with gravity and seismic reflection data.' In Grady *et al.* (1998b), 155–76.

Hill, D. H., Boynton, W. V. and Haag, R. A. 1991. 'A lunar meteorite found outside the Antarctic'. *Nature*, **352**, 614–17.

Hughes, D. W. 1998. 'The mass distribution of crater producing bodies.' In Grady *et al.* (1998b), 31–42.

Hutchison, R. 1995. 'Clues from Nature's space probes'. *Geoscientist*, **8**(10), 18–20.

Krinov, E. L. 1960. *Principles of Meteoritics*. Pergamon, Oxford, 535pp.

Kyte, F. T. and Brownlee, D. E. 1985. 'Unmelted meteoritic debris in the Late Pliocene iridium anomaly: Evidence for the oceanic impact of a non-chondritic asteroid'. *Geochimica et Cosmochimica Acta*, **49**, 1095–1108.

Kyte, F. T., Zhou, L. and Wasson, J. T. 1998. 'New evidence on the size and possible effects of a Late Pliocene oceanic impact'. *Science*, **241**, 63–5.

Lodders, K. 1998. 'A survey of shergottite, nakhlite and chassigny meteorite whole rock composition'. In Sears (1998a), A183–92.

Macleod, N. 1998. 'Impacts and marine invertebrate extinction'. In Grady *et al.* (1998b), 217–46.

Macleod, N. *et al.* 1997. 'The Cretaceous–Tertiary biotic transition'. *Journal of the Geological Society, London*, **154**, 265–92.

Marvin, U. B. and Mason, B. 1980. *Catalogue of Meteorites from Victoria Land, Antarctica, 1977–1978.* Smithsonian Contributions to the Earth Sciences, No. 23, 49pp.

McCall, G. J. H. 1967. 'The progress of meteoritics in Western Australia and its implications'. In Moore, P. (ed.), *1968 Yearbook of Astronomy*. Eyre & Spottiswoode, London, 146–55.

McCall, G. J. H. (ed.) 1977. 'Meteorite craters'. In *Benchmark Papers in Geology*, Vol. 36, Dowden, Hutchinson and Ross, Stroudsburg, Pennsylvania, 364pp.

McCall, G. J. H. (ed.) 1979. 'Astroblemes and cryptoexplosion structures'. In *Benchmark Papers in Geology*, Vol. 50, Dowden, Hutchinson and Ross, Stroudsburg, Pennsylvania, 437pp.

McCall, G. J. H. 1997. 'The enigma of tektites'. In Moore, P. (ed.), *1998 Yearbook of Astronomy*. Macmillan, London, 165–86.

McCall, G. J. H. 1998a. 'The Mundrabilla iron meteorite from the Nullarbor Plain, Western Australia: An update'. In Moore, P. (ed.), *1999 Yearbook of Astronomy*, Macmillan, London, 156–68.

McCall, G. J. H. 1998b. 'Meteoriticists at Dublin'. *Geoscientist*, **8**(10), 6–7.

McCall, G. J. H. and de Laeter, J. R. 1965, 1968, 1972. *Catalogue of Western Australian Meteorite Collections*. Special Publication No. 3, Western Australian Museum, 139pp with two supplements.

Melosh, H. J. 1998. 'Impact physics constraints on the origin of tektites'. In Sears (1998a), A104.

Milner, A. C. 1998. 'Timing and causes of vertebrate extinction across the Cretaceous–Tertiary boundary. In Grady *et al.* (1998b) 247–57.

Monteiro, J. F., Munha, J. and Ribeiro, A. 1998. 'Impact ejecta horizon near the Cenomanian–Turonian boundary, North of Nazare, Portugal'. In Sears (1998a), A112–13.

Sears, D. W. G. (ed.) 1998a, '61st Meteoritical Society Meeting, July 27–31 1998, Trinity College, Dublin'. *Meteoritics and Planetary Science*, **33** (supplement), 249pp.

Sears, D. W. G. 1998b. 'The case for asteroid sample return'. In Sears (1998a), A140–41.

Scherer, P., Patsch, M. and Schultz, L. 1998. 'Noble gas study of the new lunar highland meteorite Dar-al Ghani 400'. In Sears (1998a), A135–6.

Shoemaker, E. M. 1997. 'Long-term variations in the impact cratering rate on Earth'. In Abstract Volume for the Fermor Lecture Meeting of the Geological Society, 'Meteorites: Flux with Time and Impact Effects', 41–3.

Shukolyukov, A., Lugmair, G. W. and MacIsaac, Ch. 1998. 'Chromium in the Cretaceous–Tertiary boundary layer: First isotopic evidence for an impactor and its type'. In Sears (1998a), A144–5.

Spray, J. G. 1998. 'Localised shock- and friction-induced melting in response to hypervelocity impact'. In Grady *et al.* (1998b), 195–204.

Zipfel, J., Spettel, B., Palme, H., Wolf, D., Franchi, I., Sexton, A. S., Pillinger, C. T. and Bischoff, A. 1998. 'Dar-al Ghani 400: Chemistry and petrology of the largest lunar meteorite'. In Sears (1998a), A171.

Zolensky, M. E. 1998. 'The flux of meteorites to Antarctica'. In Grady *et al.* (1998b), 93–104.

Optical Astronomy, the Early Universe and the Telescope Super-league

FRED WATSON

About fifteen years ago, a most unusual astronomy book was published. No doubt some readers will remember it. Written by an astronomer working with a designer of folded-paper models, it was an ambitious and elaborate 'pop-up' book of the Universe.

The book made a heroic effort to represent the wonders of the cosmos in three dimensions, and I think it had its moment in the bookshops. But, with all due respect to the authors (one of whom I still count among my friends), it has to be said that the wonders of the cosmos really don't lend themselves to paper models, certainly not like the usual stock-in-trade of the pop-up genre: Jemima Puddleduck, Postman Pat and Thomas the Tank Engine.

When it comes to planets, stars and galaxies, the medium becomes *seriously* inadequate. To be brutally honest, a folded-paper planet looks more like a hibernating armadillo. A star in the process of formation resembles ... well, something you'd hang on a Christmas tree. And a galaxy looks strikingly like the aftermath of some bizarre culinary accident involving dynamite and a soufflé.

Of all the pop-ups in the book, though, the most spectacularly inappropriate is – the pop-up Big Bang! Here, the cataclysmic explosion that gave birth to the entire Universe is reduced to a series of creaks and shuffles as you open the book. No bang. Not even a pop. Just a garish paper splodge lurching unsteadily into existence before your eyes.

'Well, what do you expect?' I can just hear the indignant author saying over my shoulder. And she would have a point. What *do* we imagine the Big Bang to have been like? Nothing, absolutely nothing in our experience allows us to even remotely envisage the power of this most significant event in the Universe's history.

We can imagine explosions, of course, even nuclear ones. But in our mind's eye we always see them from the outside. And the trouble with the Big Bang is that when it went off, so to speak, some thirteen billion (13×10^9) years ago, it not only produced everything now contained in the Universe, but created space and time as well. There was no 'outside' for the infant Universe to explode into – all of space was contained within its violently expanding boundaries. And there was no 'before': time itself started with the instant of creation.

THE WAY ASTRONOMY WORKS

There are a few people for whom the mechanics of the Big Bang are relatively straightforward to imagine, in a mathematical sense. These are the physicists and cosmologists whose work involves building computational models of the processes that took place as the event progressed. Thus, we have stages such as the postulated 'inflationary epoch' (when the force of gravity became repulsive instead of attractive), which began 10^{-43} seconds after the Big Bang, and ended when the Universe was a comparatively mature 10^{-35} seconds old. Such phenomena – not to mention the time scales on which they occurred – are completely foreign to everyday experience. Yet, to the scientists whose research takes them into these exotic regions, they are (almost) as ordinary as walking down the street.

How do we know that such fantastic ideas represent the reality of what happened, and don't just belong in the annals of Great Hoaxes in Science? The mathematical models of the Big Bang that cosmologists build to incorporate inflation, for example, can be run on 'fast-forward' to see how the embryonic Universe develops with time. In fact, they can be run forward well beyond the embryonic stage, thirteen or so billion years to the present day. And then the cosmologists can have a look to see how well they conform to the real Universe.

For scientists trying to understand the processes of the Big Bang, the appearance and vital statistics of today's Universe are very important. Clearly, for example, any computer-based model of the Big Bang that doesn't manage to produce galaxies when fast-forwarded thirteen billion years has serious problems. And, just as the origin of galaxies must be explained by theories of the early Universe, so also must their present-day arrangement in space – the pattern in which they are distributed throughout the cosmos.

What sort of pattern do the galaxies follow? Forty years ago, it was believed that on the whole they were evenly distributed, although evidence for clumpiness was already at hand in the form of clusters of galaxies (Figure 1). Today, we know of superclusters (clusters of clusters), and other structures like 'walls' of galaxies apparently with completely empty space on either side. There is further evidence that some of these walls might butt together to form giant honeycomb cells enclosing vast tracts of nothingness, as though the Universe today were made up of a 'froth' of galaxies. Such a distribution would, if confirmed, tell us something about the physics of the Big Bang itself. Hence the importance of today's much-heralded surveys to map the three-dimensional positions of hundreds of thousands of galaxies in the 'local' Universe – of which more later.

This stepwise process of theoretical modelling, followed by observa-

Figure 1. A cluster of galaxies in the Southern-Hemisphere constellation Pavo, photographed with the UK Schmidt Telescope. Galaxies are aggregations of up to several hundred billion stars, and are the largest single objects we recognize. They populate the Universe to the current limits of visibility, often in clusters like this one. [© *Royal Observatory, Edinburgh*]

tion to confirm or refute the model, followed – usually – by more modelling to refine the fit to the observations, is at the heart of all science,
and nowhere more significantly than in astronomy. Here, direct exper-
imentation is impossible, and the answers to astronomical questions
rely on the combination of theoretical modelling and the facts we glean
from the radiation reaching the Earth. It is the same for our understanding of the finer details of stellar atmospheres, for example, or the
rotation of galaxies, as it is for the big questions about the origin of the
Universe.

OPTICAL ASTRONOMY RULES OK

Contemporary astronomy is, perhaps, most succinctly characterized by
its access to observations from virtually every part of the electromagnetic spectrum. Since the beginnings of radio astronomy in the 1940s,
the invisible wavebands have been opened up for observation, one by
one, by the arrival of new technologies such as Earth satellites, super-
conducting microwave devices and infrared imagers (Figure 2).

It goes without saying that optical astronomy (that is, astronomy
using visible-light observations) predates every other branch of the science by a third of a millennium – even discounting the vast quantity of
naked-eye data accumulated before Galileo applied the newly invented
telescope to celestial observation. Yet, despite its antiquity, optical
astronomy continues to make a vigorous contribution to modern
astrophysics.

There are several reasons for this. The most basic is to do with the
temperatures at which we observe 'ordinary' matter in the Universe.
Such material, at temperatures between 3000 and 10,000 K, radiates in
the visible waveband, so that optical observations remain of singular
importance in building up a coherent picture of our surroundings in
the cosmos.

When visible light from celestial objects is dispersed into a spectrum
of rainbow colours, it covers a range of wavelengths between about 330
and 1000 nm. These limits are defined by the atmospheric transmission
'window', and cover rather more than those to which the human eye is
sensitive (about 400 to 750 nm, or deep violet to deep red). But it happens that this region of the electromagnetic spectrum is rich in the tell-
tale bright and dark features that arise from atoms and some molecules.

Figure 2. Infrared astronomy is optical astronomy's closest relative and, thanks to advances in technology, the methods employed are becoming ever more similar. One of the first large, purpose-built infrared telescopes was this one, the 3.8-m UK Infrared Telescope in Hawaii. It illustrates well the basic principles of most optical and infrared telescopes: a large, concave main mirror (bottom) whose diameter defines the aperture of the telescope, a smaller secondary mirror (top) to reflect the light back down through a hole in the main mirror, and an open mechanical structure supporting the optical components. [© *Royal Observatory, Edinburgh*]

Thus, the optical spectrum of an object remains one of the most informative signatures of its true nature, its motion and, often, its environment.

There are other reasons for the continuing importance of optical astronomy. One is simply the stimulus created by the new astronomies themselves, so that discoveries in any region of the electromagnetic spectrum are likely to prompt optical observations. This is especially true when particular objects or classes of objects are observed, but it also applies in a wider sense, as in the cosmological studies already referred to. For example, observations in the microwave region of the radio spectrum (using wavelengths in the region of 10 mm) have influenced the strategies adopted by optical astronomers.

Many readers of the *Yearbook of Astronomy* will be familiar with the cosmic microwave background, an almost uniform glow of radiation that bathes the Universe. Discovered back in 1965, it has a spectrum identical to that of a glowing body at a temperature of 2.7° above absolute zero – unimaginably cold by earthly standards, but positively balmy in the eyes of low-temperature physicists.

The existence of this all-pervading radiation is one of the cornerstones of the Big Bang theory. What we believe we are seeing is the echo of an instant about 300,000 years after the Big Bang, when the Universe ceased to be a glowing 3000 K fireball, and became transparent. Instead of being locked in the brightly glowing gas, light could suddenly move freely about. The Universe began to look a little more like it does today.

The reason we don't now see the entire sky shining as brightly as the Sun is that the Universe is expanding. The expansion stretches the fabric of space, and with it the wavelength of any radiation moving through it (light, for example, or radio waves). And as the wavelength is stretched, so the intense glow of white light becomes red, then infrared, and finally the weak, millimetre-wavelength radiation we see today. This is the phenomenon we call redshift and, in a sense, it corresponds to the cooling of the fireball to the present 2.7 K. Why does the microwave background radiation appear the same to us in all directions? The reason is simply that we are *inside* the redshifted, glowing ball, seeing everywhere this tangible relic of the Universe's distant past.

Cosmologists can learn a lot by studying the details of the background radiation. Is it, for example, *exactly* the same in all directions (what those in the trade call 'isotropic')? If there were small fluctuations – some parts of the sky slightly warmer or cooler than their surroundings – this would tell us much about the uniformity of the Universe at 300,000 years of age. And it would help cosmologists to understand the physics of earlier stages of the Big Bang.

Indeed, there *are* ripples in the intensity of the background radiation, but they are almost imperceptibly slight. Ground-based microwave observations are not sensitive enough to detect them, and they were first observed by the Cosmic Background Explorer satellite (COBE), launched in 1989. So great is the potential of more detailed observations that two more orbiting microwave observatories are planned for the early years of the new millennium. They are NASA's MAP (Microwave Anisotropy Probe) and ESA's Planck Surveyor, and they will be used to investigate the characteristic angular size of the ripples – their separation in degrees on the sky.

COBE was sensitive to fluctuations on a scale of a few degrees, which are thought to have originated in the very earliest stages of the Big Bang. The finer detail that will be detected by the new satellites will show ripples imprinted on the background radiation when the cosmic fireball was at a later stage. Cosmologists hope this information will provide clues to the material nature of the fireball and, perhaps, the curvature of the Universe itself.

The effect on optical astronomy of all this, particularly the COBE observations, has been to breathe new urgency into the mapping of today's Universe (out to around two billion light years) as completely as possible. This has resulted in the three-dimensional galaxy surveys already mentioned. It is a case of an exotic new technique prompting a fresh look at the Universe with an old one – albeit, as we shall see, an old one enhanced beyond all recognition by the latest technologies.

There is one more argument that must be brought to bear by any apologist for optical astronomy, and it concerns the information content of observations. Modern optical telescopes are characterized by high sensitivity (the ability to detect faint sources), high spatial resolution (the ability to perceive fine detail in the image) and high spectral resolution (the ability to perceive fine detail in the spectrum). Separately, these do not uniquely characterize optical observations. Radio telescopes, for example, often out-perform optical telescopes in all these respects. It is the *simultaneous* combination of these attributes that gives optical astronomy its edge over work in other wavebands. As a rule, the information content per single observation remains higher for optical astronomy than for any of its sister disciplines.

WHY BUILD TELESCOPES WITH THEIR FEET ON THE GROUND?

The main purpose of this article is to celebrate the present and future of large, ground-based optical telescopes. But the world's most prominent telescope today does not quite fit into that category. Since its launch in April 1990, the Hubble Space Telescope (HST) has captured the public imagination as optical astronomy's most spectacular toy. Once that dreadful problem with the main mirror had been fixed in December 1993 (the mirror having been made with sublime precision to the wrong shape), the telescope quickly shed its image of an expensive white elephant and began producing the dazzling new images that we've become accustomed to seeing on our TV screens every few weeks.

Placing a diffraction-limited (optically perfect) 2.4-m telescope above the Earth's atmosphere allows very special kinds of observations to be carried out. First, eliminating the need to peer through an atmospheric window means that the range of wavelengths to which the telescope responds can be extended far into the ultraviolet (to much shorter wavelengths than visible light) and the infrared (to longer wavelengths). Thus, the HST is an optical telescope in the very broadest sense of the term.

Secondly, the elimination of atmospheric turbulence allows the formation of essentially perfect images. This doesn't merely give us crisply detailed electronic portraits of celestial objects. By virtue of the concentration of light into compact, unblurred images, it allows extremely faint sources to be analysed spectroscopically, penning – for ever-dimmer objects – those informative signatures I spoke of earlier. An additional contributor to this sensitivity is the absence of the atmospheric component of the night sky's background glow, something that becomes more and more significant as observations are extended further into the infrared.

Every single class of astronomical object has come under the scrutiny of the HST. The planets of our Solar System, the stars in our Galaxy at every stage of their evolution, the clouds of gas that betray both the formation of stars and their death-throes. Galaxies have been studied, not only in the neighbourhood of our own, but also at great distances from it.

Perhaps most spectacular of all, and closely related to the ancillary theme of this article, are the images of apparently blank bits of sky that are now known as the Hubble Deep Fields. The Hubble Deep Field itself (HDF) was observed in 1995 and its Southern-Hemisphere counterpart, the HDF-S, followed in 1998. Staring at these fields for days at a time, the HST revealed faint galaxies existing in an era when the Universe was perhaps 20 or 30 per cent of its present age. They might not be the first generation of galaxies to have formed after the blinding flash of the Big Bang gave way to a transparent Universe, but their observed properties certainly hint at the early days of galaxy evolution.

With such awe-inspiring observations coming from the HST, the question is often asked, 'What is the use of ground-based optical astronomy? Can't the Hubble do *everything*?' The proliferation of giant, new ground-based telescopes will speak loudly for itself in the remainder of this article, but I shall nevertheless venture some answers to that question. The main limitation of the HST is that it is unique – there is only one of it. A price-tag of at least $US 2 billion (1990 dollars) ensures that it will remain unique for quite some time – although plans for a 6-m to 8-m class spaceborne optical/infrared instrument (the Next Generation Space Telescope, or NGST) are already well advanced.

Two billion dollars will buy upwards of *twenty* ground-based telescopes in the 8-m to 10-m class. And imagine how much more a space-based telescope costs to run than a ground-based one. But, economics aside, there are other reasons for continuing to develop and build new ground-based facilities. Demand from the astronomical community is one reason – there are many, many interesting objects in the Universe that do not require the attributes of an HST to have important questions answered about them. The specialized nature of the Hubble is another: it was designed with a very narrow angular field of view primarily to study single objects in great detail. It is thus unsuitable for statistical studies involving the simultaneous observation of many objects of the same type in the same field of view. And there are more mundane considerations that restrict its applicability. The maximum slewing rate from one target to another, for example, is a languid 6 degrees per minute – the same speed as the minute hand of a watch. Hardly appropriate for darting about the sky in pursuit of fleeting transient phenomena.

Perhaps the most significant reason for continuing to develop ground-based telescopes is that, with foreseeable technology at least, it will always be possible to build instruments with larger mirrors on the ground than in space. In contrast with almost every other branch of technology, 'bigger' usually means 'better' in telescope-building circles. Primarily, this is because of the ability of a larger mirror to collect more light from faint objects. The latest developments in TV-type CCDs (charge-coupled devices) make possible electronic cameras that record *every* incident photon ('particle' of light) rather than just a small fraction of them. Thus, the scope for increasing the sensitivity of telescopes is now limited to increasing the collecting area. Gathering more photons means not only that fainter objects can be detected, but that the brightness limit for recording the spectra of faint objects is pushed down, too.

It is a consequence of the wave nature of light that larger mirrors also have the capacity to reveal more detail in an image than smaller ones – in other words, they provide higher spatial resolution. But once the mirror diameter exceeds 0.25 m or so, the detail is limited by atmospheric turbulence. Even in very stable conditions, turbulence might inflate the diameter of a star image to, say, 0.5 arcseconds, or 1/7200 of a degree. How can you reconstruct the intrinsic 0.02-arcsecond detail yielded by an 8-m diameter mirror in the presence of such blurring?

The answer lies in adaptive optics – the use of deformable optical elements in the telescope that can add to the incoming light an equal and opposite instantaneous error to that which the atmosphere introduces. Adaptive optics technology is far from easy to deploy, and depends on having a reasonably stable atmosphere to start with, but the directors of 8-m class telescopes are confident that their instruments will eventually challenge the HST in the detail they will resolve, at least in the near-infrared waveband (which is less susceptible to turbulence).

A prerequisite of such sparkling performance is an optical system that is essentially perfect. This means that surface errors in the main mirror must not exceed 150 nm or so. Imagine an 8-m mirror of such exquisite quality magnified to be the diameter of the Earth: the largest ripple on it would then be the height of a doorstep. This awe-inspiring accuracy has already been achieved with the mirror of the northern Gemini Telescope in Hawaii, and others of the 8-m class.

Optical perfection demands mechanical perfection in the structure of the telescope. It demands perfection in the control of the telescope, and in its response to temperature changes, wind buffeting and other external influences. As we shall see, modern engineering has the wherewithal to provide solutions to these challenges, ensuring that large ground-based telescopes remain more than competitive in the HST era.

THE TELESCOPE SUPER-LEAGUE –
I. BACK IN THE 1970S . . .

The second half of the twentieth century has brought a proliferation of ground-based optical telescopes. The remarkable pattern of growth we see today was initiated during the 1960s, surprisingly, perhaps, as much by the advent of wide-bodied jet aircraft as by developments in astronomical technology. As rapid and relatively cheap intercontinental travel became widely available, astronomers were able to take a global view in choosing where to locate their telescopes. An extensive campaign of site testing got under way, and many astronomers of my generation had a first-hand involvement in it.

Together with colleagues at the (sadly, now-defunct) Royal Greenwich Observatory, I too played a small part in this. One of our tasks was to determine the latitude dependence of the total number of dark hours experienced throughout the year at an observing site. The results, shown here in Figure 3, were somewhat surprising to us. They show that at middle latitudes, say within 30° of the equator, the number of dark hours remains relatively constant, but as latitude increases beyond 40° there is a rapid fall-off. Neglecting the effects of moonlight, an observatory at, say, latitude 50° would need about 30 per cent clearer weather than one at latitude 30° to compensate for the loss of dark hours.

Other, climatic considerations also lead to a choice of latitude between 20° and 40° (north or south of the equator) as optimal. In addition, the requirements for atmospheric stability (and transparency in the infrared) point to the ideal observing site as a high mountain-top near the eastern boundary of an ocean. If the mountain peak is on an offshore island and streamlined with respect to the prevailing wind, so much the better. Finally, but perhaps most importantly, a complete absence of sky-glow caused by artificial lighting is essential.

Following the site-testing campaigns came a spate of telescope-building that occupied most of the 1970s. By the end of the decade, a new world map of the largest optical telescopes had emerged. I drew it at the time for an article not unlike this one; it is shown in Figure 4.

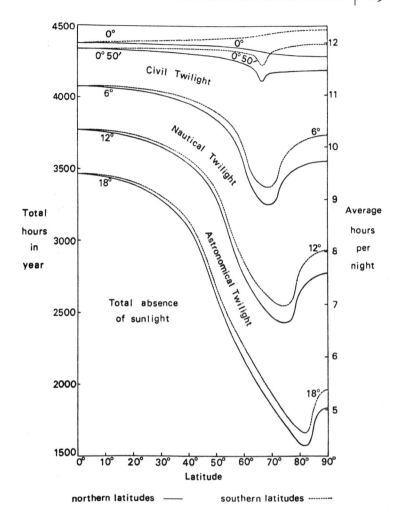

Figure 3. One reason for siting observatories in middle latitudes is that the total number of available dark hours falls off rapidly towards the poles. This diagram shows the total number of hours per year for which the depression of the Sun's centre below the horizon is greater than 0° (when the Sun's true centre is on the horizon), 0° 50' (when the refracted upper limb is on the horizon – i.e. apparent sunrise or sunset), 6° (limit of civil twilight), 12° (nautical twilight) and 18° (astronomical twilight, beyond which is total absence of sunlight). [From Yallop, Watson and Milsom, *The Observatory*, **96**, 196–8, 1976]

Clearly, the choice of telescope sites broadly conforms to the geographical conditions outlined above. But perhaps the most remarkable aspect
of this 'new world order' was the proliferation of telescopes in the 4-m
class.

The reasons why this size emerged as the norm seem to be mostly
circumstantial. A 4-m mirror is considerably easier to manufacture
than one of 5 or 6 m (6 m was then the world's largest), yet it produces
a gain in performance of two or three times over a telescope in the
'medium-size' (2.5-m) class. The success of the first of these instruments, the 4.0-m Mayall Telescope of the Kitt Peak National
Observatory in Arizona, was probably also a factor.

Throughout the 1980s and 1990s, the telescopes in Figure 4 were
responsible for many of the most exciting discoveries in astronomy,
and they are still very much the workhorses of optical and infrared
observers. Their state of health can be judged by the fact that most of
them continue to be oversubscribed: that is, several astronomers or
groups of astronomers wish to use each telescope on any given night.
Competition for telescope time is still fierce.

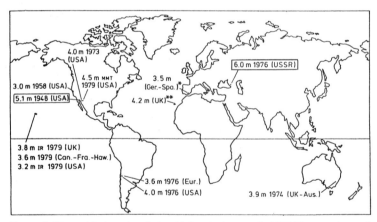

Figure 4. The world's largest optical and infrared telescopes in 1980. The map shows all
telescopes with an aperture of 3 m or greater. Two of them (boxed) are bigger than 5 m. It is
remarkable that only two of the thirteen instruments shown here existed before 1970. The
MMT is the Multiple Mirror Telescope, which, at that time, had six 1.8-m mirrors with a
combined effective aperture of 4.5 m. The Calar Alto 3.5-m telescope (marked *) was under
construction, while the Anglo-Dutch 4.2-m William Herschel Telescope (marked **) was only
at the planning stage in 1980.

THE TELESCOPE SUPER-LEAGUE –
II. THE NEW MILLENNIUM

Around a decade or so ago, events in the telescope-building world were also moving on. In particular, new ways of making mirrors in the 8-m to 10-m class were being developed. Three basic types emerged:

- 'segmented' mirrors: mosaics of many smaller mirrors (as used today in the Keck Telescopes and the Hobby–Eberly Telescope);
- thin, monolithic (one-piece) meniscus mirrors (as in the two Gemini Telescopes, the Japanese Subaru telescope and the four component telescopes of the Very Large Telescope);
- 'conventional' borosilicate glass mirrors cast in a rotating oven (as in the University of Arizona's Large Binocular Telescope and the twin telescopes of the Magellan project).

Because of advances in mechanical engineering, these new mirror types could be made much lighter than those of earlier generations, which had relied on massive proportions to maintain the shape of the reflecting surface. The mirror of the 25-year-old Anglo-Australian Telescope (AAT), for example, has a diameter (3.9 m) that is a little more than six times its thickness, whereas the corresponding ratio for one of the 8.1-m diameter Gemini mirrors is 40.5. This represents an enormous saving in weight that translates into a less costly structure for the telescope. It is made possible by a complex active support system that maintains the shape of the mirror at all elevations of the telescope.

Crucially, new optical techniques also enabled these mirrors to be designed with very low focal ratios (the ratio of focal length to diameter), so the new telescopes could be made shorter and their enclosures smaller. Again comparing Gemini with the AAT, the Gemini dome is actually smaller than that of its Australian cousin, despite the fact that the aperture of the telescope inside is more than twice as big.

Another advance that has promised to enhance the performance of modern ground-based telescopes is the control of the local air turbulence induced by the telescope and its enclosure. This demands active thermal control of the telescope and its systems, and an enclosure that controls the surrounding airflow and the exchange of outside and inside air. Once more, comparing the AAT with Gemini, the older telescope has a solid dome with an aperture to the outside world little bigger than the mirror diameter, whereas the Gemini enclosure is bedecked with huge doors that allow thorough ventilation, a concept that has been proven on several new, smaller telescopes.

A final technological advance over the boom-time of the 4-m class has been the widespread application of computers in the optical and mechanical design of the telescopes, and in their control systems. Computers have helped to achieve optical and mechanical perfection in manufacture – and to maintain that perfection under operational conditions of changing elevation angles, changing temperatures, varying degrees of wind-buffeting and the exacting demands of adaptive optics.

The net result of all this advancement has been that an 8-m class telescope built today is not just twice the size of its 1970s forebear – it is also better in terms of image quality, efficiency, pointing accuracy and stability. Furthermore, it is more versatile. Improvements in infrared detectors have lowered the boundary separating traditional optical and infrared astronomy. Most of today's telescopes are equally at home in both wavebands (although segmented-mirror types can have problems at longer infrared wavelengths).

In the face of such spectacular advancement, it is perhaps not surprising that we are currently in the midst of another boom in large-telescope building, and one that far outstrips the events of twenty years ago in terms of the total light-collecting area that will result.

Figure 5 is an updated version of Figure 4, amended to reflect the situation in 2000 and slightly beyond. So dramatic have been the changes that only telescopes of aperture 5 m and above have been added to the diagram. Several 4-m class telescopes built since 1980 (e.g. the ESO New Technology Telescope and the Italian Galileo telescope) are not shown.

Immediately evident is the concentration of astronomical firepower on the island of Hawaii and the peaks of northern Chile. These places probably represent the best sites in the world for optical and infrared astronomy. In the case of Hawaii, all infrastructure facilities – roads, accommodation and other services – exist already. (In fact, Mauna Kea, the 4200-m extinct volcano in Hawaii that plays host to such a large number of the world's major telescopes, is now looking decidedly overcrowded. This is giving rise to serious concern among the site's traditional owners, with the potential for a very delicate situation.)

Other observatory sites around the world that are, or will be, graced by giant telescopes include mountain-tops in Arizona and Texas, the 2400-m Roque de los Muchachos on La Palma in the Canary Islands (home of the William Herschel Telescope) and at Sutherland in the Northern Cape area of South Africa. All have been chosen primarily for their exquisite atmospheric conditions, but due consideration has also been given to pre-existing infrastructure.

Some of the new telescopes shown in Figure 5 are the result of major international collaborations. The Very Large Telescope (VLT) is operated by the European Southern Observatory, a union of eight European countries (Belgium, Denmark, France, Germany, Italy, the Netherlands, Sweden and Switzerland). The International Gemini Project is a partnership of the USA, the UK, Canada, Chile, Australia, Argentina and Brazil. Spain is currently seeking international partners for its Gran Telescopio Canarias (GTC), but will go it alone if none are forthcoming. Likewise, South Africa has committed itself to half the cost of the Southern African Large Telescope (SALT), but is looking for partners for the remaining funding.

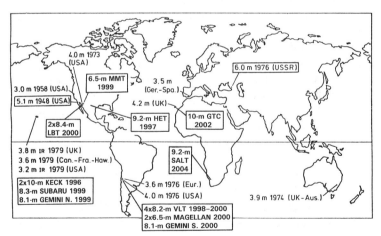

Figure 5. The world's largest optical and infrared telescopes, *circa* 2000. Instruments with an aperture of 5 m or greater (shown boxed) have been added to Figure 4. Note the concentrations in Hawaii, Chile and south-western USA. The six mirrors of the MMT have been replaced with a single 6.5-m mirror, and the telescope was scheduled to resume operations in 1999. HET is the Hobby–Eberly Telescope, and LBT is the Large Binocular Telescope. For other abbreviations, see the text.

Most of the remaining instruments in Figure 5 are funded and operated by partnerships between universities and other organizations in the USA. And finally, there is Subaru, the Japanese national large telescope, whose name speaks of the Pleiades rather than the star-bedecked motor cars usually associated with that name by Westerners.

These, then, are the countries of today's Telescope Super-league. With a fully instrumented 8-m class telescope costing typically $US 100 million (though there are exceptions), it is small wonder that a number of the projects are multinational collaborations. It is gratifying that these have emerged to bring to the world the equipment needed to carry optical astronomy into the 21st century.

AN ANGLO-AUSTRALIAN PERSPECTIVE

No one familiar with the geography and climate of the United Kingdom will be surprised that a giant telescope on British shores is absent from Figure 5. But the lack of any proposed development by her Commonwealth cousin, Australia, might well raise eyebrows. South-eastern Australia is home to the Anglo-Australian Telescope (AAT) and its wide-angle companion, the 1.2-m UK Schmidt Telescope (UKST). Both are operated by the Anglo-Australian Observatory and funded jointly by the Australian and British governments; both are rated highly for their scientific output by astronomers worldwide.

Why is there no 8-m class telescope planned for the Great South Land? Or, to put it more accurately (since aspirations for such an instrument on home ground have certainly been held by some Australian scientists), why is there no real likelihood of such a telescope being built on the Australian continent? The answer is twofold. First, Australia is a relatively small country with a population of only 18 million, despite the huge landmass enclosed by its shores. The capital and running costs of a giant telescope would almost certainly be too much for Australia alone to bear.

Australia's total annual budget for astronomy is, at present, in the region of $A 20 million. (That is considered fairly generous, but is put into perspective by the fact that the cost of this year's Sydney Olympic Games would be enough to keep the whole of Australian astronomy running for *at least* a hundred years.) A modest budget does not, of course, preclude international partnerships. Indeed, Australia's radio astronomy community, which has its own large telescope (the Australia Telescope, an array of radio dishes spread across northern New South Wales), is planning with international partners to build an even bigger one. That is the Square Kilometre Array, planned to be under construction from around 2007.

The real killer for an 8-m class optical telescope in Australia is the nation's geography. The continent, despite its size, is not blessed with any really high mountains. Siding Spring, the high ridge in the Warrumbungles Range that is home to the AAT and UKST, is only 1200 m high, and the highest mountain on the continent is no more than twice that elevation.

Neither of these peaks fits the geographical pattern described above for the ideal optical observatory site. That is not to say that Siding Spring is a *bad* site: clear skies prevail for 65 per cent of observing time, and the site is one of the darkest in the world. But in terms of atmospheric turbulence, the lack of an extra two or three thousand metres and an ocean just to the west are keenly felt. Star images at Siding Spring are typically 1 arcsecond or so in diameter, quite a bit larger than those required for an all-purpose 8-m class telescope. And site testing has shown that there is probably nowhere in Australia with observing conditions that are significantly better.

Keenly aware of this deficiency, the Anglo-Australian community has taken steps to ensure that the two telescopes of the AAO remain competitive in the 8-m era by building unique instrumental facilities to exploit particular niches in astronomy. It is well known that the AAT now boasts a field of view 2° in diameter, the largest for any telescope of its size in the world. That is to allow the robotic 2dF instrument (2dF = two-degree field) to position a set of optical fibres in alignment with no less than 400 target stars, galaxies or quasars that appear within the huge field of view at a single pointing of the telescope (for an example, see Figure 9). The light from these objects is transmitted by the fibres to two spectrographs, where it is spread out into its component rainbow colours, and those valuable signatures I spoke of earlier are recorded and analysed for each of the 400 objects simultaneously. A similar robotic instrument is currently being built for the UKST. Whimsically christened 6dF (the telescope having a 6° square field), it will replace the manual FLAIR fibre-optics system that has been in use there for some years.

While 2dF is intended to be a general-purpose spectroscopic survey instrument, one project in particular stands out. It is to carry out the biggest of the three-dimensional galaxy surveys referred to at the start of this article. The exact positions in space of some 250,000 galaxies will be determined and plotted, allowing astronomers to discover whether today's Universe is, indeed, characterized by a honeycomb 'froth' of galaxies. How can measurements with a spectrograph reveal the three-dimensional position of a galaxy? Bearing in mind that the direction of the galaxy is already known from photographs, all that is needed is its distance along the line of sight, and this comes from the galaxy's redshift.

Like the microwave background radiation, the wavelength of light reaching us from distant galaxies is stretched, or redshifted, by the expansion of the Universe. The effect was discovered more than seventy years ago, when Edwin Hubble showed that all galaxies outside our immediate locality are moving away from us – and from one another. He did this by analysing the spectrum of each galaxy in his small (by present-day standards) sample, and found they were all redshifted by an amount proportional to their distance. This result, like the more recently discovered microwave background radiation, is a cornerstone of the Big Bang theory: the galaxies are tracers of the expansion of the Universe, indicating that at some time in the distant past a cataclysmic explosion did indeed take place.

Today, we turn Hubble's discovery around, and use the amount of redshift in each galaxy's spectrum to deduce its distance, and thus plot its position in space. Figure 6 shows a simulation of the kind of map (in the form of a slice through the Universe) that the 2dF galaxy redshift survey is expected to produce on its completion. The anticipated honeycomb-type structure is clearly evident. Alongside the galaxy survey, 2dF will carry out a survey of quasars – rarer objects at even greater distances that are thought to be the central engines of infant galaxies. The relevance of both these surveys to our understanding of the early Universe cannot be overemphasized.

Notwithstanding the initiative of Australian and British astronomers in pursuing these aims, there are some observations for which they simply cannot escape the need for an 8-m class telescope. Britain has been a member of the International Gemini project since its inception, but Australian astronomers have long felt at risk of being left behind. After some delicate negotiations, Australia finally joined the project in May 1998, with a 4.8 per cent share of costs and telescope time. The UK has

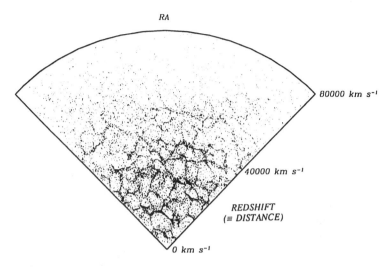

Figure 6. A slice through the Universe, in which each dot represents the position of a galaxy. Our own position is at the apex of the diagram, and the circular boundary is at a distance of about two and a half billion light years. This simulation of the 2dF galaxy redshift survey by Joss Hawthorn shows the expected large-scale 'honeycomb' structure. Results so far bear out this prediction. [© Anglo-Australian Observatory]

a 23.8 per cent share, while the USA is the largest stakeholder in the project with a share of 47.6 per cent.

Gemini consists of two 8.1-m telescopes, one at Mauna Kea, Hawaii, and the other at Cerro Pachón, Chile, to provide unobstructed coverage of both northern and southern skies. At the time of writing (December 1998) the northern Gemini Telescope has just produced its first test images, while the Chilean instrument is expected to be operational late in 2000. The essential structure of a Gemini telescope is shown in Figure 7. The two are identical, although they will carry differing suites of auxiliary instruments. Gemini North, in particular, is optimized for infrared observations as well as those in the optical waveband. Both will eventually be equipped with adaptive optics systems that will provide corrected images less than 0.1 arcsecond in diameter.

The Gemini Telescopes are truly general-purpose instruments and, despite our preoccupation with it here, it would be a great mistake to imagine that the early Universe will be the only focus of those who use them. However, the infrared optimization does lend itself to the study

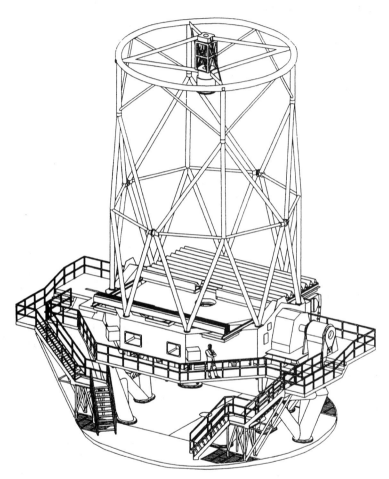

Figure 7. Schematic diagram of one of the two Gemini Telescopes. The 8.1-m mirror is seen partly obscured by its concertina-type protective cover, while at the top the support structure for the small secondary mirror is visible. The telescope rotates on the turntable at the bottom, and swings between two elevation bearings. Thus, it can point to any part of the sky. This type of mounting (altazimuth) has been used for most large telescopes built since 1980. [Courtesy Gemini UK Project Office]

of origins – of galaxies and stars. The light from the earliest generations of galaxies has experienced such a high redshift that the most intense part of the spectrum is moved out of the optical region into the infrared. It should be possible for Gemini to look back to within a billion years of the Big Bang to see galaxies in the process of formation. Likewise, the early history of stars and their planetary systems deep within dust clouds that are opaque at optical wavelengths will be revealed by means of dust-penetrating infrared radiation.

These are exciting times for Australian and British astronomers, and it is fitting that the relationship that has worked so well in operating the Anglo-Australian Observatory should continue into the Gemini era.

WHAT COMES NEXT?

Beyond the current generation of 8-m to 10-m telescopes lies territory that is by no means uncharted, though it remains fairly speculative at present. For some time, delegates at conferences on optical telescopes have listened to presentations on so-called extremely large telescopes – with mirrors of 25 m and larger.

Most of these ELT designs utilize segmented main mirrors of the kind used in the Keck Telescopes. That avoids the difficult technical problems that would arise in the fabrication and polishing of monolithic mirrors in this size range. Building up a large mirror simply by increasing the number of smaller elements is an extension of proven optical technology, and throws the emphasis of the technical challenge onto the mechanical structure and control systems.

One way of meeting that challenge is to build the telescope on the simplest possible mounting, and a suitable model for that already exists in the 9.2-m (effective aperture) Hobby–Eberly Telescope at the McDonald Observatory in Texas (Figure 8). This remarkable instrument consists of a telescope structure permanently tilted at an angle of 35° from the vertical. There is no elevation (i.e. up-and-down) motion, and the telescope is pointed simply by rotating it on a horizontal turntable. Clearly, this movement provides access to a limited part of the sky only; to access any other part, observations are scheduled so that the nightly rotation of the sky brings the target field within range of the telescope. Once the field is acquired, there is a limited tracking time for which it can be followed. Given the radical design of the telescope, this

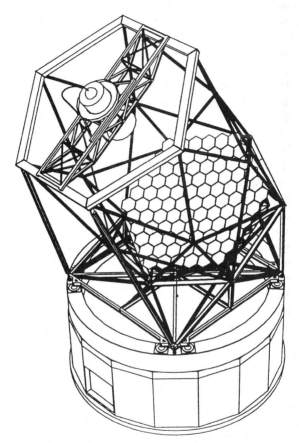

Figure 8. The unusual mounting of the 9.2-m Hobby–Eberly Telescope allows it to rotate only about a vertical axis. However, its permanent tilt of 35° from the vertical, together with the apparent rotation of the sky, enables it to access a large part of the celestial sphere. Note the 91-element segmented main mirror. The simplicity and low cost of the mounting makes this design a candidate for an extremely large telescope in the 25-m class. [Courtesy Hobby–Eberly Telescope]

is reasonably generous, ranging from 50 minutes to rather more than 2 hours depending on the position in the sky.

The novel approach taken with this instrument has allowed it to be built at a cost of around $US 20 million, one-fifth the going rate for a 'standard' 8-m telescope. But its proven effectiveness has led to an almost identical design being adopted for the Southern African Large Telescope.

If the Hobby–Eberly Telescope design is scaled up to an effective aperture of 25 m, it leads to cost estimates of around $US 150 million (1996 dollars). This compares very favourably with a 'conventional' 25-m (i.e. a scaled-up Keck or Gemini), whose cost is likely to exceed $US 1 billion by a considerable margin.

At this level of expenditure, astronomers need to take a hard look at what they would get from a smaller, space-based telescope such as the New Generation Space Telescope. It is the declared aim of NGST proponents to build and operate an orbiting 6-m to 8-m segmented-mirror telescope for a total cost of around $US 1.4 billion – much less than the HST. As we have seen, in the infrared (where significant astrophysical interest lies at faint magnitudes), space-based observation gains significantly over observation from the ground because of the absence of terrestrial background sky-glow. The NGST would compare favourably with a larger, ground-based telescope because of this.

What sort of science could we expect to come from such instruments? Observations of the first generation of galaxies (perhaps those currently seen in the Hubble Deep Fields but which are too faint for spectroscopy with present-day instruments)? Observations of the first generation of stars and the first supernova explosions? The distant host galaxies of gamma-ray bursts, revealing the nature of these energetic and enigmatic phenomena? Brown dwarf stars, and clues to the nature of the invisible matter in the Universe? Direct studies of extrasolar planetary systems? Certainly, all these are possibilities, but there is also the excitement of the unknown, the unexpected discovery that could profoundly alter our entire understanding of the Universe. It is impossible to predict what new knowledge such instruments could bring.

Finally, returning closer to home, what lies beyond Gemini for the Anglo-Australian community? For British astronomers, there is some possibility of involvement in the Spanish GTC project on La Palma. This telescope will be a 10-m segmented-mirror instrument based on the Keck design, and a share of the observing time would be a valuable supplement to Britain's share of Gemini. A decision on this issue was expected to be made during 1999.

Australia is pursuing a different tack, though still with some involvement from the UK. The astonishing effectiveness of 2dF on the AAT has turned heads among astronomers working on some of the 8-m telescope projects. Most notably, the operators of the VLT and Subaru have looked with envy on the multi-object capability that the robotic 2dF design brings. They are in the process of contracting a consortium of (primarily) Australian organizations, led by the AAO, to build similar instruments for their own telescopes. The first of these is OzPoz, a robotic fibre positioner, which should be operating on the VLT by 2001.

The image of a telescope's field of view, strewn with 400 accurately positioned optical fibres terminated with the tiny magnetic 'feet' that hold them in place on a steel field-plate, has become something of an icon within the Anglo-Australian community. Figure 9 shows such an image from the mimic display of the 2dF control computer. Here, to

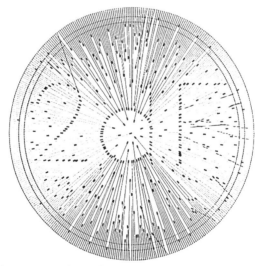

Figure 9. The 400 optical fibres of the Two-degree Field facility (2dF) at the Anglo-Australian Telescope can be placed anywhere in the 2° field of view with an accuracy of about 0.01 mm. Each is fitted with a magnet to hold it in place, and a small prism to direct light from the telescope into the fibre. Normally the fibres are arranged in a pattern to match that of the target objects in the field, but in this example of the computer mimic display, 2dF has engaged in a little self-promotion. [© Anglo-Australian Observatory]

demonstrate its robotic prowess, 2dF has even written its own name. With an identical number of fibres, the OzPoz mimic display will have a similar overall appearance, so the icon will continue to stand for Anglo-Australian excellence in astronomical technology for years to come.

For that reason alone, Figure 9 provides a most appropriate point at which to end this survey. But there is another, slightly less serious reason that makes it doubly fitting. If you turn Figure 9 upside-down, and have a look at it through half-closed eyes, you will find that it bears an uncanny resemblance to ... yes, you've guessed it – the pop-up Big Bang!

The discoveries that will come from the optical and infrared telescopes of astronomy's Super-league will be exciting, far-reaching and probably very surprising. It's hard to imagine how the essence of this could be distilled into even the most spectacular folded-paper model. Maybe pop-up book designers should stick to Thomas the Tank Engine after all.

USEFUL SITES ON THE INTERNET

Anglo-Australian Observatory
http://www.aao.gov.au/

Australia Telescope National Facility
http://www.atnf.csiro.au/

Gemini Telescopes
http://www.gemini.edu/

Hobby–Eberly Telescope
http://www.as.utexas. edu/mcdonald/het/het.html

Hubble Space Telescope
http://www.stsci.edu/

W. M. Keck Observatory
http://astro.caltech.edu/ mirror/keck/

Large Binocular Telescope
http://medusa.as.arizona.edu/ lbtwww/lbt.html

Southern African Large Telescope
http://www.da.saao.ac.za/~salt/

Subaru
http://www.naoj.org/

UK Infrared Telescope
http://www.jach.hawaii.edu/

ESO Very Large Telescope
http://www.eso.org/ projects/vlt/

Author's e-mail address
fgw@aaocbn.aao.gov.au

NOTE

This article is based on the 1998 Questacon Lecture, presented in Canberra, June 1998.

White Dwarf Stars

NIGEL BANNISTER

HISTORY

In 1834, the German astronomer and mathematician Friedrich Wilhelm Bessel used oscillations in the proper motion of Sirius to deduce that it was part of a binary system. Twenty-eight years passed before the American optician Alvan Clark observed a faint companion in the over-powering glare of the bright star, so confirming Bessel's work (Figure 1).

In 1915, the astronomer Walter S. Adams, working at the Mount

Figure 1. The white dwarf star Sirius B (arrowed), just visible in the overpowering glare of its primary, Sirius A – the brightest star in the sky. The difficulty of observing white dwarfs in binary systems, where the main sequence star dominates, is well illustrated in this image. Spectroscopic observations are now used to detect white dwarfs in binary systems. [UCO/Lick Observatory photo]

Wilson Observatory in the United States, was able to obtain a spectrum of the companion, designated Sirius B. He found that although it had a luminosity comparable to that of a cool main sequence star (only 0.3 per cent as luminous as the Sun), both its colour and its spectrum suggested that it was very much hotter, with a surface temperature of around 30,000 K. This implied that Sirius B was much denser than any 'normal' star. In fact, the observations indicated a density of around 3 billion kilograms per cubic metre, with a mass comparable to that of the Sun packed into a body only 0.008 times the Sun's radius – about the size of the Earth. Clearly Sirius B belonged to a hitherto undiscovered class of object, and with the discovery of similar objects orbiting Procyon, 40 Eridani and several other stars, it was a class whose membership was growing at a steady rate. The stars were small, and often very hot, and were thus given the title 'white dwarfs'.

PHYSICAL NATURE

With such large densities, white dwarfs represented matter of a type completely unknown and inexplicable to astronomers of the 19th century, many of whom found it difficult to believe that the suggested figures were correct. In order to understand these objects, science had to wait until the 20th century for one of the most outstanding successes of modern physics – the development of quantum mechanics.

Quantum mechanics describes the behaviour of particles and matter on very small scales. It was not until this comparatively new branch of physics was developed in the early 20th century that inroads could be made in the study and understanding of white dwarfs. Of particular consequence is a prediction of quantum mechanics known as the Pauli exclusion principle, which essentially states that 'in a multi-electron atom there can never be more than one electron in the same quantum state'. The term 'quantum state' refers to a combination of particular properties of the electron such as its spin, angular momentum or magnetic orientation. The effect of this principle is that nature imposes limits on the extent to which material can be compressed. During the formation of a white dwarf, the outer layers of the star's gaseous envelope fall towards the centre under the influence of gravity, and the core of the star is compressed so much that this limit is reached. Any further compression would force electrons of the same configuration to occupy similar locations, and this is expressly forbidden by the exclusion principle. As a result, the matter resists any further compression, and in doing so it provides an outward pressure which balances gravity. Physicists call material in this state 'degenerate', and the result is a stable body made from a material of colossal density, as observed in Sirius B.

It was the eminent astrophysicist Subrahmanyan Chandrasekhar (Figure 2), researching the structure of white dwarfs, who first predicted that these stars could exist only up to a maximum of 1.4 times the mass of the Sun. Above this limit, a stellar core collapses beyond the degenerate white dwarf state to form a tiny neutron star. Chandra, as he was affectionately known to his friends, determined a relationship between a white dwarf's mass and its radius while he was travelling by ship from India to take up a post at Cambridge in 1939. He was finally awarded a Nobel Prize for Physics in recognition of this work in 1983. He sadly passed away in 1995.

FORMATION

The main sequence is that part of a star's life in which it generates energy by using nuclear reactions to convert hydrogen into helium. The amount of time a star spends on the main sequence depends on its mass. Stars of 30 solar masses exhaust the majority of their hydrogen in less than 6 million years, while stars like the Sun last nearer 10 billion years; very-low-mass stars use their fuel more frugally, and can live to twice this age. However, every star eventually exhausts its hydrogen supplies. When this happens, a star moves off the main sequence, and its structure changes dramatically. The nature of these changes depends on the mass of the star. High-mass stars pass through a sequence of nuclear reactions which create a range of atomic elements in the core, before ending their lives in the transient brilliance of a supernova explosion, and leaving as their epitaph a rapidly expanding cloud of gas which may contain a neutron star. In contrast, stars of under approximately seven solar masses are less self-destructive, and evolve towards the white dwarf phase ('approximately' because the upper mass limit of white dwarf progenitors is the subject of continuing investigation).

On the main sequence, a star like the Sun is powered by energy generated through hydrogen fusion. The radiation produced gives enough

Figure 2. Subrahmanyan Chandrasekhar (1910–95). In 1999 the third of NASA's 'Great Observatories', formerly known as the Advanced X-ray Astrophysics Facility (AXAF), was renamed the Chandra X-ray Observatory in his honour before its launch. [Courtesy the University of Chicago]

outward pressure to support the overlying layers of the star, which would otherwise collapse towards the centre under gravity. In other words, there is equilibrium between gravity and radiation pressure, leading to stability. However, with the depletion of fuel comes a reduction in energy output, and this balance is destroyed: gravity now wins the battle, and the star begins to contract. With the outer layers of the star bearing down on the core (which has been turned into helium during the period of steady hydrogen burning), immense pressures are created at the centre of the star. Under these conditions, the core of the star is compressed to the point where electron degeneracy pressure prevents further collapse. Hydrogen still burns in a shell around the core, producing more energy; the resultant radiation pressure overcompensates for gravity, and the outer layers of the star are blown away. The star increases its size, and at the same time the outer layers cool, becoming redder, and so we call this stage of a star's life the red giant phase. The Sun will enter this phase in around 5 billion years' time, expanding to around 100 times its current radius, and producing 1000 times its present luminosity.

In the red giant phase the hydrogen-burning shell continues to produce helium, which falls onto the helium rich core, increasing the temperature and pressure further until the temperature is high enough to initiate new reactions which convert helium into carbon. This process starts explosively because of the nature of the degenerate core, but eventually settles down to a steady controlled burning of helium, which becomes the star's main source of energy. At this point in the evolution of the star there are dramatic transformations in the internal structure: convection becomes an important mechanism in energy transport from the central regions to the outside, and the star becomes unstable, its outer layers beginning to oscillate. Astronomers refer to this stage in a star's life as the 'thermal pulsing phase'. The oscillations grow until the process 'runs away', and the star sheds its outer atmosphere, leaving the small degenerate core behind. This is the process responsible for the formation of planetary nebulae (Figure 3), shells of ex-stellar gas expanding into space at velocities upwards of 10 kilometres per second. The naked core left at the centre of the nebula is known as a 'planetary nebula nucleus' (PNN), and is the immediate progenitor of the white dwarf. The gas in the nebula is illuminated by the PNN, which has a surface temperature in excess of 100,000 K. The rapid expansion into surrounding space means that in just 100,000 years the nebula diffuses into the interstellar medium, and the central star collapses and cools into a hot, young, degenerate white dwarf.

The size of the original main sequence star played a principal role in determining the mass of the new white dwarf, but now the nuclear reactions that powered the star have all shut down, and even further gravitational contraction is prevented by electron degeneracy pressure. The object now shines by the energy that was stored up in the material during the collapse of the core of the progenitor star – energy known as

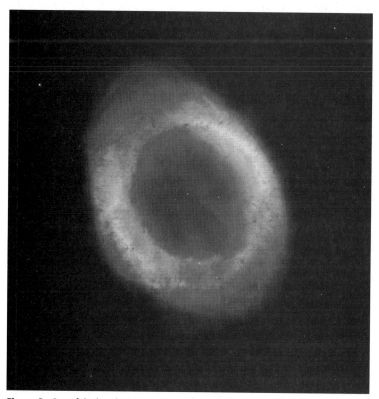

Figure 3. One of the best-known planetary nebulae in the sky, the Ring Nebula (M. 57), as imaged by the Hubble Space Telescope in 1998. Planetary nebulae precede the formation of white dwarf stars. The gas, shed from the red giant progenitor, glows as a result of being ionized by the small, hot white core left at the centre. The temperature of the white dwarf at the centre of the Ring Nebula is estimated to be 120,000 K. [Courtesy the Hubble Heritage Team (AURA/STScI) and NASA]

the 'heat of formation'. With no way of replacing the energy that it radiates out into space, all that lies ahead of the star is a slow but inexorable fade into the obscurity of a cold, black dwarf.

CLASSIFICATION AND EVOLUTION

Just as normal stars are divided into the familiar classes of the Harvard Spectral system (O, B, A, F, G, etc.), there exists a classification system for white dwarf stars, also based on observed spectral characteristics. Their very high densities mean that white dwarfs have very high gravitational fields (typically 10 million times that of the Earth), and since they lack the usual means by which a star generates energy, we observe a wide range of temperatures: from a few thousand Kelvin for old stars which have cooled down, to 100,000 K or more for young white dwarfs. A white dwarf's gravitational field exerts an influence on the various atomic constituents in its atmosphere. The heavier elements sink into the core, leaving an outer gaseous atmosphere a few kilometres thick which is made up chiefly of hydrogen and helium. This would lead to a white dwarf spectrum showing features from only those two elements. However, the initially simple picture is complicated by other factors. The apparently layered or 'stratified' structure may be compromised by processes such as convection in the inner regions, in which hot material in the core rises into the upper, cooler layers and is mixed in with the lighter elements. At temperatures in excess of 40,000 K, radiation pressure in hot white dwarfs can push heavier elements into the outer atmosphere and suspend them there, where they contaminate the otherwise pure hydrogen–helium spectrum. White dwarfs are therefore classified according to their spectral characteristics. Since these depend on temperature, the resulting classes may be broadly divided into hot and cool objects, with some overlap between the temperature groupings.

Hot white dwarfs

DA white dwarfs   Objects with atmospheres particularly rich in hydrogen, with only traces of helium and other elements. This class contains stars encompassing a broad temperature range, from around 6000 K to over 80,000 K.

DO white dwarfs   Helium-rich objects, with temperatures in excess of 45,000 K. The spectrum is dominated by the signature of ionized helium, although hydrogen and higher elements may also be observed in smaller amounts.

DB white dwarfs   This class may be regarded as an extension of the DO group into lower-temperature regions (below around 30,000 K). The cooler temperatures are insufficient to ionize helium, so the spectrum is dominated by neutral helium lines, with only trace amounts of hydrogen (only 1/10,000th of the observed helium abundance).

Cool white dwarfs (below 11,000 K)

DQ white dwarfs   Stars with predominantly helium atmospheres, showing lines of molecular or atomic carbon in any part of the spectrum. In addition, these stars are cool enough for hydrogen atoms to join together into molecules, so the signature of molecular hydrogen may also be observed.

DZ white dwarfs   Stars exhibiting only metal lines from, for example, calcium and iron. No hydrogen or helium present.

DC white dwarfs   Stars showing relatively featureless spectra, because the temperatures are insufficient to excite the atomic hydrogen and helium into a state where they produce emission/absorption.

This classification system was suggested by E. M. Sion and co-workers in 1983. 'D' signifies a degenerate object; the letters that follow were chosen for a variety of historical and practical reasons. The designations may be combined where stars show features typical of two classes. For example, stars which show mainly hydrogen lines but have some contribution from helium are given the label DAO.

It is believed that this classification is directly related to the evolution of white dwarfs, as they cool. The groups can also be divided into two categories based on atmospheric composition: those with hydrogen-rich atmospheres (DA types), and those with a majority of helium (DO/DB). Thus we might expect to find a separate evolutionary path for these two classes. However, there is an apparent flaw in the idea.

The problem is known as that of the 'DO/DB gap'. The hydrogen-dominated objects are found throughout the entire range of observed temperatures, as may be expected. However, when astronomers examine the temperature of helium objects, initially believed to have their own evolutionary path, they find a gap between 30,000 and 45,000 K where none exist. This gap may indicate that as the white dwarf evolves, it can undergo changes which alter the spectral type, causing the object apparently to change class. It has been suggested that as a helium-rich (DO) white dwarf drops below 45,000 K, any traces of hydrogen in the bulk of the atmosphere float up to the surface to form a very thin layer which effectively shrouds the helium from observation, and causes the star to take on the hydrogen signature of a DA type. Dropping below 30,000 K, processes such as convection may be able to stir up the atmosphere to reveal the helium again, giving the object the appearance which is ascribed to the DB class of star. The precise mechanisms behind these changes are as yet poorly understood, and researchers are currently trying to identify white dwarfs which have made this temporary move into the hydrogen group. Figure 4 shows the proposed evolutionary track.

CURRENT RESEARCH

In the early days of this field, potential white dwarfs were identified by looking for particularly blue objects (due to the high temperatures), and also by searching for stars with high proper motion. Today, instruments carried on spacecraft such as the Extreme Ultraviolet Explorer (EUVE), and ROSAT, which ceased operation only recently after a spectacularly successful eight-year career, have extended the range of observation into higher energies, up to extreme ultraviolet (EUV) and X-ray wavelengths. These observations are particularly important since the youngest white dwarfs, with effective temperatures ranging from 20,000 K to beyond 100,000 K, emit strongly in the short-wavelength region, and can be used to investigate white dwarf evolution. The University of Leicester's X-ray Astronomy Department is home to one of the world's leading white-dwarf research groups. Led by Dr Martin Barstow, and collaborating within an international community of similarly interested scientists, the team of astrophysicists is addressing some of the most important current questions.

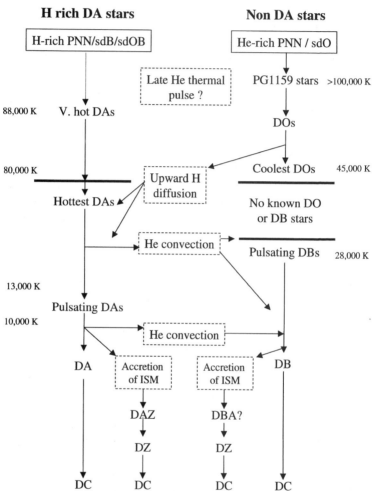

Figure 4. The evolutionary sequences of hydrogen- and helium-rich white dwarfs, showing the temperature gap in helium-rich stars, and processes which may affect the atmospheric composition of the stars (ISM stands for interstellar medium). [Courtesy M. Barstow, Leicester University]

One debate concerns white dwarf atmospheres. At temperatures greater than 40,000 K, radiative levitation counteracts the pull of gravity, allowing heavier elements to be suspended in the atmosphere. UV and EUV spectra have revealed the signature of heavy elements in many objects, and as a consequence models have become more complex in an effort to solve the discrepancy. For instance, the EUV luminosity of the star G191–B2B was found to be lower than expected, suggesting that energy is being absorbed by heavy elements in the atmosphere. Spectra from the International Ultraviolet Explorer (IUE) confirmed this by revealing the signature of elements such as iron and nickel (Figure 5), and a great deal of effort has been invested in modelling the star. Until recently such accurate models would not have been possible, the most complex treating around 30,000 spectral lines from the iron and nickel groups. But as a result of recent work by atomic physicists around the world studying the transitions of these elements, current models include over 9.4 million lines from iron and nickel. The results give good agreement with observation, but only when large amounts of ionized helium are assumed to exist in order to explain certain features. It has been suggested that this helium is in the form of a circumstellar shell, removing the need to account for an unusual amount of helium in the intervening interstellar medium. Although no shell has been observed in G191–B2B, the star REJ0457–281 has a similar spectrum, and a circumstellar shell *is* apparently observed around the star, although in this case the results of spectral modelling are less accurate than in the case of G191–B2B. Clearly, models are becoming increasingly accurate, but the results are posing further questions about white dwarf stars and their immediate environments.

The question of whether hydrogen-rich DA white dwarfs really do contain a significant amount of helium, as required by current models, is one of the driving forces behind the development of a new type of very-high-resolution detector. One suggested explantation for the absence of helium features in observed spectra is that the resolution of currently available instrumentation is insufficient to pick out helium absorption lines from the huge number of features produced by heavy elements such as iron and nickel; instead, only 'blends' of many lines are observed. The Joint Astrophysical Plasmadynamic Experiment (JPEX) is a new type of spectrometer which incorporates the latest developments in high-energy detector technology to deliver a resolution far higher than was achieved by previous instruments. Designed

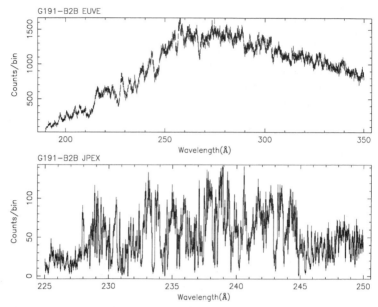

Figure 5. Top: The EUVE spectrum of the white dwarf G191-B2B, showing blends of hundreds of unresolved lines from iron, nickel and other heavy elements. The signature of helium may be hidden inside this spectrum; higher-resolution instruments will be able to detect individual lines. Bottom: A model spectrum of G191-B2B, showing the improvement in resolution which should be obtainable with the JPEX detector currently under development. Note the finer wavelength scale compared with the EUVE spectrum. [Courtesy M. Barstow, Leicester University]

and built in a collaboration between the US Naval Research Laboratory, the Lawrence Livermore National Laboratory, the University of Leicester and the Mullard Space Science Laboratory, the first test flight of JPEX is scheduled to take place in October 1999, the primary target being the white dwarf G191–B2B.

Astronomers are also investigating alternative explanations for the discrepancy between observation and theory. In a recent paper, Martin Barstow (Leicester) and Ivan Hubeny (Goddard Space Flight Center, USA) describe how some aspects of this problem can be understood if, rather than being a mixture of gases, the atmosphere of a white dwarf star is modelled as a stratified series of layers containing different elements and abundances. By increasing the complexity of such models (accounting for many more of the spectral features produced by heavy elements, and no longer assuming local thermal equilibrium to exist within the atmosphere), some of the earlier problematic observations can be explained. Nevertheless, complete agreement between models and observation is yet to be achieved, and helium is still required to explain certain features. Certainly, the direct observation of helium in an isolated hydrogen-rich white dwarf would be an important breakthrough in this area of research.

Before the arrival of spaceborne instrumentation, objects which are members of binary systems were under-represented in white dwarf surveys – a serious defect since over half of all stars are members of multiple systems. The signal from these small, faint white dwarfs was drowned out by the luminosity of the companion star, as evidenced by Sirius B, which was only discovered because the system is so close to Earth (8.8 light-years). Had this distance been any greater and the apparent separation between Sirius A and B been correspondingly smaller, the white dwarf would never have been observed. Many other white dwarf candidates must have been overlooked because of this effect. However, instruments aboard ROSAT and EUVE identified apparently normal main sequence stars which were inexplicably bright in the EUV region. This unexpected short-wavelength signal was explained by the presence of white dwarf companions. The IUE spacecraft was invaluable in confirming the existence of these objects by taking spectra of the stars. The brightness of a normal main sequence star decreases towards ultraviolet wavelengths, but in contrast, hot white dwarfs are much brighter at these wavelengths than in the optical. Thus IUE was able to use the ultraviolet spectrum to show the white dwarf signal rising out of the main sequence star's features (as shown in Figure 6). The neglect of white dwarfs in binary systems is thus now being redressed, and the information they provide can now be included in current studies of the whole white dwarf population. Unfortunately, this entire area of research received a severe blow when the tremendously successful IUE spacecraft was switched off in September 1996, a victim of budgetary constraints.

Despite this setback, Matt Burleigh and Martin Barstow recently announced the discovery, using spectra from EUVE, of a non-interacting binary system consisting of a B star and a hot white dwarf. This extremely important finding allows a lower limit to be placed on the maximum mass a white dwarf progenitor star can have. Determining the spectral type of the main sequence object allows its mass to be estimated. Since we know that higher-mass stars evolve more rapidly, and that the white dwarf is by definition more highly evolved than the main sequence star, it is clear that the progenitor to the white dwarf was more massive than the companion star (provided that no significant mass transfer between the stars has occurred). Hence, by using the main sequence object we can estimate a lower limit to the mass of the white dwarf progenitor; we might assume, for example, that the progenitor had a mass only slightly greater than that of its companion. The discovery of the white dwarf around the early, massive B star HR2875 effectively places a lower limit on this mass: we now know that white dwarfs can be formed from progenitors which have at least as much mass as a typical B star, or approximately 6.5 solar masses. The data also suggest that the mass of this particular white dwarf is around 0.9 solar mass, significantly higher than the 0.5 solar mass which the vast majority of these objects contain. Future observations of this star will aim to detect variations in radial velocity, which in turn give an independent measure of mass. The discovery of HR2875 is a significant aid to our understanding of white dwarf stars, and provides an indication that stars in other early-type systems await discovery. This is helping astronomers to understand more comprehensively the link between a white dwarf and the star from which it formed.

White dwarf stars are not only interesting in themselves: they also provide a very effective probe of the local interstellar medium (LISM). In this respect, a white dwarf can be thought of as a light bulb shining through the clouds of hydrogen and helium which lie in space between the star and ourselves. Spectra of these white dwarfs taken from the EUVE spacecraft can be used to measure the density of hydrogen and helium in the LISM by studying the hydrogen and helium absorption lines and comparing them with a knowledge of abundances within the star itself using atmospheric models. Using such a method, it is found that the Sun lies within a 'bubble' of gas with a lower density than that of the surrounding regions, probably as a result of a number of fairly recent supernova explosions which have swept much of the gas out of the vicinity.

In recent years, several white dwarfs have been observed which exhibit complicated brightness variations. These so called 'pulsators' have been divided into several classes according to their surface temperature, and their behaviour has been attributed to the presence of

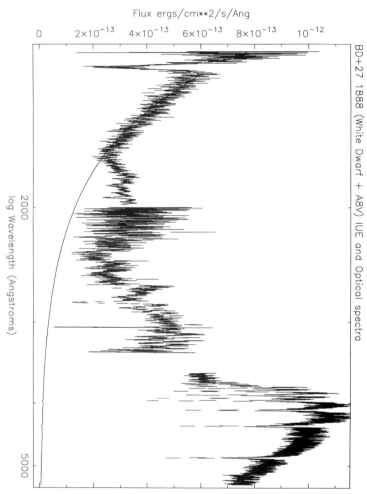

Figure 6. IUE and optical spectra of an A-type star and its white dwarf companion. The IUE data run from 0 to 3300 Å, and the optical spectrum occupies the range above about 3600 Å. Also shown is a model spectrum for a white dwarf with a temperature of around 34,000 K (the smooth curve). Flux from the A star falls away towards shorter wavelengths, while the white dwarf signal rises at wavelengths below 2000 Å. The large 'spike' at 1216 Å is due to the hydrogen Lyman-alpha absorption line, and is used to determine the temperature and gravity of the star. [Courtesy M. Burleigh, Leicester University]

various 'instability strips' at different temperatures. It is thought that within these temperature regions, strong convection zones form within the star and cause large disruptions in temperature and internal structure. As the star cools, it passes through a succession of these instability strips, so explaining the various types of pulsator observed. It is hoped that careful observation of these 'starquakes', a branch of astrophysics known as *astroseismology*, will reveal important information about the inner structure of white dwarf stars, in the same way that vibrations of the Sun are used to probe the layers below the visible photosphere.

Since they have no internal energy source of their own, white dwarfs cool steadily, and it becomes possible to find a star's age by determining its temperature. Surveys of white dwarf luminosity show that low-brightness objects outnumber their more luminous counterparts to a significant degree, but that there is also a minimum luminosity below which no more are found, even though detection techniques are capable of revealing fainter objects if they existed. This suggests that no white dwarf has existed long enough to cool below a certain temperature, and so by improving our knowledge of the cooling processes it should be possible to determine very accurately the age of the dimmest object – an age which would provide a good estimate of the age of our Galaxy.

In 1994, over fifty years after Chandrasekhar made his prediction about the upper limit of white dwarf masses, the Leicester team discovered the most massive white dwarf ever found. At 1.35 times the mass of the Sun, REJ0317–853 (another Rosat EUV source) exists on the verge of the Chandrasekhar limit. Quite how such a massive white dwarf could be formed by normal stellar evolution is a mystery, but it is possible that REJ0317–853 is the end result of a merger of two less massive white dwarfs. The star is also remarkable in possessing an enormous magnetic field, the second most powerful ever seen in a white dwarf; furthermore, it is a rapid rotator, with a period of 725.4 seconds measured at optical wavelengths. Only 2 per cent of all white dwarfs appear to have magnetic fields, and their origins are unknown. Most highly magnetic white dwarfs appear to be isolated objects, and are relatively cool (few have temperatures greater than 25,000 K). By studying magnetic white dwarfs, astronomers can gain a greater understanding of the role such fields play in stellar formation.

The Leicester team, led by Matthew Burleigh with the help of German astrophysicist Stefan Jordan (Kiel), have studied RE J0317–853 intensively with the Anglo-Australian Telescope, the Hubble Space

Telescope, the Extreme Ultraviolet Explorer and the Shuttle-borne Orfeus ultraviolet telescope. Their work is already beginning to produce interesting results, and suggests that the magnetic axis of the star is not only inclined to the rotational axis (as it is in the Earth), but also that the magnetic field is offset along this axis. The team continue to try to fathom the mysteries posed by this unique object: a record-breaking star, and a stellar laboratory for the study of atomic physics.

CONCLUSION

The examples of current research mentioned here cover only a few of the problems which are occupying today's white dwarf researchers – problems which not only relate to white dwarf stars themselves, but have important implications for our understanding of stellar and galactic astrophysics as a whole. With the immense amount of data obtained from both ground and spaceborne instruments, and the prospect of even better-quality data from future spacecraft equipped with improved detectors, many questions will be answered, and our understanding of these amazing objects will grow. But this is not just the study of dead stars whose lives are far behind them. By turning our eyes and telescopes towards the dim light arriving from these dying objects light-years distant, we are observing the closing stages of an ancient star's life, and witnessing the ultimate fate of our own Sun 5 billion years hence, when it becomes the newest white dwarf in the Galaxy, orbited by a charred, barren rock called Earth.

ACKNOWLEDGEMENTS

I would like to thank Dr Martin Barstow and Dr Matthew Burleigh of Leicester University's X-ray Astronomy Department for their advice and proofreading, as well as for explanations and data from their latest white dwarf research projects.

FURTHER READING

General

Adouze, J., Israël, G. and Falque, J. C. (eds), *Cambridge Atlas of Astronomy*, 3rd edn, Cambridge University Press, 1993.

Maran, S. P., *Astronomy and Astrophysics Encyclopaedia*, Cambridge University Press, 1991.

Zeilik, M., Gregory, S. A. and Smith, E. v. P., *Introductory Astronomy and Astrophysics*, Saunders College Publishing, 1992.

Advanced

Barstow, M. A., 'White dwarfs'. *Advances in Space Research*, Vol. 11, No. 11, pp. 47–56, 1991.

Barstow, M. A. (ed.), *White Dwarfs: Advances in Observation and Theory*, Kluwer, 1993.

Barstow, M. A., 'Hot white dwarfs: An observational viewpoint', *Contemporary Physics*, Vol. 37, No. 5, pp 359–74, 1996.

Barstow, M. A. *et al.*, 'ROSAT studies of the composition and structure of DA white dwarf atmospheres', *Monthly Notices of the Royal Astronomical Society*, Vol. 264, pp. 16–34, 1993.

Diamond, C. J., Jewell, S. J. and Ponman, T. J., 'ROSAT EUV observations of DA white dwarfs and late-type stars and the structure of the local interstellar medium', *Monthly Notices of the Royal Astronomical Society*, Vol. 274, pp. 589–601, 1995.

Sion, E. M. *et al.*, 'A proposed new white dwarf spectral classification system', *Astrophysical Journal*, Vol. 269, pp. 253–7, 1983.

Supernova Searching in the New Millennium

RON ARBOUR

INTRODUCTION

It has been said that we could not build the pyramids today because of the lack of available manpower over such a long period of time. Likewise, it is difficult to see how we could revert to the kind of lifestyle enjoyed at the beginning of the 20th century. Our lives have changed in innumerable ways. We are accustomed, for example, to travelling great distances. Just by taking away the motor car, our lives would change dramatically. If you wanted to visit friends or relatives for an evening in a rural area 50 miles from where you live, it would not be practical. You would not have the freedom to travel where and when you like. Your job opportunities would also be much reduced. In another 10 years many of us could be working at home for a day or two a week, thereby reducing the need to travel. The technology for this exists today, and it could help reduce traffic congestion, the fatigue of travel and costs. During the last 20 years, modern technology in the shape of the microprocessor has revolutionized the way we work, live and play. In the office we have word processors, laser printers, scanners and fax machines. In our homes we have intelligent CD players, video recorders, mobile phones and electronic personal organizers. By going back just 20 years life would be very different, and in some cases difficult.

When I was writing the article 'The amateur's search for supernovae' for the *1987 Yearbook of Astronomy*, few could have predicted the effects that modern technology would have on *all* aspects of supernova searching. From 1957 to 1987, only 24 supernova discoveries had been made by amateurs. Since 1987 the total has increased by 111; of these, 8 were photographic, 45 were visual and 58 were by CCD camera. Of the 45 visual discoveries, 16 were made by a solitary amateur, the Revd Robert Evans, bringing his total to date an amazing 36 (see his article in the

1998 Yearbook). At the time of writing (April 1999), most of the recent amateur discoveries are being made using CCD cameras and computerized telescopes. However, no amount of money thrown at technology will guarantee success without high levels of effort and determination. You don't make discoveries lying in bed or just talking about it.

UK DISCOVERIES

I felt very proud when in October 1996 Mark Armstrong made the first amateur supernova discovery from the UK. Apparently, Mark decided to make a serious search for supernovae after reading my article in the *1987 Yearbook*. It was a very well deserved discovery, as Mark observes on virtually all clear nights and often all night until dawn. His 16th-magnitude supernova, designated SN 1996bo, was discovered on October 23 in the galaxy NGC 673. Mark has since discovered three more, incredibly, all in a matter of 50 days!

In 1996 there were only three UK amateurs seriously searching for supernovae. Serious searching is defined as 'on every possible occasion at the exclusion of virtually all other observational interests and having one's social life determined by the phases of the Moon and the latest weather forecast'. The other two UK observers were the writer, who had been searching for some 18 years, and Tom Boles, who inaugurated his search some five weeks after Mark's first discovery.

The second UK success came six months later on April 7, 1997, when Stephen Laurie made his first discovery, the 16th-magnitude SN

SN designation	Date	Mag.	Galaxy	IAUC	Type	Discoverer	Codiscoverer(s)
1996bo	Oct. 23, 1996	16.5	NGC 673	6497	Ia	Armstrong	BOA survey, Okazaki
1997bq	Apr. 7, 1997	16.1	NGC 3147	6616	Ia	Laurie	Zissell
1997dn	Oct. 29, 1997	16.0	NGC 3451	6763	II	Boles	
1998V	Mar. 10, 1998	16.0	NGC 6627	6841	Ia	Armstrong	
1998an	Apr. 6, 1998	15.7	UGC 3683	6871	Ia	Arbour	
1998aq	Apr. 13, 1998	14.9	NGC 3982	6875	Ia	Armstrong	
1998bp	Apr. 29, 1998	14.8	NGC 6495	6890	Ia	Armstrong	
1998eg	Oct. 19, 1998	16.0	UGC 12133	7033	Ia	Boles	
1998ey	Dec. 5, 1998	17.0	NGC 7080	7065	Ic	Arbour	
1999aa	Feb. 11, 1999	15.5	NGC 2595	7084	Ia	Arbour	
1999bt	Apr. 9, 1999	17.0	Anon -----	7142	1a	Boles	
1999by	Apr. 30, 1999	15.1	NGC 2841	7156	1a	Arbour	Lick Observatory

Table 1. UK amateur supernova discoveries, October 1996 to April 1999.

Figure 1. Four UK amateur discoveries: (1) SN 1997bq, by Stephen Laurie (image by David Strange), (2) SN 1998aq, by Mark Armstrong, (3) SN 1998eg, by Tom Boles, and (4) SN 1998ey, by Ron Arbour.

1997bq in NGC 3147, after patrolling only a thousand galaxies. Using similar techniques and equipment, Stephen has also discovered several dozen minor planets, a quite incredible achievement. Then, on October 29, 1997, Tom Boles made his first discovery, the 16th-magnitude SN 1997dn in the galaxy NGC 3451, after a total of 3970 galaxies had been patrolled. It will be seen that one must be prepared to devote considerable time to making a discovery. Stephen Laurie's success after only a hundred patrols is the exception to the rule. The writer spent some 20 years before success came.

From the number of recent UK discoveries (Table 1, Figure 1), it might seem that supernova searching is quick and easy. This is not so.

Before success came, Mark Armstrong spent 285 hours, Tom Boles 246 hours and the writer an incalculable amount of time in the first 18 of 20 years of searching. It is only in the last 2 years that I have had any reasonable chance of success, with over 8000 patrols in 1998 alone (with a month lost modifying equipment).

AUTOMATED SEARCHES

Many professional schemes to computerize telescopes for automated supernova searching have either failed or lingered on for many years without success. Believed to be the first automated telescope was that of the Space Astronomy Laboratory of the University of Wisconsin. It was a 200-mm (8-inch) reflector designed for photometry of bright stars. The first telescope automated purely for supernova searching was a 0.75-m (30-inch) $f/6$ reflector designed and built by Sterling Colgate, purported to search 1000 galaxies per hour, and was believed to have found at least one supernova. Today there are several professional computerized telescopes conducting supernova searches. Without doubt the most efficient is the 0.76-m (30-inch) $f/2.5$ Katzman Automatic Imaging Telescope (KAIT) at the Lick Observatory in California (Figure 2). After many years of effort, this telescope, operated by the Berkeley Supernova Search Team and renamed the Lick Observatory Supernova Search (LOSS), is enjoying incredible success. The year 1998 saw 19 single discoveries made in just over 9 months! Other patrols, such as the Supernova Cosmology Project, the Mount Stromlo Abell Cluster Supernova Search, and the High-z Supernova Search Team, have made many discoveries in a short time. These were made by very large telescopes recording long exposures on very distant clusters of galaxies, a technique which ensures that several discoveries are made in a single observing run. The KAIT programme targets individual galaxy fields containing brighter galaxies at intermediate distances.

Completely controlled by computer, KAIT is programmed to slew to a predetermined list of galaxies, take a CCD image, call up and align the corresponding master image and subtract one from the other. What remains should be a supernova suspect. This idea sounds like the obvious way to go about detecting supernovae, since any object left after the subtraction must be a supernova. Unfortunately, cosmic ray impacts,

Figure 2. The Katzman Automatic Imaging Telescope (KAIT). [Reproduced by kind permission of the Lick Observatory Supernova Search (LOSS)]

camera artefacts and differing sky brightness conspire to create false alarms. Residual artefacts can look exactly like supernovae and cause much wasted time and effort to eliminate. The Berkeley team have gone to great lengths to reduce this effect with their software.

For any patrol to have a good chance of success, a large number of galaxies must be patrolled on a regular basis. It is hard to imagine a system that is more efficient than the KAIT telescope. It can take CCD images at the rate of 80 to 90 an hour from its target list of 5000 galaxies. Half of this total are recorded by the end of every third night. It employs a very sensitive CCD detector that can record images down to magnitude 19.5 in just 30 seconds. By comparison, photography would be very inefficient for supernova searching. To reach a similar limiting magnitude would require an exposure in the region of 15 minutes, thirty times longer. And that does not include loading a camera, processing the plates and the onerous task of visually inspecting dozens of plates. Computerized checking, by comparison, is effortless.

This is only part of the story. A team of programmers have made important advances in the efficiency of spreadsheet galaxy selection (using a spreadsheet to select only those galaxies that meet certain criteria, to optimize telescope time and maximize the chance of success), telescope pointing, target sequencing, automatic checking and image measurement routines. Projects such as this require several man-years of labour, but the LOSS has shown that it is very worthwhile.

IMPROVING PRODUCTIVITY

So what has changed since 1987 to have significantly increased the rate of amateur discoveries? Undoubtedly, the phenomenal success of Robert Evans has inspired many amateurs to take up supernova searching. To date, his total of discoveries stands at 36 and will be difficult to overtake. He may become a victim of his own success, with all the increased competition, and the LOSS supernova 'gobbler' will have an impact by discovering more supernovae in the brighter galaxies. As mentioned above, it is only in the last 2 years that I have stood any chance of success myself. Before then I used photographic methods for searching with a manually operated telescope. The change to automated searching has been responsible for my success. Replacing film with a CCD camera and the manual 400-mm (16-inch) Newtonian telescope with a computerized Schmidt–Cassegrain has revolutionized my patrols.

Several attempts since 1982 to automate the 400-mm Newtonian were only partially successful, actually lowering the productivity that could be obtained by using the instrument manually. Where it was once a struggle to patrol a couple of dozen galaxies per 5-hour session with Tri-X film, the CCD camera and computerized 300-mm catadioptric instrument will cover 200-plus, and my personal record stands at 251 on a single night. Within 2 years of operation I have built up a database of over 1500 CCD master images, which is still being added to, and enabled four discoveries to be made in less than 13 months.

The most powerful tool that is available to the amateur supernova searcher is one of the commercial computerized telescopes. They have revolutionized the acquisition of deep-sky targets. Armed with a good set of charts and pristine skies, the experienced visual observer can star-hop to a few dozen deep-sky objects in an evening session. Realistically, with increasing light pollution, this has become difficult for the average amateur. For the serious supernova searcher, time is a critical factor and cannot be wasted. Successful discoverers will confirm that supernova searching is a frantic exercise in the UK climate, followed as it is by having to capture a few hours' sleep before going to work.

The computerized telescope can increase the number of patrolled galaxies to several hundred per session, depending on how long the observer wishes to remain in the great outdoors. With a CCD camera the time spent on each galaxy will be about a minute or two. Visually, it could be a lot less. Robert Evans is said to spend only a few seconds on each galaxy, and can observe 500 galaxies a night. But he has committed most of them to memory and knows immediately if something has changed. The writer believes strongly that visual observers would increase their chances significantly by using computerized telescopes (unless their surname is Evans).

The ultimate computerized amateur supernova search must be that of Michael Schwartz of Cottage Grove, Oregon. He currently operates a 360-mm (14-inch) *f*/7 Celestron Schmidt–Cassegrain telescope on a precision-engineered mounting from Software Bisque. It will point with a precision of 1 arcminute over the entire sky, and is supplied with a software suite that integrates target selection, telescope positioning control, CCD camera integration and image processing. The telescope, located in Arizona, is controlled from Michael's home in Oregon over the Internet and is believed to be the first commercial amateur remotely controlled robotic telescope. To date, Michael ranks as the second most successful amateur supernova searcher with fifteen discoveries to his credit. This is bound to increase soon with the completion of his automated 0.8-m (32-inch) reflector in Arizona. It will be interesting to compare the success of this system with that of the LOSS.

I purchased a commercial Meade 300-mm (12-inch) LX200 Schmidt–Cassegrain (Figure 3) with the sole intention of using it, combined with a CCD camera, to search for supernovae. These telescopes can automatically slew to one of many thousands of galaxies in its built-in database. As mentioned earlier, no time can be wasted on imaging incorrect fields or having to continually refocus. So before the telescope was used in anger, several months were spent on modifications that would improve efficiency.

Because the field size of the CCD detector is only 11 × 8 arcminutes, special attention was paid to polar alignment to improve pointing accuracy. The usual 'wedge' that is provided with Schmidt–Cassegrains was not considered to be suitable. Adjustments are normally made around a 125-mm (5-inch) radius. An adjustment of only 0.1 mm (0.004 inch) results in a huge shift of nearly 3 arcminutes of the polar axis. With this in mind, a steel pier 230 mm (9 inches) in diameter with walls some 6 mm (0.25 inch) thick was built with large feet that rotated about a 1.5-m (5-foot) radius. A 0.1-mm adjustment corresponds to only 13 arcseconds of movement. A dial gauge was used to make adjustments more predictable and reliable. The task of polar alignment was far more predictable than the usual 'suck it and see' methods. The drift method was used initially, but replaced with the photographic King test when very small adjustments were needed to eliminate errors that cannot be detected by the drift method.

It was found that the mirror would tilt with the telescope's changing attitude and an object would drift out of focus. Modifications to the mirror support system have improved but not entirely eliminated this problem. The whole support system will have to be rigidly 'fixed' in position and a separate focusing device fitted. As the instrument is never used visually, this is not a problem.

I felt that entering a galaxy's name or position into a hand-held keypad would be too slow, and that there was a risk of wasting time if incorrect data were entered. As the LX200 has the facility of accepting commands from a personal computer, via an RS232 communication

Figure 3. The author with his LX200 telescope.

link, a program has been written, with the help of David Briggs, largely to automate the process of galaxy acquisition and CCD camera operation. Under optimum conditions, 40 to 50 galaxy fields can be acquired and imaged per hour, a massive improvement over manual operation. After a file of galaxies for a particular night has been loaded from a database of over 8000, the telescope automatically slews to each galaxy field in turn, and the CCD makes a timed integration. Meanwhile, the equivalent master image is displayed on a second monitor, and compared with the new image for additional objects. This process is repeated until all the galaxies on the list are observed, cloud interrupts or the operator becomes tired – or, on some occasions, falls asleep! The program can be interrupted if a suspect is found and a second exposure is needed. All the images are inspected at the telescope, but are also saved on a Zip disk for transportation indoors and further scrutiny, especially when a suspect supernova is found. This is where the important work of verification and confirmation begins.

ELIMINATION OF FALSE SUPERNOVAE

Over many years I have developed a systematic checking routine for the elimination of suspects that can look exactly like supernovae, for example minor planets, variable stars, cosmic ray strikes and camera artefacts. It has often happened that an observer has alerted the Central Bureau for Astronomical Telegrams (CBAT) only to find that the 'supernova' is a bright minor planet, variable star or just a figment of a CCD camera's imagination. With the proliferation of CCD cameras in amateur hands, reports of suspect supernovae are becoming very frequent. Reporting false supernovae does not enhance one's credibility. All possible checks must be carried out before the suspect is announced to the professional community or even other amateurs, especially to newsgroups over the Internet! The latter should be avoided at all costs. In my experience the news of an actual discovery will get around the Internet very quickly indeed. Here is my checklist of steps to be followed once a suspected supernova has been found:

1. Check against a master image.
2. Take an additional, longer exposure and see if the 'suspect' still exists.
3. Check, if possible, against archived images taken on other dates.

4. Check Megastar, Guide, The Sky or a similar software program for minor planets.
5. Check the Digitized Sky Survey Website for the relevant Palomar field.
6. Check the CBAT Minor Planet Checker Website.
7. Check CBAT for the latest known supernova discoveries.
8. Measure the object's precise position using an astrometry program.
9. Take another image about 30 minutes later and check by eye for movement of the suspect.
10. Measure the precise position of the object on the second image, and check for any change.
11. Ask an experienced amateur to confirm suspect's existence.
12. Notify CBAT or a supernova search organization.
13. Await notification of your supernova and its designation on an IAU *Circular*.
14. Await spectroscopic confirmation.

Nowadays, a visual discoverer will find it difficult to convince CBAT of a supernova's reality unless the observer is known to be reliable or has previously been successful. Help must then be provided by an experienced amateur who is suitably equipped to take CCD images of a suspect and measure its precise position. This will confirm the object's existence and rule out the possibility of a minor planet near its stationary point without having to wait for 24 hours to detect any motion.

I would encourage all amateurs to search for supernovae, but it must be understood just what damage a false alarm can cause. The further you go down a false trail, the bumpier it becomes. Rule number one: always seek advice from experienced observers. Don't tell the whole world, but quietly seek help. Don't be worried that someone will steal your discovery – if you confide in a true supernova searcher, then you can be virtually certain that your discovery is safe. A real searcher will not get any pleasure from pretending he's found your supernova. Tell the world on the Internet, and someone will probably claim they found it the day before!

If a second exposure shows the object in the same apparent position as the first, move the telescope 10 to 30 arcseconds and take a third exposure. This will place the object in a different position on the CCD detector and rule out a 'hotter' than usual grouping of pixels giving the appearance of a stellar-like object. If the object still exists, compare another image of the same galaxy taken on a previous occasion because the master may prove to be inferior: for example, the seeing, transparency or focus may be poorer.

Now it is a good idea to check against other sources and the Bible for the SN searcher is *Vicker's CCD Atlas*. It contains negative prints of some 1700 galaxies, and shows stars to about magnitude 20. Although some of the nuclear regions are overexposed, it can be thoroughly recommended and is also useful to have while building up a set of master images. With its help, I have found several minor planets, independently found two supernovae and rediscovered five more, in addition to confirming one of my own, SN 1998ey in NGC 7080. There is no other paper publication that shows so many galaxies as well as this for supernova work.

You must be able to check all stars to at least half a magnitude fainter than your suspect. The very best deep-sky atlas is the *Palomar Sky Survey*. Not many amateurs have access to this fine resource, but it is available at a much lower resolution on eight CD-ROMS as *Real Sky*. If you enter a galaxy's name or coordinates, *Real Sky* will display an image of the relevant galaxy. The *Palomar Sky Survey* can be viewed at higher resolution on the digitized Sky Survey Website (Figure 4). By entering a galaxy's designation or field centre coordinates, you can download an image of the field which contains your suspect.

If the suspect has passed these tests, then the object is real and you now have to determine what it is. If the galaxy is near the ecliptic there is a strong chance that it is a minor planet. If it is brighter than 17th magnitude, it could be a known minor planet. There are many software programs available that show, at any given time, the positions of at least 6000 numbered minor planets. Most show many more and can be updated by inclusion of additional orbital elements as well as known and suspected variable stars. For the serious supernova searcher, such a program is mandatory.

Passing the above check does not exclude the suspect from being a recently discovered minor planet, which can be easily eliminated by visiting CBAT's Minor Planet Checker Website. After completing their form (Figure 5), all the known minor planets within the specified radius and brightness range will be listed. This does not rule out the possibility that you may have found an unnamed or unnumbered minor planet, as did Mark Armstrong with minor planets 1997 WQ_{28} and 1998 EN_{20}.

Of course, the suspect could be a supernova that has already been announced by CBAT, so it is important to see if you have been pipped to the post by viewing the CBAT Website devoted to recent supernova

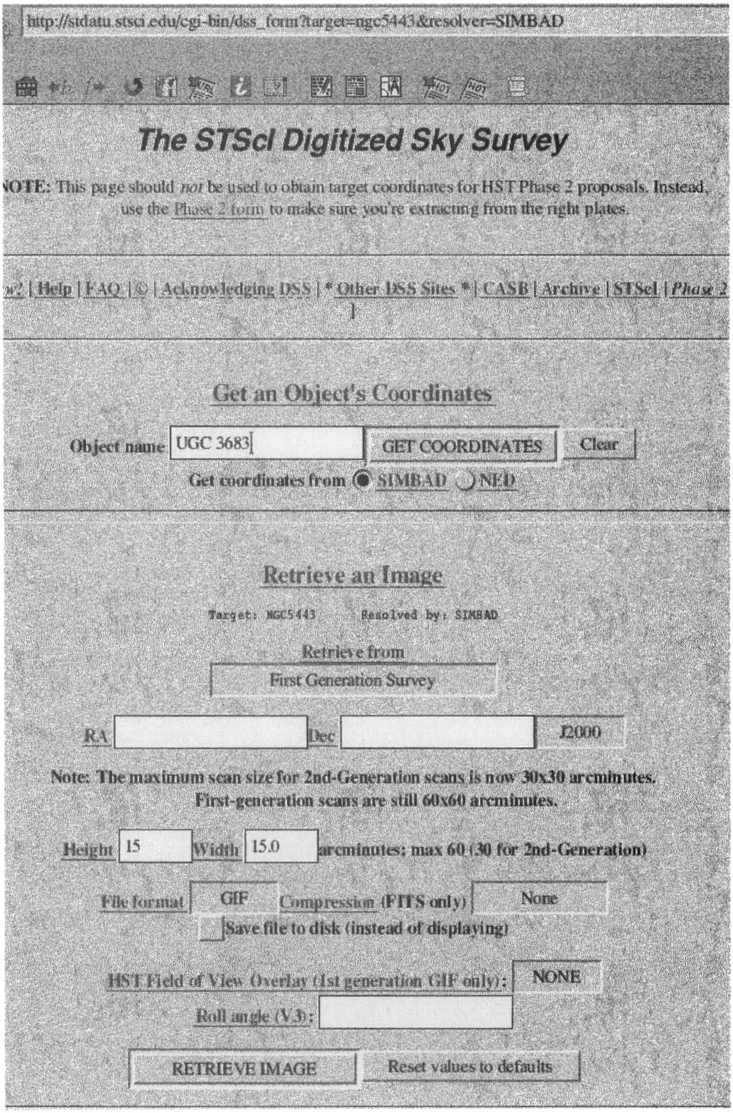

Figure 4. The Digitized Sky Survey form for requesting galaxy images. [Reproduced courtesy of the Space Telescope Science Institute (STScI)]

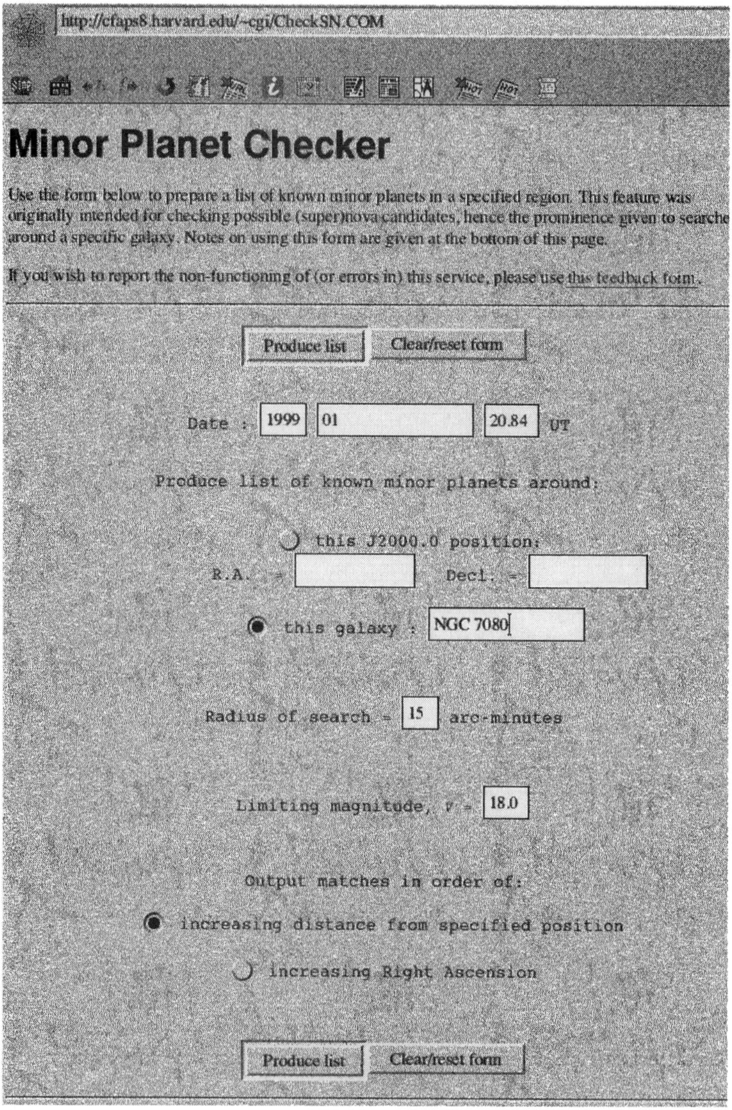

Figure 5. The Minor Planet Checker form for requesting details of minor planets in the region of interest. [Reproduced by kind permission of the Central Bureau for Astronomical Telegrams (CBAT)]

discoveries. A very interesting site containing a lot of information and images of recently discovered supernovae is David Bishop's Bright Supernovae page. Check to see that it is the same object – it could be another supernova in the same galaxy!

If your suspect has survived this far, then it is advisable to measure its position very accurately down to a fraction of an arcsecond. If it is a new minor planet, this is the accuracy to which it must be reported; if it is a supernova, professional astronomers will want to know exactly where to point the slit of a spectrograph. Today, we can measure, 'astrometrically', as it is known, the position of objects to this precision on CCD images with several software programs in combination with a CD-ROM containing some 15 million stars from the *Guide Star Catalogue*. The most popular of these programs is *Astrometrica*. Making an astrometric measurement will prepare us for the next stage.

We must now take another CCD image of the 'suspect' to see if it has moved. If it is a minor planet near its opposition point, any movement over 30 minutes can be seen by casual inspection. If near the stationary point, movement can be very difficult to detect, so it is very important to compare the precise positions on the first and last images using an astrometry program. At the same time you must measure the offsets: the direction and distance from the suspect to the centre of the galaxy (e.g. 12 arcseconds north, 27 arcseconds east). This is usually written as '12″ north, 27″ east'.

OBTAINING CONFIRMATION

If, after 30 minutes to an hour, no apparent motion can be detected, then another experienced observer should be asked to confirm the object's existence. Before the days of sending images by email, all information relating to suspects was relayed by telephone (some still is). What should be a straightforward description of where the suspect is in relation to the parent galaxy and surrounding stars can be very difficult to relate. On one occasion I was congratulated on a discovery by another observer when comparing notes from the verifier's master image, only to be told an hour later that the verifier was holding his image upside down!

A CCD image is easily sent by email to a verifier, and it is a good idea to label not only the suspect, but north and west as well. It is also a good idea when starting to take master images to orient your image so that north is to the top and west is to the right. Software can 'flip' images, but mistakes are easily made. All CCD images must have north at the top! Accurate orientation also makes the offsets more reliable.

If the verifier is able to say that there is an object of a similar brightness at the exact position you stated, then you should now recheck all you have done. If the suspect still passes every test, now is the time to tell someone about it. Many countries have an organized amateur supernova search programme. In the UK there is the UK Supernova Patrol, run jointly by the British Astronomical Association and *The Astronomer* magazine under the coordination of Guy Hurst. SunSearch is the equivalent organization in the USA, run by supernova discoverer Wayne Johnson.

If you are not very experienced at reporting suspects, then it is strongly suggested that you contact one of these organizations for help. They will 'interrogate' you to make sure that all the necessary checks have been completed efficiently. With each stage of checking that your 'suspect' survives, the excitement mounts. The adrenaline starts accelerating while the brain starts decelerating, and it is at this time that silly mistakes can easily be made. With experience, the prospective discoverer will gain confidence and will be able to contact CBAT directly. But be warned that if you do not complete all the necessary checks and get some of your facts wrong, egg stains can be very difficult to wash off. If your local organization is satisfied, it will relay details of your suspect to the CBAT. Now you wait. It is now, and only now, that you are allowed to panic!

You may have to wait anything from a few hours to several days to see if the discovery will be announced in one of the IAU *Circulars*. It is a common misconception that if amateurs make an actual discovery they will be sent either a telegram or a confirmatory email, but unfortunately this is not the case. You need to be a subscriber to the relevant *Circular* to receive notification, or to rely on a friend to inform you of your discovery. It can also be several days before spectroscopic confirmation is obtained by a large professional telescope, and spectrograms can be viewed on a special CBAT Website (Figure 6). The Internet really makes discoveries much more interesting, by showing you all the associated activity that your supernova creates. I personally find it fascinating that a very faint smudge on a CCD image can make a 1.5-m professional telescope take time out to point to an object that was first seen via a small telescope in a back garden. As we enter the new millennium, it is difficult to appreciate that hardly any of the technology described above was available to the average amateur when the *1987 Yearbook* article was written. Would we amateurs be able to make so many discoveries without this technology today? Definitely not!

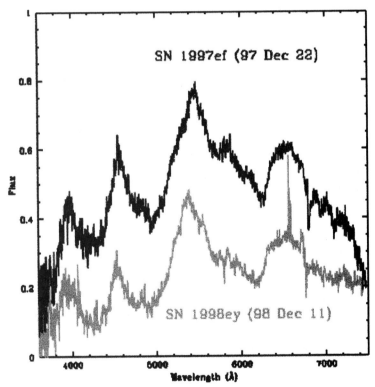

Figure 6. The spectra of supernovae SN 1998ey and SN 1997ef compared. Both are peculiar Type Ic supernovae. [Reproduced by permission of the Supernova Group at the Harvard–Smithsonian Center for Astrophysics (CfA)]

SOURCES

UK Supernova Patrol: Co-ordinator, G. M. Hurst, 16 Westminster Close, Kempshott Rise, Basingstoke, Hampshire RG22 4PP.

Websites
Digitized Sky Survey
http://archive.stsci.edu/dss/

CBAT Minor Planet Checker
http://cfa-www.harvard.edu/ps/CheckSN

CBAT Recent Supernova List
http://cfa-www.harvard.edu/iau/lists/RecentSupernovae.html

Dave Bishop's Bright Supernovae
http://www.ggw.org/freenet/a/asras/supernova.html

International Supernovae Network
http://www.supernovae.net/isn.html

CBAT Bright Supernovae Spectra
http://cfa-www.harvard.edu/cfa/oir/Research/supernova/RecentSN.html

A Cool Look at the Universe with the Infrared Space Observatory

HELEN J. WALKER

The Infrared Space Observatory (ISO) satellite observed a part of the spectrum we cannot access from the ground, in between the optical and the radio regions. Although operations ceased only in April 1998, the impact of ISO on many areas of astronomy has already been apparent, from Solar System science to cosmology and the origin of the Universe. During its 29-month lifetime, ISO made over 26,000 observations for astronomers from 19 countries, and its data archive will be a treasure trove for many years.

ISO was a large astronomical satellite, 5 metres high and 3.6 metres wide, built by the European Space Agency (ESA). It was launched on November 17, 1995, and scientific operations were terminated on April 8, 1998, when the liquid (superfluid) helium coolant finally ran out. At the heart of ISO was a (small) 60-centimetre telescope, with four scientific instruments (see Figure 1). One instrument was a small camera, which took pictures at various wavelengths between 2 and 17 micrometres. The photometer measured brightness in the infrared (from 2 to 240 micrometres), in a similar fashion to an ordinary camera's light meter. There were also two spectrometers on board, which split the light into infrared 'rainbows'. One advantage of having a small telescope was that the telescope itself, as well as the instruments, could be effectively cooled by the liquid helium coolant, although the computers and electronics which ran the instruments had to be placed in a service module outside the cold part of the satellite, since they would not work well if cooled by liquid helium. A thermos flask filled with 2000 litres of liquid helium at –269°C (4 degrees above absolute zero) surrounded ISO, which stopped the detectors from being 'blinded' by the heat from the satellite itself, so ISO could look into the cool, dim regions of deep

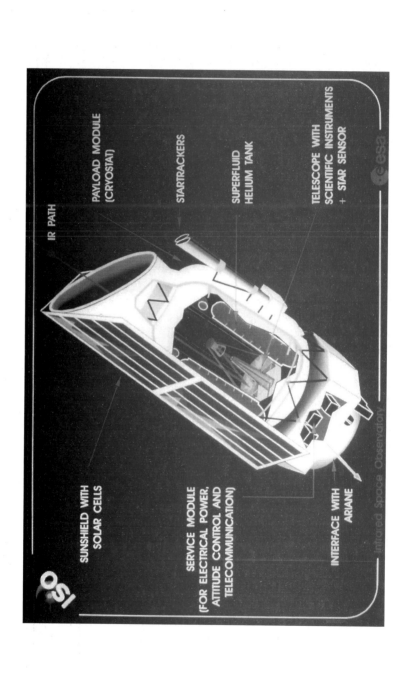

ISO

SUNSHIELD WITH
SOLAR CELLS

SERVICE MODULE
(FOR ELECTRICAL POWER,
ATTITUDE CONTROL AND
TELECOMMUNICATION)

INTERFACE WITH
ARIANE

IR PATH

PAYLOAD MODULE
(CRYOSTAT)

STARTRACKERS

SUPERFLUID
HELIUM TANK

TELESCOPE WITH
SCIENTIFIC INSTRUMENTS
+ STAR SENSOR

G eesa

Infrared Space Observatory

space. ISO had to avoid looking at the Sun, the Earth and the Moon because they were so bright they would damage the instruments. This meant that ISO could observe only a limited region of the sky at any one time, and the region moved round the sky as the mission progressed. The liquid helium gradually boiled away as the observations were made. ISO was designed to last for 18 months, and after launch we thought there would be enough helium coolant for 24 months. However, even that proved to be a conservative estimate, and the coolant lasted for almost another 5 months. Fortunately the instruments, which were also naturally designed to last 18 months, also worked flawlessly throughout the extended period. Everyone was very pleased when ISO lasted almost 29 months, since it meant the important regions in Orion and Taurus could be observed towards the end of ISO's lifetime. (They had been inaccessible for the first two years of ISO's operation because of their position relative to the Sun, Earth and Moon.)

ISO has opened a window onto the Universe which we cannot see from the ground, because the Earth's atmosphere absorbs it. Things which appear dark to the Hubble Space Telescope glow brightly for ISO, so we get a complementary view of astronomical objects. ISO is particularly useful in investigating molecules and dust in the colder parts of the Universe, where most other telescopes see nothing at all. The IRAS satellite, which was launched in 1983 and operated for 10 months, found almost a quarter of a million objects, and ISO gave us the opportunity to study some of them in more detail. One of the exciting techniques used on ISO was to switch on the most sensitive far-infrared detectors as ISO moved from one target to the next, giving what we call the Serendipity Survey. A test scan of the Coma Cluster of galaxies showed that when the four far-infrared detectors from the photometer scanned from one galaxy to a second galaxy, a third galaxy on the scan line was recorded by three of the detectors during the scan. This meant that the signals obtained during the scans could be verified

---

Figure 1 (see opposite). A cutaway diagram of ISO, showing the main components of the satellite. The telescope and instruments were placed inside the tank filled with liquid (superfluid) helium; the electronics and computers to run the instruments were placed outside the tank (in the service module). ISO pinpointed its position in space using the (optical) star-trackers. [Courtesy of ISO/ESA]

as real, and were not just noise in one or two detectors. Figure 2 shows where ISO travelled during its period of operation. The map (using infrared data from the earlier IRAS mission) is displayed with the centre of our Galaxy at the centre of the picture, and the infrared Milky Way as the bright broad band along the middle. There was a clustering of scans across the north ecliptic pole early in the mission, and then later scans were made across the Large Magellanic Cloud, which is very close to the south ecliptic pole. Finally, scans were made near Orion (on the right edge), which became accessible to ISO towards the end of the mission. Over 29 months, 17 per cent of the sky was surveyed and a large number of distant galaxies were observed (probably around 4000), of which some will be new. In our own Galaxy the survey has revealed very cold dust clouds, places where stars could form in the distant future.

SOLAR SYSTEM SCIENCE

Jupiter has been observed at several different ISO wavelengths, each wavelength looking at a different depth in the atmosphere and each giving a very different view of Jupiter (Figure 3). At 3.0 micrometres Jupiter appears rather similar to the normal view we see, with several bands visible, and the bright blob below centre is indeed the Great Red Spot. At 3.3 micrometres, methane everywhere in the atmosphere absorbs the radiation, so Jupiter looks completely dark. At 5.7 micrometres there were hot spots where ISO was peering deep into the atmosphere, through dry anticyclonic regions of sinking gas. At 7.6 micrometres the stratosphere was seen, high in Jupiter's atmosphere, and at 9.4 micrometres the cloudy zones, which were previously bright, were now relatively dark. The results from this global view can be compared to the very detailed picture given by the Galileo probe, which investigated one point in great detail, and the information we gained from the impact of Comet Shoemaker–Levy 9.

ISO observed Comet Hale–Bopp, but since it could not point very close to the Sun, the observations were when the comet was still far away in the outer Solar System. In the optical there was a beautiful tail of gas and dust blown out from the comet by the solar wind. There was also a blue ion tail. In the infrared it was perhaps less spectacular, for here we saw only the dust carried away from the comet's nucleus. ISO

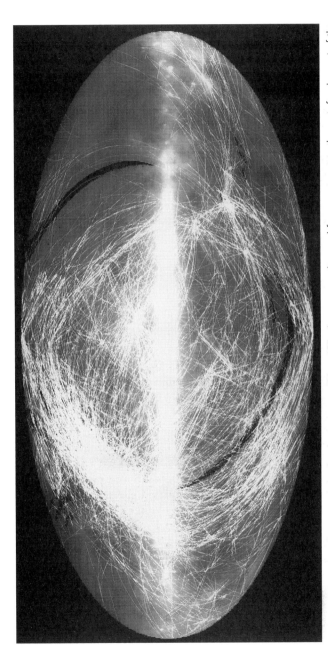

Figure 2. Two years of scans made by the photometer on ISO at 175 micrometres as it moved from one target to the next, forming part of the Serendipity Survey. The background is taken with the IRAS satellite at 100 micrometres, with the centre of the Galaxy in the middle; the Milky Way is the bright band across the middle of the picture. [Courtesy of the Max Planck Institute of Astronomy, Heidelberg]

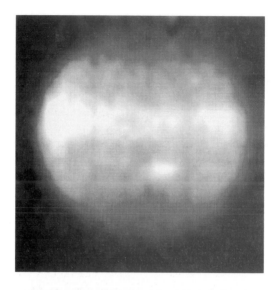

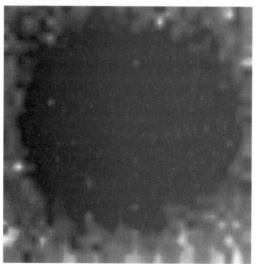

Figure 3. Two pictures of Jupiter taken with the camera on ISO. At 3.0 micrometres (top) the planet shows several bands; these correspond to the bright zones seen by optical observers. The bright patch below centre is the Great Red Spot. At 3.3 micrometres (bottom) Jupiter looks completely dark because the methane in its atmosphere absorbs the light. [Courtesy of Encrenaz and ESA/ISO]

observed Comet Hale–Bopp at 4.6 AU from the Sun, so the comet was almost as far away as Jupiter, and we were looking at the region very close to the nucleus of the comet, which was very small, and at that time not very warm and not very active. Carbon dioxide was seen evaporating from the nucleus, but water was not evaporating yet, which was surprising. Water was seen later, when the comet was 2.9 AU from the Sun, and carbon monoxide was seen then as well. The comet was warming up as it approached the Sun, and it may be that the dust shielded the water from evaporation for longer than was expected. ISO could not observe Comet Hyakutake because the comet moved too quickly for ISO to be able to track it safely. However, several other comets were monitored.

Titan, Saturn's largest moon, was another place where ISO found water. Titan is one of the few moons in the Solar System which we know has an atmosphere. NASA and ESA are sending the Cassini/ Huygens pair of probes to Saturn and Titan to study the system in detail. Athena Coustenis (Paris Observatory) and Alberto Salama (ISO Operations Centre, Spain) found carbon monoxide, carbon dioxide, hydrocarbon and nitrile molecules in the atmosphere as well as water. The scientists working with Cassini/Huygens have several years to consider the impact of the ISO data on their own plans.

NEW STARS

Water was also found where new stars are forming, in the constellation of Orion, where the bright Orion Nebula is seen optically. It is encouraging to find water molecules in the hostile environment of a bright nebula such as this, particularly since we would like the water to be present when planets are forming around the new stars.

The camera on ISO took pictures (at several different wavelengths) of the dust clouds in Ophiuchus, where new stars are being formed. The new stars form in cool, dark clouds, which are collapsing, and so the dust is slightly warmer than the surrounding cloud, due to the warmth from the collapse and the birth of the new star. When the ISO pictures were combined these warmed clouds were very conspicuous, even though they were still only a few degrees warmer than their surroundings. Most of the clouds that were found in Ophiuchus will each form a star about as massive as the Sun, but one very bright cloud was found which concealed a star one hundred times as massive as the Sun. Lynds 1689 is a known dark cloud in the constellation of Ophiuchus, so cold that even as seen with the camera on ISO the cloud was still dark. Derek Ward-Thompson (formerly at the University of Edinburgh, now at the University of Cardiff) found a star in the earliest stages of formation. The picture was taken at the longest ISO wavelengths available, with the photometer. When he looked at these wavelengths he found a cloud of gas and dust, almost twice the mass of the Sun, just about to start collapsing and warming up. The cloud was so cold that it was not detected by IRAS, which could not measure such cool temperatures. The 15-metre British James Clerk Maxwell Telescope in Hawaii could detect it at submillimetre wavelengths (longer than ISO and shorter than radio telescopes like Jodrell Bank detect), as could the 30-metre submillimetre telescope in the Sierra Nevada in Spain (IRAM), but could not define the temperature very precisely. The ISO observations were very close to the peak energy emitted by the cloud, and accurately measured its temperature to be –260°C (13° above absolute zero), to the nearest degree. This cloud has a long way to go before it becomes a star like the sun.

DUST RINGS AROUND NORMAL STARS

I wrote about dust rings around normal stars in the 1998 *Yearbook*, and in particular about maps I had made of the dust ring around the nearby bright star Vega (α Lyrae). The dust ring was very unusual because a star as old as Vega should have lost all of its dust. We think the dust ring might be a failed attempt to form planets, with not enough dust present. The instrument team realized that ISO was pointing very precisely indeed, so we made some high-resolution scans to look at the ring in more detail. We scanned (with very small steps from one position to the next) across an ordinary star (γ Draconis) to check what we were seeing, since γ Dra has no dust ring; then we scanned across Vega and its ring, in order to find out more precisely how big the ring was. The ring was almost 500 AU across, similar to the Oort Cloud around our own Solar System, which is where we think the long-period comets come from. However, there was less material in Vega's dust ring than there is in our own Moon. Vega is 25.4 light-years away. Thanks to the extended lifetime of ISO, I was able to make the same type of high-resolution scan across another normal star with a dust ring, β Pictoris, further away than Vega at about 62 light-years distant. This star is known to have a dust ring, which is edge-on as viewed from Earth, unlike Vega's which we believe is face-on. We made several scans, along the ring, perpendicular to the ring and at three other angles. We found the ring to be about the same size as that around Vega, even though the star is farther away, and to be a little more massive, possibly almost three times the mass of the Moon. I also looked at a ninth-magnitude star in the constellation Scorpius, which is a lot farther away, around 900 to 1000 light-years, and younger than either Vega or the Sun. It has a much bigger ring, more than 1000 AU across, which I can just about resolve with ISO using this special technique. It contains more material (possibly ten times the mass of Jupiter), so this might be a better place to find planets.

OLD STARS

As a star grows old, it accumulates either an excess of oxygen in its stellar atmosphere, which combines with the ever-present hydrogen to form water (when the outer parts of the stellar atmosphere are cool enough), or an excess of carbon. One of the big surprises with ISO was to find a planetary nebula (which is an old star throwing off its outer atmosphere, and nothing to do with planets) which was rich in carbon, but also managed to have features associated with water. This was NGC 7027, a ninth-magnitude planetary nebula in Cygnus. Investigations by Mike Barlow's group at University College, London, have shown that the gases in the nebula around the star (blown out from it) can heat up to the point where oxygen atoms are separated from the carbon-rich molecules, with enough opportunity to combine with hydrogen instead of recombining with the carbon, as was expected. Another surprising discovery was that some dust features in planetary nebulae were caused by crystalline silicate dust. The dust grains were formed in the cool parts of the nebulae in the amorphous form, but they have been heated and cooled so that very tiny crystals have formed. Up until now, the models used for the dust around stars have always assumed that the dust remains in the amorphous form.

IRC+10 216, a star with a telephone-number name, is too faint to be seen with an optical telescope (IRC stands for Infra-Red Catalogue), because it has a large, thick dust shell round it, but it glows very brightly in the infrared. It is an old star, and Mike Barlow found he could model its atmosphere very well indeed by assuming a mixture of carbon monoxide and hydrogen cyanide – not a pleasant star to live near. When the model was compared with the data from the Long Wavelength Spectrometer, the match was very good indeed, showing that the group understood what happened to a star's atmosphere as it grew old. It is very important to make these models, since only after the data have been matched to the model will the unexpected, new features be clearly seen, and astronomers can hunt for their identification and learn more about stellar evolution.

Although IRC + 10 216 has a lot of carbon in its atmosphere, this is a small amount compared with some stars. R Coronae Borealis (R CrB) is an example of a sooty star: it has an enormous amount of carbon in its atmosphere. You can just about see the star with the naked eye, if you know where to look. When I used ISO to look at it in February 1996, I found the spectrum to be totally unlike anything else I had observed with ISO. This spectrum was taken just after a minimum (the star is variable), and showed a broad plateau instead of sharp molecular features as in IRC+10 216. I was so surprised that I asked for the observation to be repeated, and I was even more surprised when the second observation showed the same feature, but the strength of the feature had changed. My colleagues in the instrument team assured me that the instrument was not faulty. I now have four spectra of R CrB, and the feature has continued to change during the two years I have observed it with ISO. There were several features I had expected which were not present: the features due to the molecules normally present in the dust around carbon-rich stars (such as carbon monoxide, hydrogen cyanide or silicon carbide), or the signature of molecules combining carbon and hydrogen, but none of these normal features were there. As far as I can tell, the dust cloud puffed out from R CrB really was pure soot (amorphous carbon, to be more technical), although when I compared it with soot found on Earth, the local soot proved to have more hydrogen and oxygen mixed in. I think the cloud of soot was formed quite close to the star, as carbon gas, which very suddenly condensed into soot. Due to the lack of hydrogen, the carbon gas could condense at higher temperatures than is normally possible. The soot was then blown away from the star by radiation pressure (like the solar wind from the Sun) and gradually the soot spread out into the interstellar medium.

OTHER GALAXIES

Since ISO was very sensitive to the cool dust warmed by new stars forming, it was very good at detecting this in galaxies other than our own Milky Way. Figure 4 compares an optical photograph of M.101, a beautiful spiral galaxy in the constellation of Ursa Major, with the map produced by the photometer on ISO. The optical picture was taken with the 2.2-metre telescope at Calar Alto in Spain, which was a much bigger telescope than ISO, so it saw more detail in the galaxy. The bright patches in the ISO picture are where large numbers of stars are being formed; for example, the bright patch at the lower left of the picture was about 30 times brighter than similar regions in the Milky Way. There were several very large regions where massive stars were being formed, 10 to 50 times the mass of the Sun. The match between features in the optical and infrared was not exact, because the dust obscured the optical light and shone brightly in the infrared. The galaxy M.31 in the constellation of Andromeda was thought to be very similar to our own Galaxy, but my colleagues Dietrich Lemke and Martin Haas (of the Max Planck Institute of Astronomy in Heidelberg) did not see the normal spiral arms (as in M.101), but instead a ring of stars forming around the centre, a ring over 30,000 light-years from the centre of M.31 (the Sun is roughly this distance from the centre of our Galaxy). This means that M.31 is not as close a twin of the Milky Way as was thought.

The cluster of around 500 galaxies in the constellation Coma Berenices is sitting in a sea of hot gas, at about 80 million degrees. The X-ray satellite Rosat observed X-rays from the gas. When my colleagues Manfred Stickel (Max Planck Institute of Astronomy, Heidelberg) and Kalevi Mattila (Helsinki Observatory) scanned across the cluster with ISO, they expected to see two peaks where the scan crossed the two bright galaxies in the centre of the cluster, since these galaxies should have dust in them. Instead they found that the dust had been stripped out of the galaxies and was spread throughout the cluster. This could have been due to collisions between galaxies within the cluster, or there could have been a merger between the Coma Cluster and another cluster of galaxies. The dust is very cold, around −220°C to −250°C (20 K to 50 K) and is sitting in the enormous cloud of very hot gas, which is emitting the X-rays. The dust will gradually evaporate as the X-rays

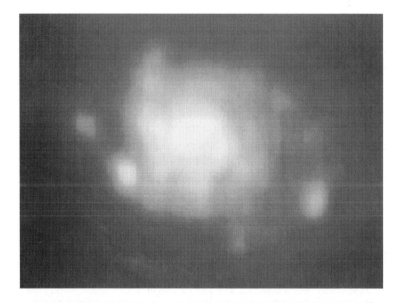

Figure 4. Two pictures of the spiral galaxy M101: at 100 micrometres as seen by the photometer on ISO (top), and at optical wavelengths as seen by the 2.2-metre telescope at Calar Alto (bottom). [Courtesy of the Max Planck Institute of Astronomy, Heidelberg]

heat it, and it will all disappear into the gas in around 100 million years. This is about 1 per cent of the age of the galaxies, so disruption was a fairly recent event. We had not expected to find the Coma Cluster to be a place where things were so dynamic.

The Hubble Space Telescope has looked at two very small patches of space, one in the Northern Hemisphere and one in the Southern, to see how many galaxies were present. The pictures it took looked very deep into space: for example, the exposure for the southern field lasted for 10 days. The camera on ISO has also looked at these patches of space, although not for so long. ISO saw the dusty galaxies in the fields, and in the southern field Michael Rowan-Robinson (Imperial College, London) and his colleagues have identified one galaxy which the Hubble Space Telescope did not see, due to the dust in it.

PROBING THE BIG BANG

ISO can also make a contribution to cosmology and our understanding of the origin of the Universe, but in a slightly unusual way – through observing the amount of deuterium in the atmospheres of the giant planets Saturn and Jupiter. When Saturn and Jupiter formed from the solar nebula, they captured deuterium made in the Big Bang. Since the planets do not create or destroy deuterium, the amount we detect with ISO must be that original amount. The result found by ISO from observations of Saturn disagreed with the amount found by Galileo for Jupiter. Astronomers are not too worried about this yet, since there is always a lot of work involved in calibrating satellite instruments. ISO now has data for Jupiter as well as Saturn, and Uranus and Neptune have also been similarly observed. Uranus and Neptune trap more hydrogen in their cores than do Saturn and Jupiter, so comparatively more deuterium (with respect to hydrogen) will be detected. When the analysis of all four planets is completed (and the analysis of the Galileo data), a very significant result will be available to the astronomical community about the amount of deuterium in the nebula from which the Sun formed.

THE FUTURE

The data-taking stage of ISO has come to an end, and this is now followed by a 3.5-year period when we sort out the more than 26,000 observations to create an archive of data which astronomers worldwide can use. After ISO, ESA has plans for two larger satellites, called FIRST and Planck Explorer, which will work at longer wavelengths (85 to 600 micrometres). FIRST will look at very cool material, and Planck Explorer will look at the cosmic background in detail, following up the work of COBE. The satellites will have 3-metre telescopes, last for 4.5 years and be launched around 2006. NASA/JPL will launch their infrared satellite, SIRTF, before that, in December 2001. SIRTF will be similar to ISO but it will have new instruments which can look at fainter signals than ISO could detect. NASA is also building SOFIA, which is a 3-metre telescope in a Boeing 747 jumbo jet. This will fly very high in the atmosphere, and has the great advantage over a satellite in that the engineers can fly with the instrument, and can fix any problems as and when they occur.

Gravity Waves: A Lot of Fuss over Nothing?

CHRIS KITCHIN

INTRODUCTION

Suppose that you, as an amateur astronomer, were contemplating buying a telescope. You could spend £20 ($30) on a second-hand throwout from someone at the local astronomical society in a jumble sale, £500 ($750) on a new 150-mm (6-inch) Newtonian, or between £1500 and £6000 ($2500 and $10,000) on a Schmidt–Cassegrain or Maksutov, or even up to £20,000 ($30,000) on a state-of-the-art, computer-controlled, large Schmidt–Cassegrain. But as you do so it is in the sure and certain knowledge that when you look through the eyepiece of your investment, there will be something to see. Would you spend the same money if there might or might not be anything to see? I suspect not. Yet research councils and governments are spending not a few thousands, but hundreds of millions on building telescopes whose certainty of detecting (seeing) anything is quite unknown. Those telescopes are dedicated to looking for gravity waves.

The familiar optical telescopes receive radiation with wavelengths in the region from 700 nm (red) to 380 nm (violet). We are also quite used to the idea of radio telescopes working in the region from millimetres to tens of metres. Rather less widely known, telescopes on board spacecraft are capable of probing the Universe at wavelengths ranging from gamma rays (0.001 nm), through X-rays (1 nm), ultraviolet radiation (100 nm), infrared radiation (10 μm) to microwave radiation (100 μm). But all these are just different forms of electromagnetic radiation, and almost all (99.9999 per cent) of our knowledge of the Universe is based upon what this radiation tells us. The only information about the Universe that is independent of electromagnetic radiation comes to us from cosmic rays[1] and neutrinos.[2]

Our view of the Universe is therefore very much prejudiced by the ways in which we can look at it. An independent means of observing the Universe could be expected to provide quite different insights into its nature, and quite possibly an entirely different picture of what the Universe is all about. Gravity waves may provide that independent view of the Universe, and that is why so much is currently being spent in attempts to observe entities which may not exist.

WHAT IS A GRAVITY WAVE?

Newton's apple showed us that all material objects have a gravitational field which affects all other objects in the Universe. Einstein then went on to interpret the effect of mass not as a force but as a distortion of the fabric of spacetime. The apparent force of gravity is then just due to an object moving along the shortest distance between two points within that curved space (Figure 1). Either way, if an object with mass moves or changes, then generally its gravitational field or the curvature in spacetime that it induces will also change. Information on that change will then propagate outwards at the speed of light as a ripple in the grav-itational field intensity or in the curvature of spacetime. That ripple is a gravity wave.[3] Thus if you walk across the room, about two and a half million years later the Andromeda Galaxy (M.31) will notice a small change in the direction of the force of gravity acting upon it from you. Of course that change would be exceedingly tiny, and quite unde-tectable, but if a neutron star collapsed to a black hole or two white dwarfs collided, then the gravity waves from those events might be found.

General relativity is needed to predict exactly what may happen with a gravitational wave, but we are so used to the idea of gravity as a force in our everyday lives that it is easier to describe what is happening in Newtonian terms, and that is the approach we shall take in the rest of this article. However, a word of warning is needed: general relativity has been an outstandingly successful theory – correctly predicting the orbital motion of Mercury, the bending of starlight as it passes the Sun, and so on – but it is not the only replacement for Newtonian gravity that has been suggested. There are several other theories of gravity such as Fred Hoyle and Jayant Narlikar's C-field theory, and Carl Brans and Robert Dicke's scalar tensor theory. These alternatives make different predictions about gravity waves. In particular, most alternatives to

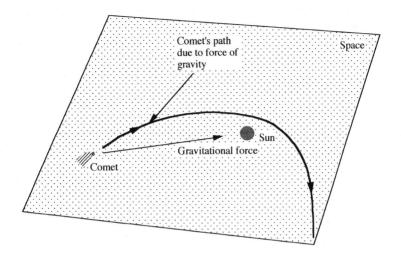

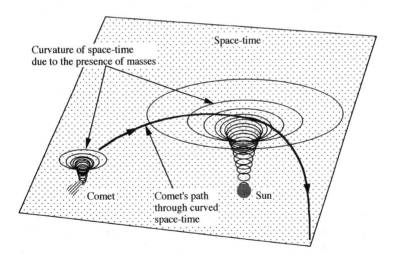

Figure 1. Newton's (top) and Einstein's (bottom) views of gravity.

general relativity suggest an intensity of gravity waves from a binary star about a factor of a hundred higher than is predicted by general relativity. One of the motivations for trying to detect gravity waves is thus the possibility of testing against these various theories of gravity against one another. At the moment, most evidence does support general relativity, but should it turn out to be wrong (and all theories fail eventually), then some changes are likely to be needed to the predictions discussed below.

Suppose, then, that a gravity wave arrives at the Earth, coming from, say, Sirius. What would we experience? Such a gravity wave would result in an alternating increase and decrease in the gravitational force towards Sirius. It might therefore seem that if it were strong enough we would suddenly fly up towards Sirius in the sky, followed shortly afterwards, as the weakening part of the wave arrived, by being slammed back down onto the Earth's surface. But however strong the gravity wave, that is not what would happen, because of course the Earth is affected by the wave as well as ourselves. We, other animals, the Earth, trees, houses, oceans, clouds, and so on would all move simultaneously, and in fact we would hardly notice that the gravity wave was passing through. The only effect we might detect is due to the variation in the intensity of gravity over the gravity wave. Thus, if the wave had a frequency of 12 Hz, corresponding to a wavelength of 25,000 km, then since the Earth is 12,500 km across, one side of it would experience the high-intensity part of the gravity wave at the same time as the other side was in the low-intensity part of the wave. The Earth would therefore be slightly stretched or compressed by the different forces from the gravity wave acting at different points across it. As the wave moved through, that stretching and compression would alternate, and the Earth's shape would oscillate slightly at the frequency of the gravity wave.

We experience just such an effect all the time because of the changing position of the Moon, and thus of the direction of its gravitational force, as it moves around its orbit. The point on the Earth closest to the Moon experiences a greater gravitational force than the point on the opposite side of the Earth. The Earth is therefore distorted into an elliptical shape (Figure 2). As the Earth rotates, and the Moon orbits the Earth, that distortion moves around the Earth. We experience the effect as the tides,[4] and can see it most dramatically at the seaside where it is amplified by the movement of the water and by the shelving of the land at the edge of the sea. However, tides occur in the solid land as well as

Figure 2. Tidal effects on the Earth and Moon (the amount of distortion and the difference between the forces on opposite sides of the Earth and Moon have been very greatly exaggerated).

the seas, and with the Moon overhead we are about 30 centimetres further from the centre of the Earth than when the Moon is on the horizon. The Earth's gravity has a similar distorting effect on the Moon, but because the Moon keeps the same face towards the Earth, the tidal bulge does not move around the Moon.

The effect of differences in gravitational force is thus revealed through tides. With gravity waves it is therefore their tidal effect that produces results that we can experience. These then cause the shape of an object to change, and it is alternately stretched in one direction while simultaneously being compressed in the perpendicular direction, and vice versa (Figure 3). The change in the shape of an object can be measured by the strain, which is the amount of the change divided by the original size. Thus, if an object is 1 metre long and the change in length is 1 millimetre, then the strain is 0.001 (1 mm divided by 1000 mm). For the changes shown in Figure 3, the strain is about 0.1, and would clearly be noticed by the person involved. That being so, why have we

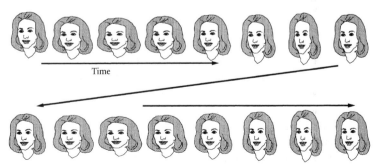

Figure 3. The effect of a gravity wave (the wave here is passing through perpendicularly to the page).

not observed or even felt the strain induced by gravity waves? The answer is that the strains induced by real events in the Universe are vastly smaller than those shown in Figure 3. The star ι Boötis is a nearby binary with a period of just 6 hours, and may be expected to be one of the brightest continuous sources of gravity waves in the sky. Yet the predicted strain produced here on Earth by ι Boötis is just or 5×10^{-21}. This would change the width of the lady's face shown in Figure 3 by just 10^{-21} m, or about 10^{-10} of the width of a hydrogen atom. Thus we cannot expect to feel gravity waves directly.

WHERE DO GRAVITY WAVES COME FROM?

Any object changing its shape, size or position can produce gravity waves. Thus binary stars like ι Boötis are one possible source. Most binaries, though, will produce effects even smaller than those expected from ι Boötis. Sirius, for example, is a binary with a white dwarf as its companion. But though it is only a tenth of the distance from us of ι Boötis, Sirius would have an effect 10^{14} times smaller than ι Boötis because of its lengthy (50-year) orbital period. Gravity wave detectors (see below) are soon expected to be able to detect strains of 10^{-22}. The possible sources that they may then be able to 'see' therefore include:

- the close binaries forming novae and dwarf novae out to distances of a few hundred light-years,
- pulsars out to a few thousand light-years,
- supernovae out to a few tens of thousands of light-years,
- coalescing binary systems, especially two white dwarfs, out to the nearest galaxies,
- neutron stars collapsing to black holes, out to tens of millions of light-years,
- coalescing binary systems involving pairs of neutron stars or pairs of black holes, out to hundreds of millions of light-years.

ARE THEY THERE TO BE FOUND?

No gravity waves have yet been definitely detected (see below), but none the less there is evidence for their existence, and that they behave as general relativity predicts. The evidence comes from a rotating neutron star, or pulsar, which forms a binary system with a second neutron star. The pulsar is in Aquila and is called PSR 1913+16. Its pulsation period is 59 milliseconds, and its orbital period around the second neutron star (which is not pulsing) is 7.75 hours. Timing the pulses from the pulsar enables the details of the orbit of the system to be found to a very high degree of precision. The orbit is highly elliptical, and the two neutron stars should be radiating gravity waves as they move around it. Now, the effect of radiating gravity waves on a binary system is to cause the size of the orbit to shrink. In extreme cases it can lead to the components of the binary colliding with each other and coalescing. In PSR 1913+16, the shrinkage of the orbit should cause the orbital period to shorten. The observed shortening of the orbital period is by 75 microseconds every year, and this is almost exactly the value predicted by general relativity for the system. Thus PSR 1913+16 not only provides evidence that supports the existence of gravity waves, but also indicates that they are behaving as general relativity, and not the other theories of gravity, would suggest.

HOW CAN WE FIND GRAVITY WAVES?

Detecting gravity waves involves measuring the strain that they produce in objects. As we have seen, this is likely to be very tiny indeed. Gravity wave detectors therefore need to be quite extraordinarily sensitive. The first such detector was built by Joseph Weber some 35 years ago. It comprised an aluminium bar 2 m long and 0.5 m wide. It had a natural vibration frequency around 1 kHz, which is the expected frequency for the gravity waves from several of the possible astronomical sources. Gravity waves of that frequency would resonate with the bar and so increase the likelihood of their detection. Vibrations in the bar were detected by piezoelectric crystals attached to it. Numerous precautions, for example to isolate the bar from external disturbances, and to keep its temperature constant, needed to be taken. The detector was able to measure strains down to 10^{-15} corresponding to a change in its width by just a ten-thousandth of the size of an atom. None the less, such a sensitivity is at least a factor of a thousand too poor to catch the predicted strains from astronomical gravity wave sources. However, Weber's bars (he used two and looked for coincident detections) in 1969 did seem to detect gravity waves coming from the centre of our galaxy. No one else, though, was able to detect the waves, and his results are something of a puzzle. Most people do not now think that it was a real detection of gravity waves, although what caused the disturbances in the bars remains unknown. Modern variants of Weber's bar are cooled by liquid helium and use niobium in place of aluminium. They are predicted to be able to detect strains down to 10^{-18}, and so should be able to 'see' the brightest astronomical gravity wave sources, though none has yet done so.

The main modern gravity wave detectors, which are all still under construction, operate quite differently from the bar detectors. They are based upon the interferometer design that Albert Michelson and Edward Morley used in 1887 to show that the speed of light was constant in all directions despite the Earth's orbital motion through space.[5] In a Michelson interferometer-based gravity wave detector, light from a laser is split into two beams which are sent out on two perpendicular paths (Figure 4). The beams are reflected back and recombined to produce an interference pattern. Any change in the path length of one of the light beams will cause a shift in the interference pattern. Thus a

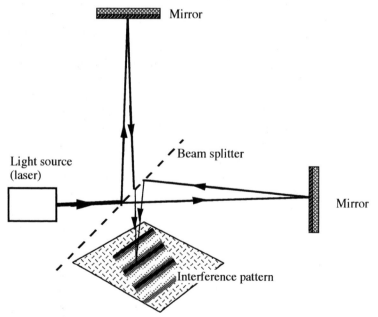

Figure 4. The Michelson interferometer.

gravity wave, which is likely to change one path length by a different amount from the other as it passes through the interferometer, can be detected through the resulting changing interference pattern.

Michelson interferometer-based gravity wave detectors should be able to detect strains of 10^{-22}, and so find many astronomical sources. However, to reach that level of sensitivity great care and numerous precautions have to be taken. The light paths have to be several kilometres long, and their effective length expanded many times[6] by multiply reflecting the light beams back and forth. The whole light path must be in a vacuum, and the instrument as isolated as possible from external disturbances, the mirrors have to be flat to a few nanometres, scatter must be less than 0.01 per cent of the light, the frequency of the laser source must be stabilized to a few parts in 10^{18}, and so on.

Several such detectors are under construction at the moment. One of the most ambitious is LIGO (Laser Interferometer Gravity wave Observatory) in the USA. This will have two Michelson-type interferometers with 4-kilometre arms. One detector will be in Louisiana, the other 3000 km away in Washington state. The separation of the detectors means that coincident detections are much more likely to be due to gravity waves and not to, say, local disturbances. Other detectors are under construction in Italy, Germany and Japan. The building of several detectors is not as wasteful as it may seem, because they are just detectors, not telescopes. That is to say, an individual instrument will only detect a gravity wave; it will not determine from where in space it has come. Several well separated instruments are therefore needed so that the delay times between their detections of the same gravity wave can be used to locate its source in space. Even more grandiose ideas are planned for future gravity wave detectors, such as a space-based interferometer system which would have arms 5,000,000 km long and need at least six spacecraft whose positions would need stabilizing to a fraction of a nanometre.

CONCLUSION

Gravity waves will almost certainly be detected within the next decade – and possibly within a year or two. When they are found we can expect them to reveal the inner workings of supernovae, white dwarfs and neutron stars, and show black holes in the process of formation. Much of what gravity waves may reveal is already predicted by theoreticians, but the real excitement, as with any new means of observing the Universe, will come from what has not been expected. What 'dragons' are there out there to be discovered by the first gravity wave astronomers? We do not know the answer now, but it is likely that we shall not have to wait for it for much longer.

NOTES

1. Particles such as protons and helium nuclei which pervade the Galaxy, and possibly the whole Universe, travelling at velocities from 90 to 99.999999 per cent of the speed of light. They are thought to originate in solar flares and supernovae.
2. Electrically neutral, low- or zero-mass subatomic particles involved in many nuclear reactions. So far they have been observed to come from nuclear reactors, the Sun and the Large Magellanic Cloud supernova (1987A).
3. Oscillations of the Earth's atmosphere may also be called gravity waves, but they are quite different from what is being discussed here.
4. The differential gravitational force from the Sun also contributes to the effect.
5. So eventually leading to the formulation of the special theory of relativity.
6. As strain is the change divided by the original length, a strain of 10^{-22} would change a path length of 10 m by just 10^{-21} m. But the same strain would change a path length of 1000 km by 10^{-16}m.

The Royal Observatory, Greenwich: The Finding of Longitude at Sea and the Advancement of Astronomy, 1675–1998

ALLAN CHAPMAN

The closure of the Royal Greenwich Observatory in 1998 severed Britain's longest-standing and most fruitful link between government and astronomy. A 'Memorial' meeting was held at the Royal Astronomical Society in January 1999 to which I had the honour of being invited to give the paper dealing with the old Royal Observatory's pre-20th-century history. As we now enter the new millennium, we should remember that institution which, between 1675 and 1998, did so much not merely to put British astronomical excellence on the world map, but to create large areas of that map in the first place.

We should not forget, however, that if official cheese-paring attitudes were responsible for ending the Royal Observatory, then it was official bungling almost worthy of a Gilbert and Sullivan opera which brought it into being in the first place. In 1674, England was well on her way to becoming Europe's foremost maritime power, though even the most powerful fleets afloat often found it difficult to rendezvous or to lay down an exact course because of their inability to find the longitude at sea. While Robert Hooke, Christiaan Huygens and others had experimented with 'sea clocks' as a way of longitude-finding (a method which John Harrison would perfect a century later), it was the 'Lunars' method which most people favoured. To make this method work, it was simply necessary for a navigator on a ship at sea to measure the angular distance between the Moon and a given star, and compare his locally measured angle with that printed in a table prepared by a home-based observatory. But in 1670, no observatory in the world had instruments that were sufficiently accurate to measure lunar and stellar positions to the level of precision that was required to calculate the necessary tables.

Then a young French adventurer turned up in London. He was Le Sieur De St Pierre, who was trying to use his influence with King Charles II's current French mistress, Louise de Kéroualle, later the Duchess of Portsmouth, to gain an audience with the king. St Pierre had a method of finding the longitude at sea using the Moon and a star, and when Louise mentioned St Pierre to the king, his majesty was very interested. Charles II was one of Britain's most intellectual monarchs, who, in addition to being an inveterate womanizer, connoisseur and spendthrift, was a keen lover of science, and founder of the Royal Society. The technical details of St Pierre's method were handed over to a committee of the Royal Society for consideration, which in turn consulted the 28-year-old son of a Derby brewer who was currently in London on business, and had many friends in the Royal Society. John Flamsteed, in fact, was acknowledged in the Society as one of the most accomplished astronomers working in Britain, and his report on St Pierre's method was damning. Of course one could find the longitude at sea using the Moon and stars, Flamsteed said, but St Pierre clearly had no practical knowledge of astronomy, for if he had, he would have known that the finest astronomical tables then available, those of Tycho Brahe, were nowhere near accurate enough to generate the necessary predictive tables.

King Charles asked Flamsteed what would be needed to provide lunar tables of the requisite quality, and he was told that a wholesale re-observation of the sky using the latest instruments, instead of those made by Tycho 90 years before, was necessary. The king resolved that an observatory was to be built in the Royal Park at Greenwich, and commissioned his architect, Sir Chrisopher Wren, FRS, to provide a good, cheap building. As it was the king's lady friends and select courtiers who seem to have got most of what money the hard-up Charles II had, this observatory had to be a bargain-priced Royal foundation. Money was raised from the sale of 'decayed' gunpowder – in which the saltpetre, sulphur and charcoal had settled out of the mixture – stored at the Tower of London. The money raised from the chemical dealers was used to buy second-hand building materials, from the recently demolished fort at Tilbury, further down the Thames. Wren's resulting building, 'for use, and Little for Pompe', must rank as the finest cheap building in the whole history of architecture. It cost only £519 – just £14 more than the large wooden builder's model for the future St Paul's Cathedral, which Wren had also just designed.

The building was erected during the summer of 1675, though when Flamsteed took possession as 'Our Astronomical Observator', or Astronomer Royal, he found it quite empty. The Royal Foundation Charter failed to provide him with any instruments! Fortunately, Flamsteed possessed instruments of his own, brought down from Derby, while his friend Sir Jonas Moore, the Master General of the Ordnance, provided him with an excellent iron sextant of 7 feet (just over 2 metres) radius, and pendulum clocks. Over 30 years later, Flamsteed would recollect that he would have achieved little at Greenwich had he not had private money. In short, while he had an official salary of £100 per annum, paid erractically by the government, it was his own private funds that actually made the Royal Observatory a success, for Flamsteed was really a grand amateur astronomer in charge of an ill-administered official observatory.

But what made the Lunars method of finding the longitude look feasible in 1675 was the revolution in instrumentation that had recently taken place. Not only was the telescope now in regular use, but the Yorkshireman William Gascoigne had successfully adapted it to become a precise measuring instrument. The same William Gascoigne had also invented the screw micrometer which, along with the telescopic sight, enabled astronomers to measure angles to seconds of arc, rather than to mere fractions of a whole degree. And by 1658 the Dutchman Christiaan Huygens had perfected Galileo's pendulum to produce clocks that were over a hundred times more accurate than they had been in 1655.

All of Flamsteed's instruments incorporated this new precision technology, which had an impact on the astronomy of the 1670s that was as great as that produced by CCDs, computers and adaptive optics on the astronomy of the 1990s. But in the 44 years that he worked on Greenwich Hill, John Flamsteed never succeeded in observing the lunar orbit with sufficient accuracy to facilitate the production of longitude tables. The finest instruments of Thomas Tompion, Abraham Sharp and others all failed, because graduation, systematic and other errors could still not be eliminated or quantified by the time of Flamsteed's death, on New Year's Eve, 1719. Yet on the way, Flamsteed's micrometers, clocks, sextant, mural arc, telescopes and other instruments made possible a wholly new type of astronomical catalogue. For the *Historia coelestis Britannica* ('British Account of the Heavens') which Margaret Flamsteed and his old Assistants published in three big folio volumes in 1725 would provide the definitive Northern-Hemisphere sky survey for the next 80 years. Even Sir William Herschel, in 1795, would relate his nebula discoveries to Flamsteed's catalogue.

The 64-year-old Edmond Halley succeeded Flamsteed in 1720. Flamsteed had loathed Halley, and his widow Margaret began a lawsuit to claim all her late husband's instruments and papers to stop them falling into Halley's grasp. She won. Yet this stripping of the Royal Observatory would be a healthy development, for the wily Halley insisted that it was the government's responsibility, and not the Astronomer Royal's, to provide the instruments. Halley also won his claim, much to the financial advantage of future Astronomers Royal.

With the generous £500 grant which Halley got out of the government of King George I, he commissioned the clockmaker George Graham, FRS, to provided a set of instruments that would become prototypes for 18th-century observatories from St Petersburg to Philadelphia, USA. Like Flamsteed, Halley realized that observing angular positions of the Sun, Moon and stars, in right ascension and declination, was best done in the meridian.

First of all, he commissioned a new type of instrument from Graham: a transit telescope, set on eastern and western trunnions, so that it described an exact meridian circle. Whenever a body passed its meridional wire, Halley could measure its position from the next object, or from the first point of Aries, by simply timing it with one of Graham's beautiful pendulum clocks. These sidereal angles could either be expressed directly in hours, minutes and seconds of time, or easily converted into degrees of arc.

Secondly, Halley commissioned an 8-foot (2.5-metre) radius iron quadrant to be set in the meridian. The telescopic sight, micrometer and precision 90° brass scale of this quadrant enabled Halley to observe declinations with unprecedented accuracy, so that with his new instruments he was in a strong position to fulfil his vow to the Admiralty – and quite an optimistic vow it was for a 64-year-old to make 280 years ago, when only a fraction of people saw 70 – that he would observe the Moon in the meridian through its entire 18.6-year cycle. And what is more, Halley kept his word!

Yet Edmond Halley was so different in character from Flamsteed. He was a bon viveur, a wit and a shrewd businessman. Almost certainly it had been the promised £20,000 prize for finding longitude at sea, by the Act of 1714, which had inspired him to petition the government for Flamsteed's old job. As a former Royal Naval captain, moreover, Halley got his £100 per annum as Astronomer Royal augmented by the half-pay, or pension, of a captain, in addition to which he retained his Savilian Professorship of Geometry at Oxford University, with its stipend and students' fees. He was well off, though in full justice to a man of 70-odd years, he fulfilled his duties with amazing energy. It was said that he never missed a visible transit of the Moon in 21 years. Halley's death, indeed, was of a piece with his life. Warned by his doctor to cut down on his drink, the jovial Halley told his son-in-law to pour him a bumper of his favourite wine, on 14 January 1742. He drank it, licked his lips, sat down, and promptly died. He was in his eighty-sixth year.

For the last 30 years of his life, Halley had been the patron and friend of a brilliant young Oxford astronomer, the Revd Dr James Bradley. Even as a student, Bradley had shown his genius both as a practical and as a mathematical astronomer, and it was via Halley that he began his friendship with and discipleship of Sir Isaac Newton, of whose *Principia* (1686) Halley had been publisher. Halley had also been instrumental in getting Bradley appointed to his own companion chair at Oxford, when Bradley became the Savilian Professor of Astronomy in 1721, while during the 1720s and 1730s he was a regular visitor at Greenwich. It had been Bradley's meticulous work, both as an observer and as an experimental physicist, that led him to realize that, over 20 years, George Graham's beautiful 8-foot quadrant at Greenwich had developed a tiny scale error of 15.75 arcseconds. Bradley traced it to a distortion caused by the different coefficients of expansion between the brass and the iron parts of the instrument. When Bradley succeeded Halley as Astronomer Royal in 1742, he ordered a new 8-foot quadrant by John Bird with the £1000 overhaul grant which the Admiralty gave to the Royal Observatory. Every part of the instrument, barring the lenses and micrometer screws, was of brass so that thermal homogeneity would be maintained. It was the first time that such a concept had been applied to a large engineering structure, and the quadrant's 1-arcsecond scale error remained stable until it was finally superseded in 1812.

James Bradley brought a degree of precision to astronomy that would have seemed impossible in the days of Flamsteed. The direction of Bradley's future career, in fact, had already been firmly laid down in 1728 when he had discovered the aberration of light, using a zenith sector by George Graham. This was a 12½-foot (3.8-metre) refracting telescope hung on gimbals, pointing exactly to the zenith and measuring to 0.5 arcseconds with a micrometer. Observing the star Gamma Draconis from his private observatory at Wanstead, Essex, he noticed that it displayed a six-monthly motion that was not a stellar parallax, but was none the less caused by the Earth's movement in space – the first observation to demonstrate unequivocally that the Earth rotated around the Sun. And then, in 1748, he extracted a second motion from his zenith sector observations. This was a gravitational nodding effect caused by the Moon upon the Earth across its 18.6-year cycle. Being a fine classical scholar, Bradley called the new phenomenon 'nutation' from the Latin *nutare*, 'to nod'.

It was also James Bradley who recognized that the refractive index of the atmosphere was sensitive to barometric pressure and temperature, and from 1750 onwards he accompanied every Greenwich observation with a meteorological reading. From his pressure and temperature readings he could make refined corrections to his right ascension and declination observations, and thereby compensate for tiny fluctuations in air conditions that would distort the true position of a star. Bradley's formulae still form the basis for the refraction tables we use today. And as a by-product, this gave Greenwich one of the oldest and most accurate runs of meteorological data in the world.

By the 1750s, therefore, everything seemed in place to enable longitude to be found by Lunars: observatory quadrants reading to a single arcsecond in declination, observatory regulator clocks that enabled right ascension to be measured to one-tenth of a second of time, tables to correct for atmospheric distortions, and an increasingly refined knowledge of the complex orbit of the Moon. Then, building on the work of Flamsteed, Halley and Bradley, came two other men. The first was Tobias Mayer, of Göttingen, Hanover, a German Fellow of the Royal Society, and the second, the Revd Dr Nevil Maskelyne, the future, and fifth, Astronomer Royal.

Yet what Bradley, Mayer and Maskelyne also had in common was the fact that they all observed, from Greenwich or from Göttingen, with superb large brass quadrants made by John Bird, a former Durham weaver who by 1755 was acknowledged as the world's leading quadrant builder.

By the time of his death in 1762, Tobias Mayer had produced a set of lunar tables, using his 6-foot (1.8-metre) radius Bird quadrant, that were of good enough quality to predict accurately the future motions of the Moon. This meant that they could be used to generate published tables from which the longitude could be extracted. The claims put forward by Mayer's widow were taken seriously in London.

James Bradley died after a short illness in 1762, at the age of 69, and he was succeeded as Astronomer Royal by another Oxford man, the Revd Dr Nathaniel Bliss. Sadly, however, Dr Bliss died after only two years in office, so that he had no chance to draw conclusions from any long, detailed runs of observations. Dr Maskelyne, of Trinity College, Cambridge, came next, and was to hold the post of Astronomer Royal for a record 47 years, dying in office in 1811.

It is unfortunate that in Dava Sobel's recent bestseller, *Longitude*, Dr Maskelyne emerges as the villain of the piece who blocked John Harrison's rival claim for the Longitude Prize, in which a chronometer or sea clock was being advocated instead of the Lunars method. This is, however, a distortion of historical fact, for being a very practically minded scientist and a conscientious civil servant, he was all too aware of costs. Maskelyne made no bones about the fact that he believed it was more practical to find the longitude at sea by observing the Moon than it was from a delicate and fantastically complex piece of mechanism. He openly backed the claim of Tobias Mayer, and used Mayer's, Bradley's and his own Greenwich observations to publish the first edition of the *Nautical Almanac* in 1767.

Now the *Nautical Almanac* came to contain positions of the Moon for up to three years into the future, so that even a ship away from Britain for several years could still continue to find its precise position anywhere in the world. And with all the observations already in the bag, or at least in continuous production, all that one needed to do was reduce and publish them, and issue a volume to every ship in the Royal Navy. The *Nautical Almanac* has been in continuous, updated production ever since, and has laid one of the essential foundations of modern astronomical navigation.

And to use these cheaply produced tables (cheaply produced because the research capital had already been spent over the previous 92 years), all that one required was a good octant or sextant, and a sailing master (or navigating officer) who could do complex calculations. Jesse Ramsden had already developed a machine upon which accurate scales could be generated and engraved on brass sextant bodies for only a few shillings apiece – one of the first examples of precision mass-production miniaturization – so that the Lunars method looked vastly cheaper to put into practice than Harrison's chronometer. As Maskelyne and others very correctly pointed out, it would cost vast sums of money to equip each and every ship in the Navy with a Harrison chronometer, whereas all that was required with the Lunars method was to supply them with a mass-produced sextant costing about £10 and a printed book!

The real flaw in the Lunars method, however, was the inability of most officers to do the four hours of complex calculation that had to follow *every* sextant observation of the Moon before one could derive a longitude fix. Georgian naval officers were essentially fighting men, and not higher mathematicians, and Maskelyne realized the fact. Over his years in Greenwich, therefore, he set about simplifying the calculations, wherever possible, and greatly reducing the toil. And, hand in hand with the mathematical simplification, between 1767 and the Napoleonic Wars 30 years later the mathematical skills of officers improved considerably, for while Lunars were in fairly general use by 1800, chronometers, even of the types simplified from Harrison's designs by craftsmen such as Thomas Earnshaw and John Arnold, were still relatively scarce and expensive, and frequently the personal property of individual officers rather than standard Navy issue.

In addition to his work on Lunars and longitude, Dr Maskelyne was a founder of the science of geophysics. In 1774 he made a series of observations of zenith stars upon a meridian line passing through the mountain Schiehallion in the Scottish Highlands. By measuring the tiny deflections caused by the granite mass of the mountain upon the known density of the lead of his zenith sector plumb-bob, he was able to compute a value for the density of the mountain. And as Schiehallion was made of primary rock, he argued that, from its density, the Earth itself must be 4.5 times the density of water (the modern figure is 5.51). In short, he was the first scientist to calculate 'big G', or the gravitational mass of the Earth. Now that the density of one planet in the Solar System was known, it was possible to extract the densities of all the others, from their already known proportionate pulls upon one another as derived from Newton's *Principia*.

By the early years of the 19th century, many astronomers were coming to feel that the 75-year-old Maskelyne and his 50-odd-year-old instruments were no longer at the cutting edge of research. Then in 1806 Mr John Pond, who maintained an excellent private observatory at Westbury-sub-Mendip, Somerset (he probably used Glastonbury Tor as his meridian mark), published a paper in which he compared the right ascension and declination positions of certain key stars measured at Greenwich and at his own observatory. It was immediately clear that the Westbury Observatory produced more consistent observations, to fractions of a single arcsecond, whereas Maskelyne's Greenwich observations were sometimes a whole second out. Maskelyne, who was nothing if not a fair-minded and honest man, admitted that a private gentleman's observatory was superior to a national institution, and agreed that the Greenwich instruments needed replacing.

Now the secret of Pond's success lay in the new type of instrument which he was using at Westbury. By 1806, in fact, it was generally agreed across Europe that the quadrant had been superseded by the astronomical circle. From the 1780s onwards, craftsmen like Jesse Ramsden and Edward Troughton, both FRSs in their own right, had been advocating full circles rather than part-circles such as quadrants; and in all fairness it must not be forgotten that as early as 1792 Maskelyne had requested a new circle to replace the old Greenwich quadrants, though his request had been ignored. A full circle was easier to graduate, its errors were more easily detectable, and when corrections were applied staggering levels of accuracy could be obtained in astrometric work. Like many of the leading astronomers of the day, John Pond was a 'grand amateur'. The son and heir of a wealthy London businessman, he had studied astronomy at school before going up to Trinity College, Cambridge; he is said to have been living in Paris at the time of the Revolution, and following his return to England, he commissioned Troughton to build him one of the new circles. He got the first paid job of his life at the age of 44, in 1811, when the government invited him to succeed the deceased Dr Maskelyne as Astronomer Royal, and began using the superb 6-foot-diameter mural circle at Greenwich, built by Edward Troughton, when it was completed in 1812.

John Pond brought Greenwich up to date in its instrumentation. He also increased its staff to institute a system of 24-hour observing, for an astronomical quadrant or circle fitted with a good telescope can be used to observe star transits in the meridian during daylight provided that the Sun is not nearby.

The Royal Observatory, indeed, had been astonishingly understaffed ever since 1675. With the exception of a £25 sum provided by the Admiralty for an Assistant – a miserable amount especially by 1750 – the successive Astronomers Royal had been obliged to dig into their own pockets to pay staff costs. But after 1822, Pond obtained a regular official grant to pay for six men to do the observing and routine calculating duties that were essential to providing the data for the *Nautical Almanac*. By the late 1820s, however, Pond was beginning to lose his grip, probably as a result of worsening health. The declining reliability of Greenwich observations became a scientific and a political scandal and, to poor Pond's embarrassment, the *Nautical Almanac* was removed from his control and placed under that of a separate office and Superintendent in the Admiralty in 1834, though it still used Greenwich observations.

And there was also a clique of assistants who, no doubt realizing the growing incapacity of the Astronomer Royal, started to take advantage. Their ringleader was Thomas Taylor, the chief assistant. He was an ex-naval officer who, while a skilled astronomer and calculator, was also dishonest, insubordinate and often drunk. And then there were two men who had come down from Yorkshire together to work for Pond. William Rogerson of Leeds proved to be a shiftless individual, whereas his friend William Richardson of Pocklington had great intelligence and zeal. Richardson won the RAS Gold Medal in 1830 for his work on refining the aberration constant; however, in 1845 he was arrested for murder!

The Augean stable of the Royal Observatory needed to be cleansed, and in 1835 the government appointed a man to replace the newly retired and terminally ill Pond. The new broom would prove to be the most formidable figure that Greenwich had ever known. Sir George Biddell Airy was only 34 years old when appointed Astronomer Royal, yet already he had an international reputation as a scientist and professorial director of the Cambridge University Observatory. A ruthlessly honest and efficient administrator, Airy had Taylor sacked as a condition of his own acceptance of the post of Astronomer Royal. He tried to get rid of Rogerson and Richardson, but their misdemeanours were less blatant, and the Admiralty protected them. Even so, Airy probably felt a certain amount of justification when Richardson was arrested for incest and murder, and automatically lost his job.

Airy swept through the Royal Observatory with an unprecedented wind of change. Within a few years all the major instruments had been replaced with new, state-of-the-art designs. As an undergraduate at Trinity College, Cambridge, Airy had been the most brilliant man of his generation. As Senior Wrangler he had carried off by far the highest First of his year, 1822; and yet he was by no means a pure theoretician. Airy applied his analytical mathematical knowledge to optics and engineering design, and during the 46 years that he was Astronomer Royal he personally designed *every* major instrument that he was to bring into use, from the great Transit Circle of 1850 to the distribution of the electric time signals, sent through the growing network of the electric telegraph to every corner of Britain by 1865, which helped establish GMT and the international status of the Greenwich meridian.

Yet Airy, though the seventh Astronomer Royal, was the first one who was not a gentleman of ample private means. He was also a layman, so unlike Flamsteed, Maskelyne and his other clerical predecessors, Airy could claim no church patronage. Unlike Halley he was not a naval captain, and unlike Pond he was not the son of a rich businessman. He was, as he bluntly reminded the Admiralty, a person who needed to be paid a decent professional salary for the job. Flamsteed, as we saw, got £100 a year, and Halley had had this sum liberally topped up by a Navy pension. Yet from Bradley to Maskelyne the Astronomer Royal's salary stuck, for 57 years, at £350 per annum, and when Maskelyne's friends tried to secure him a pay rise in 1809, the Chancellor of the Exchequer dismissed it bluntly by saying that Dr Maskelyne was privately wealthy and needed no more money. Pond did get a rise, but the hard-bargaining Airy secured a hefty increase to £800, plus a £300 a year Civil List Pension settled upon his 30-year-old wife Richarda. As Halley had established the precedent of making the government responsible for providing instruments, so Airy made it responsible for paying adequate salaries.

During his years at the Royal Observatory, Airy exerted a transforming influence, not only 'industrializing' the making, reducing and publishing of meridian observations of unprecedented accuracy, but in other things as well. Airy's Greenwich was the home of the world's first and most extensive telegraphic time service after 1852, and became a premier geomagnetic and meteorological observatory, and a critical testing place for the now vastly cheaper marine chronometers. His fascination with industrial and mechanical accuracy led to the introduction of 'foolproof' photographic and photo-electric data recording devices, as well as pioneering innovations in timekeeping, optics and geophysics.

Even people who worked at Greenwich in the early 1950s, or some 70-odd years after Airy's retirement, admit that his impact upon Royal Observatory procedures had been so great that they always felt that Sir George's ghost was still keeping an eye on them when they were there.

By the time of Airy's retirement in 1881, such was the revolution in navigation that had taken place that all the problems which the Royal Observatory had been created to address in 1675 had been solved. Lunars were standardized, greatly simplified, and in international use. Chronometers were now not much more expensive than first-class gold pocket watches, and even small merchant vessels carried them. Using either Lunars or the chronometer, a good navigator could fix the position of his ship almost to within a kilometre anywhere on the Earth's surface.

And yet no Victorian minister of state so much as suggested shutting down the nation's most illustrious scientific institution. Greenwich time, Greenwich tables, Greenwich Certificates of Warranty were international bywords for excellence and reliability, and Queen Victoria's government was deeply proud of what went on within Wren's red-brick masterpiece on Greenwich Hill.

Of course, all the traditional functions continued to be performed: meridian work, lunar orbit work and timekeeping. But after Sir William Christie succeeded Airy in 1881, Greenwich began to develop departments that enabled the cultivation of the most recent branches of astronomy, such as astrophysics. Stellar spectroscopic work began, and Walter Maunder, head of the Solar Department, started to do serious work on solar physics, discovering the celebrated 'Maunder minimum' in the sunspot cycle.

It was also during Sir William Christie's time, in 1890, that the first women were taken on at the Royal Observatory. Two young Girton College, Cambridge, graduates, Annie Dill Russell and Alice Everett, were employed on £50 a year short-term contracts – although the Cambridge University Observatory had employed women junior assistants since about 1875, and had paid them better. Annie Russell married Maunder in 1895, and while Civil Service Regulations required her to resign, she spent the next 50 years of her life as an independent solar physicist, international eclipse photographer, and driving force within the British Astronomical Association.

Eclipse work and the study of the solar atmosphere became long-term specialities at Greenwich after 1881. Christie was fascinated by the Sun, as was his successor as Astronomer Royal, Sir Frank Dyson, after 1910, and into the 20th century Greenwich was to send eclipse researchers in pursuit of shadows around the world. It was Dyson, in 1917, in fact, who first suggested that Einstein's theory of relativity could be tested experimentally by seeing whether the mass of the Sun was capable of bending a ray of starlight at the forthcoming eclipse of 1919. And, as we know, he was right.

Between 1933 and 1955, Dyson was succeeded as Astronomer Royal by Sir Harold Spencer Jones, and he in turn by Sir Richard van der Riet Woolley.

But the ever-expanding sprawl of smoke-laden London had long since made Greenwich a thoroughly bad location for an astronomical observatory, and its obvious vulnerability during the Blitz in the early 1940s began to make people wonder about the need to shift the great national institution to better skies. Even so, Greenwich served with spectacular success during World War II, and the Greenwich Park staff even formed its own Home Guard unit. Spencer Jones, the Astronomer Royal, was naturally the commanding officer, and the senior assistants became the other officers. The shortage of firearms for the unit caused one Greenwich senior assistant to go up to a West End sporting shop to provide himself with a good shotgun for when he went on duty! One does not generally associate the Royal Observatory with the antics of 'Dad's Army', although the unpublished wartime 'diary' of the late Philip Laurie, who was on the Observatory staff then, often makes entertaining reading.

Sir Richard Woolley was the last Astronomer Royal to work in the old Royal Observatory, Greenwich, for after the war moves were made to find a new permanent site, and in 1948 King George VI gave the Royal Assent to a new location and title: The Royal Greenwich Observatory, Herstmonceux. The 'RGO' was born, and over the next six years was to move from cramped Wren buildings to a spacious medieval castle in Sussex. The last meridian observation to be taken at Greenwich, after an unbroken working life of 279 years, was made on Airy's great 1850 transit circle (which still marks the international

Greenwich Meridian) on March 30, 1954. It was of the asteroid Pallas, and was made by Gilbert Satterthwaite, who was then a junior member of staff, and still works at Imperial College, London. At the time it was officially scheduled that a senior assistant would make the last recorded observation on the Greenwich site. But the final day at Greenwich was cloudy, so that Gilbert Satterthwaite's Pallas observation was the last to be officially made, and published.

At Herstmonceux, the RGO proceeded upon a new and glorious scientific career which culminated in the commissioning of the 98-inch (2.5-metre) aperture Sir Isaac Newton Telescope in 1967. Alas, even the balmy climate of Sussex was not clear enough to use the Isaac Newton to maximum advantage, and after about 15 years it was moved to La Palma in the Canary Islands, to a mountain-top site assessed by Sir Francis Graham-Smith, who would later become Astronomer Royal.

The last Astronomer Royal to be in actual charge of the RGO, both at Greenwich and at Herstmonceux, was Sir Richard Woolley. Upon his retirement in 1971, fundamental changes took place. Dr Margaret Burbidge succeeded him at Herstmonceux, but she was never given the ancient title Astronomer Royal, but simply called 'director' of the RGO. She was to be succeeded after only a year by Dr Allan Hunter, and he in turn by Sir Francis Graham-Smith; and after the move of the RGO to Cambridge in 1990, Dr Alec Boksenburg and Dr Jasper Wall took over. Responsibility for the institution had also been moved from the Royal Observatory's old master, the Admiralty, to the Science Research Council.

The office of Astronomer Royal, meanwhile, separated from the directorship of the Royal Observatory in 1972, had now become a 'floating' title which the powers that be used to grace the career of an illustrious British astronomer. Since 1972, it has been held by Sir Martin Ryle, Sir Francis Graham-Smith and Sir Arnold Wolfendale; the current holder is Sir Martin Rees. The Astronomer Royal is now something of a British astronomical ambassador, and Sir Francis, Sir Arnold and Sir Martin, both in office and in retirement, are all currently active in fostering astronomy in Britain, and are also leading figures in the encouragement of amateur astronomy.

But in 1998, the RGO was finally closed. While it is true that the growing international character of astronomy, and especially World Wide Web communications, may no longer make national observatories and national time services quite so essential as they once were, the closure of the longest-running research observatory in the history of science (the slightly older Paris Observatory was badly disrupted in the French Revolution) is a sad event by any standards. And if the exuberant circumstances of 1675 have some of the elements of a Gilbert and Sullivan comedy, those of 1998 might be likened to a funeral march played by a band of accountants.

Yet we should not overlook the fact that in its first decades and in its last, the state-of-the-art instrumentation at Greenwich and the RGO came from beer profits. For just as John Flamsteed's mural arc and other instruments derived from an inheritance which stemmed from a Derby brewery, so the Carlsberg Automatic Transit Circle, which now monitors time for Britain at La Palma, derived from monies generously provided by the Carlsberg Brewery in Denmark.

ACKNOWLEDGEMENTS

I particularly wish to thank Andrew Murray for his insights into post-1950 Greenwich and the RGO. I similarly acknowledge George Wilkins, Gilbert Satterthwaite and the late Philip Laurie.

BIBLIOGRAPHY

Eric G. Forbes, *Greenwich Observatory: 1. Origins and Early History (1675–1835)* (Taylor & Francis, 1975).

A. J. Meadow, *Greenwich Observatory: 2. Recent History (1836–1975)* (Taylor & Francis, 1975).

Derek Howse, *Greenwich Observatory: 3. The Buildings and Instruments* (Taylor & Francis, 1975).

John Flamsteed, *The 'Preface' to John Flamsteed's* Historia Coelestis Britannica. *1725*, edited by Allan Chapman, based on a translation by Dione Johnson (National Maritime Museum Monograph No. 52, 1982).

Derek Howse, *Nevil Maskelyne, The Seaman's Astronomer* (Cambridge University Press, 1989).

E. W. Maunder, *The Royal Observatory, Greenwich* (Religious Tract Society, 1900).

Gilbert Satterthwaite, 'The History of the Airy Transit Circle at the Royal Observatory, Greenwich', University of London M.Sc. Dissertation, 1995

Allan Chapman, *Dividing the Circle: The Development of Critical Angular Measurement in Astronomy 1500–1850* (Praxis-Wiley, Chichester and New York, 1990, 1995)

Allan Chapman, *Astronomical Instruments and their Users: Tycho Brahe to William Lassell* (Variorum, Aldershot, 1996)

Castle in the Sky: The Story of the Royal Greenwich Observatory at Herstmonceux

CHAS PARKER

This article is dedicated to the memory of Dr Bill Martin, one of the many wonderful characters who made the Royal Greenwich Observatory the unique place it was, and who so sadly passed away on January 15, 1999.

The Royal Greenwich Observatory, which closed in October 1998, enjoyed a glorious history spanning over three hundred years. Initially located at Greenwich, it ended its days at Cambridge, but it was during its time at Herstmonceux in East Sussex, particularly in the sixties and seventies, that it was perhaps at its most vibrant. The thing that set the Observatory apart, of course, was the people. With a staff of over two hundred in its heyday, the unique mix of skills and personalities made the place what it was and enabled it to enjoy a worldwide reputation for excellence. But how did an establishment, known as the Royal *Greenwich* Observatory, come to be situated in 380 acres of Sussex countryside just outside a village with a decidedly French-sounding name?

When the Royal Observatory was founded in 1675, Greenwich was a village in open countryside, several miles outside London. With the growth of the capital, however, the area became urbanized and gradually deteriorated as an observational site. Smoke from factories and houses, along with mercury-vapour street lighting, meant that by the end of World War II the only option for the Admiralty, which in those days was responsible for running the Observatory, was to relocate it. After what are described as 'extensive investigations', Herstmonceux in Sussex, ten miles north of the resort of Eastbourne, was selected as its new home. Because of the importance of the establishment, and the fame of Greenwich, it was renamed the Royal Greenwich Observatory, Herstmonceux. To those who worked there, and their colleagues in the astronomical community around the globe, it became known simply as 'the RGO'.

In retrospect, the site seems an odd choice. In the past three decades virtually all new observatories have been sited on mountain-tops, where the seeing qualities are excellent and the number of clear nights per year is far greater than at lower altitudes. By contrast, Herstmonceux is nearly at sea level and lies next to marshland, the mists from which sometimes made observing a problem. Even so, it probably enjoys more clear nights than any other site in the UK. Whatever the site may have lacked from a climatic point of view, it more than made up for aesthetically. The 15th-century brick castle, nestling between two gentle hills, provided the perfect environment for the astronomers and their colleagues.

Herstmonceux Castle was one of the first large brick buildings in the country. The name is derived from the Saxon word *herste*, meaning 'clearing in the woods', by which name both the manor and the family that lived there were known. A marriage between the de Herst and the de Monceux families in the 12th century gave us the present name of Herstmonceux. Originally constructed in 1441, the castle fell into decay and the interior was gutted in 1777. The ruins became a popular attraction until acquired by Colonel Lowther, who began the reconstruction and renovation of the interior in 1911. The castle later passed into the hands of Sir Paul Latham, who completed the restoration. Once purchased by the Admiralty, it became the home for the Observatory's library, refectory, offices and the director's residence, and provided accommodation for astronomers and visitors.

Before we go any further, perhaps it is useful to look briefly at what the Observatory's role was in those days. Its original purpose had been to map the heavens in order to improve navigation at sea. Over the years, this work on pure positional astronomy had led to investigations into the nature of objects such as stars and galaxies themselves, spawning the science of astrophysics. Positional work still played an important part, of course, with the annual publication of the Nautical, Air and Star Almanacs by the Nautical Almanac Office (NAO). These were published in collaboration with the United States Naval Observatory for use by astronomers, navigators and surveyors. Information included daily positions of the Sun, Moon, planets and natural satellites. The NAO was also responsible for supplying astronomical data for civil and legal purposes.

Other aspects of the Observatory's work included investigating the Earth's magnetic field, determining the rotation of the Earth, and the measurement of time. Greenwich Mean Time was, and still is, known the world over and it was the RGO's responsibility to provide a national time service and to generate the familiar six 'pips' which were then broadcast by the BBC. It was because of this connection with timekeeping that the Ministry of Defence's Chronometer Department, responsible for servicing and repairing Royal Navy chronometers and RAF navigator's watches, was also attached to the Observatory. The many departments, in turn, were supported by mechanical, electrical and electronic workshops and laboratories, a drawing office, and the usual administrative services that any large organization requires. So the work of the RGO encompassed a number of different disciplines, each of which had to be accommodated at Herstmonceux.

The move from Greenwich was not achieved overnight, of course. In fact it took ten years, mainly because of the postwar shortages of manpower and building equipment, and an initial lack of local housing for the staff. A group of Nissen huts provided temporary accommodation, and the Astronomer Royal, Sir Harold Spencer Jones, moved into the castle in 1948. No significant building work started until 1953, and it wasn't until 1957 that the scientific staff left Greenwich and started work in offices within the castle. During the war many of the departments had been evacuated from the capital, including the Time Department and the office of the Astronomer Royal, which were at Abinger, in Surrey; the Chronometer Department, which went to Bradford; and the Nautical Almanac Office, which was in Bath. Gradually the different departments and their staff transferred to Sussex and the establishment became whole again.

In addition to the facilities in the castle, a purpose-built block known as the West Building was constructed to house the Nautical Almanac Office, the Time Department, the computer installation, and various other offices, workshops and laboratories. On the east side of the estate, on higher ground than the castle, the Equatorial Group of telescopes was built. Named after the equatorial type of mounting that each of the telescopes utilized, this complex consisted of six domes, three of which were linked by a large building which housed photographic darkrooms, optical laboratories and an aluminizing plant for the telescopes' mirrors. The other three domes were accessed by raised walkways, and the whole complex was situated within an enclosure with flint-knapped walls and a large ornamental pond.

This strange edifice was constructed because of concern by the locals about the impact on the environment the arrival of the Observatory was going to have. When the first small dome was erected to house the solar telescope, local residents expressed their dismay at this strange building. The outcry led to a severe delay in the design and construction of the Equatorial Group. The Fine Arts Commission was called in to give its views, and the result was an attractive, but in some ways impractical, enclosure. The architect had a difficult task: he was expected to construct six large domes for the telescopes, together with all the necessary servicing facilities, and to make the resulting construction elegant and attractive. This he did very successfully, but the night observers who subsequently worked in it would have preferred simpler designs more suited to their professional needs. For example, one of the domes had its entrance only a few yards from the ornamental pond, and directly facing it. The story goes that one student, tired after a long night's observing, stepped out of the dome and failed to turn left or right, with the inevitable result. It was also at the Commission's suggestion that each of the domes was clad in copper so that, with the passage of time, they would gradually turn green and 'blend in with the Sussex countryside'. Once the design had been settled work was able to proceed, and the buildings were completed around 1956. The telescopes which had previously been at Greenwich, and which had been removed from their domes for safety during the war, were carefully installed in their new homes, and by 1957 most of them were operational again.

The telescopes that comprised the Equatorial Group were the Thompson 30-inch (0.76-metre) reflector, the Yapp 36-inch (0.91-metre) reflector, the Astrographic 13-inch (330-mm) reflector, the Thompson 26-inch (0.66-metre) reflector and the 'Great Equatorial' 28-inch (0.71-metre) refractor. A Schmidt camera was planned for the sixth dome but was never installed. To the north of the castle lay the Spencer Jones Group of meridian instruments. These were the Photographic Zenith Tube (PZT), which was used for time determination and for measuring latitude variation; the Danjon Astrolabe, also used for time and latitude determination; and the Cooke Reversible Transit Circle, used for determining star positions and planetary positions and motions. Located between the castle and the West Building, the Solar Dome housed the Newbegin 6¼-inch (160-mm) refractor, the photoheliograph and an underground spectrohelioscope.

Extensive plantations around the estate helped to reduce atmospheric turbulence, while the woods and castle moat provided a habitat for a variety of wildlife. Also within the grounds were a cricket pitch, tennis court, swimming pool and a clubhouse, the latter built by the staff and including a licensed bar. The cricket pitch, in particular, saw good use while Sir Richard Woolley, an ardent player, was Astronomer Royal. At one match the RGO took on, and beat, a World XI, consisting of internationally renowned astronomers, most of whom had apparently only learned the rules of the game a few hours beforehand.

Woolley had taken over as Astronomer Royal from Spencer Jones in 1956. His intention was to build up the observatory, train new astronomers and thereby promote modern research into astronomy and astrophysics. He was the guiding light that helped the RGO to establish itself at its new location and build even further on its worldwide reputation. One of the ways in which this was to be achieved was through the provision of a very large telescope on the site.

Long before the move to Herstmonceux, there had been talk of providing UK astronomers with a telescope large enough to allow them to compete on equal terms with their counterparts abroad, especially in the USA, where the 200-inch (5-metre) Hale Telescope on Mount Palomar was in operation, and in the Soviet Union, where a 6-metre instrument was on the drawing-board (it would be completed in 1975). It was eventually agreed that a 100-inch (2.5-metre) telescope be constructed, funded jointly by the Treasury and the Admiralty. The telescope would be for the use of all UK astronomers and, although located at Herstmonceux, would be administered by a Board of Management separate from the RGO. It was RGO staff, however, who were subsequently to maintain and operate the telescope. A 98-inch glass disk, originally intended for a telescope at Michigan University, was donated to form the prime mirror of the new instrument. After much discussion and delay concerning the design of the optical systems, and the mounting and guiding of the telescope, construction finally got under way. In 1967, Her Majesty the Queen performed the opening ceremony for the new Isaac Newton Telescope (INT) at Herstmonceux.

Over the years, the INT was used for a number of research projects. These included direct and electronic photography of nebulae, galaxies and quasars, infrared spectrometry and direct TV scanning of optical spectra. Meanwhile, the other telescopes continued in regular use and it was not uncommon, on a warm summer's night, to hear the strains of music across the air as one or more of the astronomers kept themselves entertained during a long observing session, playing tapes of anything from Bach to Led Zeppelin. Other research work carried out by RGO staff included the determination of radial velocities, parallaxes and proper motions of stars, the study of globular clusters and the Magellanic Clouds, the measurement of the chemical composition of different stars, and research into black holes. In 1971 an RGO team identified the X-ray source known as Cygnus X-1 with a particular star, which was thought to be part of a binary system, the partner of which was most likely a black hole.

Astronomical research is not just carried out at night, of course. The shelves of the RGO library, which occupied a large portion of the castle, contained every significant book relating to astronomy that had been published in the past three hundred years. The RGO's archives also included the correspondence of all the previous Astronomers Royal. This treasure trove of astronomical lore attracted researchers and historians of astronomy, who came from all over the world to search the records. The RGO also played a significant role in the training of new, young astronomers. Woolley was instrumental in ensuring that astronomy was included on the syllabus at the nearby University of Sussex, at Brighton. From 1965 it was a recognized subject for M.Sc. and D.Phil. degrees, and some RGO staff became visiting members of the faculty.

Other students benefited from the annual summer vacation courses run at Herstmonceux. Many of today's astronomers cut their teeth in this way, spending a summer living in the castle, observing on the telescopes at night, enjoying a game of cricket at the weekends and retiring to the bar afterwards. To a young, aspiring astronomer, it must have seemed like heaven. Another annual event was the Herstmonceux Conference. This was established by Woolley in 1957 and was held each spring on a different subject of topical interest. Over the years, leading astronomers from all over the world in a wide range of astronomical disciplines enjoyed the unique atmosphere and hospitality of these conferences. The RGO was enjoying its heyday at Herstmonceux. By the mid-seventies, though, things had begun to change, and the probable start of the decline of the RGO can be traced back to the opening of the INT in 1967.

Before the 1960s, it was only rarely that astronomers of any nationality travelled abroad to use other telescopes. In the main, they had to make do with whatever facilities were available in their own country. This put UK astronomers at an immediate disadvantage because of the unfavourable climate. With the advent of cheap air travel in the 1960s, however, it became feasible for them to travel abroad and use telescopes in better locations and collaborate on projects with overseas colleagues. The result was that, almost as soon as it opened, astronomers realized that the INT was in the wrong place. The bigger and more powerful a telescope is, the better the site it needs to fulfil its potential. A large telescope will be used to look at the faintest, most distant objects and to glean the most information possible about them. It therefore requires the very best observing conditions that can be obtained. Such conditions are found at higher altitudes than Herstmonceux, usually on the tops of mountains. Smaller instruments, like the others at Herstmonceux, which are used for different types of observation, can cope with less than perfect conditions. The INT, during its time in Sussex, was used for only about a third of the time it could have been had the climate been kinder. It was little wonder, then, that in the early seventies a decision was taken to move it to an overseas site in the northern hemisphere, where it could be put to better use. After testing various sites, including Hawaii, the Canary Island of La Palma was chosen and plans were made to establish an international observatory there. In 1979 the INT was removed from its dome at Herstmonceux to be completely refurbished and fitted with a new mirror, before being shipped to the Canaries.

Other changes were also under way. The fifties and sixties had seen great advances in science and technology, and these were to have a profound effect on the work of the Observatory. The first computer was acquired in 1958. By today's standards it was a primitive device, with a memory of one kilobyte, and its only use was to speed up calculations. Even so, it quickly made an impact and within a few years was replaced by a much more powerful machine. As computers became smaller and more powerful, they came to be used for other purposes, until it was difficult to find an instrument of any type, including the telescopes, that was not computer controlled. In the fifties and sixties most junior staff were recruited from secondary schools with 'A' or 'O' level qualifications, and they learned astronomy through the performance of their duties. The operation and maintenance of the new technology, however, required operators with specialist training in many fields to carry out the research and instrument development. As a result, by the eighties an honours degree or a Ph.D. was the minimum qualification needed to join the scientific staff.

Perhaps the greatest effect that the advance of technology had was to make some of the traditional work of the RGO redundant. In the past, the Admiralty had needed accurate time, propagated by radio time signals, as an aid to navigation. During the mid-seventies, the Time Department, in collaboration with the US Naval Research Laboratory, took part in experiments in the distribution of time using artificial satellites, which was to lead to the establishment of the Global Positioning System of navigation. This, together with the ever-increasing accuracy of atomic clocks, meant that there was no longer a requirement for a national time service. Accurate time could be easily and readily obtained via satellite. The development of automatic transit instruments and dedicated satellites also meant that observations for positional astronomy no longer had to be made at Herstmonceux.

The Solar Department was closed down, and the instruments replaced by the Satellite Laser Ranger (SLR). This instrument measures the distance to specially designed satellites to within a few centimetres, by sending a pulse of laser light and measuring the time it takes to return. The laser pulse is reflected by mirrors on the satellite which direct it back in the direction from which it came. Other stations around the globe make similar observations and the results are used to study the rotation and gravity field of the Earth. Results thus obtained meant that the Time Department's Photographic Zenith Tube was no longer required. Gradually, the need for the fundamental services which had once been the *raison d'etre* of the RGO was slowly disappearing.

Once the INT had ceased operating at Herstmonceux, all thoughts were focused on its new home. However, the work of establishing an overseas observatory, which was known initially as the Northern Hemisphere Observatory (NHO) and later as the Roque de los Muchachos Observatory, was a drain on the RGO's resources. Science, and astronomy in particular, has never been over-funded in the UK, and setting up a project team of design engineers and optical experts meant that resources for other work diminished. The result was that when maintenance or repair work was required on some of the telescopes of the Equatorial Group, there was neither the manpower nor the money to undertake it. The instruments, while still being used as best they could, began to be run down. Policy decisions within the RGO were partially to blame, as was the direction in which astronomical research had gone. The forefront of research no longer concentrated on 'nearby' objects such as stars and neighbouring galaxies, but lay instead in the farthest known objects, such as quasars and other distant galaxies. Those involved in stellar research saw their budgets cut first, and the morale of some of the staff began to fall.

It had not always been like this. In the fifties and sixties, the majority of staff lived in the nearby village of Herstmonceux itself. Private cars were relatively few, and so the facilities that the castle and clubhouse offered meant that it was only natural that staff and their friends spent much of their leisure time there. The RGO was truly a focal centre for village activities. In the sixties, as more people began to own their own cars, living close to your place of work was no longer a necessity. As some staff began to live slightly further afield, so the desire to drive back to work for leisure reasons declined. By the mid-seventies the clubhouse was still actively used, but nothing like to the extent that it had been. A decade later, with morale at an all-time low, there was little desire among the staff to socialize.

By this time, the RGO had also seen a number of changes at the top. Woolley had retired in 1971, to be succeeded by Margaret Burbidge. The powers that be took the decision that, for the first time, the posts of Director of the RGO and that of Astronomer Royal should be separated. No individual was to hold both these posts at the same time again. Burbidge's stay was a short one. She and her husband, also a prominent astronomer, were vocal in their condemnation of the siting of the INT. Their scientific conclusions were correct, but they won themselves few friends. Burbidge retired from the post in 1973 after a serious road accident. She was succeeded by the then deputy director, Alan Hunter. Hunter was a popular figure appointed to oversee the tercentenary celebrations of the Observatory in 1975. After his retirement, later that year, the post was taken by Professor Francis Graham-Smith, a radio astronomer. It was Smith who saw the RGO through the NHO project up until his own retirement in 1981. His successor, Professor Alec Boksenberg, would be the last of the directors of the RGO at Herstmonceux. Boksenberg's style was different from that of any of his predecessors. He was younger, and came from an instrumentation background (he was the inventor of the image photon counting system

(IPCS), a ground-breaking instrument which came to be universally used in astronomy).

The expertise of the RGO was now fully focused on La Palma, particularly the design and construction of the giant 4.2-metre William Herschel Telescope and all its associated instrumentation. Development of instrumentation was, in fact, one of the RGO's greatest strengths. From the early days of image tubes to the charge-coupled device (CCD) detectors of the eighties, the RGO research teams were at the forefront of development. Now, with all effort concentrated abroad, and the RGO charged with operating the La Palma telescopes on behalf of the UK astronomical community, it didn't take long for someone to question whether that role couldn't best be carried out from a different location. The arguments went along the lines of, 'Why do you need a 15th-century castle and 380 acres of Sussex countryside to run an overseas observatory?' The answer, of course, was that you don't, but many felt that if funding were made available to keep the other telescopes running, they could still be have been used for valuable research, for testing new instruments and for training students. The arguments were to fall on deaf ears. It has never been a policy of any British government to fund any basic research that does not have some practical purpose. That is left to the universities. With the decline of fundamental work, such as time determination and positional astronomy, the very need for a national observatory was being questioned.

In 1965, responsibility for the RGO had passed from the Admiralty to the newly formed Science Research Council (SRC), later to become the Science and Engineering Research Council (SERC). Report after report was instigated by the SERC, each one detailed to examine the workings of the observatories – not just the RGO, but also the Royal Observatory, Edinburgh. Instead of being able to concentrate on their work, staff spent much of their time writing reports justifying what they were doing. Many of the scientific arguments for the RGO to leave Herstmonceux were justified, but there was a feeling among some of the staff that a hidden agenda existed. Protests were dismissed as being 'parochial', and eventually it was announced that the Observatory was to relocate to Cambridge, on a site adjacent to the University's Institute of Astronomy. In 1990 the RGO moved for only the second time in its existence. Less than ten years later it was shut down completely.

From today's perspective, life at the RGO during the early years at Herstmonceux must have been unbelievably idyllic. The staff were working in extremely pleasant surroundings, many pursuing research into a subject dear to their hearts, and everyone feeling that they belonged to something worthwhile, indeed that they were doing something worthwhile themselves. This was, after all, the *Royal* Greenwich Observatory. The setting of the castle and its grounds was far removed from an office in a city centre. These were the days of jobs for life. Conditions of employment were linked to the Civil Service, and staff enjoyed good holiday allowances, a guaranteed job and a pension at the end of it. The pay may not have rivalled that available in outside industry, but that didn't matter.

Idyllic as it now sounds, it wouldn't have been any different from what people expected. The sixties were a time of optimism across the country. If you worked at the RGO, life was relaxed, there was cricket in the summer and the living was easy. The problems that afflicted the RGO during the seventies and eighties were the same problems that were affecting society: uncertainty about the future, concerns about funding, adapting to new technology and a culture change to a more commercial way of thinking.

The RGO may have only spent 10 per cent of its long history at Herstmonceux, but it is not unreasonable to describe that time as a sort of golden age when the best and most innovative work was done. Its passing from the site merely reflected the passing of an age. Its like will never be seen again. The RGO at Herstmonceux was truly unique.

BIBLIOGRAPHY

Calvert, D. A., *The History of Herstmonceux Castle*, RGO, 1980.

McRea, W. H., *The Royal Greenwich Observatory*, HMSO, 1975.

Murdin, P. G. and Parker, C. A. (eds), *Royal Greenwich Observatory, Herstmonceux Castle*, SERC, 1987.

Perkins, A. J. (consultant), *The History of The Royal Observatory and Royal Greenwich Observatory*, Laurie Project Community Programme, 1987.

Ronan, C. A., *Greenwich Observatory*, Times Books, 1975.

Part III

Miscellaneous

Some Interesting Variable Stars

JOHN ISLES

The following stars are of interest for many reasons. Of course, the periods and ranges of many variables are not constant from one cycle to another. Finder charts are given on the pages following this list for those stars marked with an asterisk.

Star	RA		Declination		Range	Type	Period	Spectrum
	h	m	°	′			(days)	
R Andromedae	00	24.0	+38	35	5.8–14.9	Mira	409	S
W Andromedae	02	17.6	+44	18	6.7–14.6	Mira	396	S
U Antliae	10	35.2	−39	34	5–6	Irregular	–	C
Theta Apodis	14	05.3	−76	48	5–7	Semi-regular	119	M
R Aquarii	23	43.8	−15	17	5.8–12.4	Symbiotic	387	M+Pec
T Aquarii	20	49.9	−05	09	7.2–14.2	Mira	202	M
R Aquilae	19	06.4	+08	14	5.5–12.0	Mira	284	M
V Aquilae	19	04.4	−05	41	6.6–8.4	Semi-regular	353	C
Eta Aquilae	19	52.5	+01	00	3.5–4.4	Cepheid	7.2	F–G
U Arae	17	53.6	−51	41	7.7–14.1	Mira	225	M
R Arietis	02	16.1	+25	03	7.4–13.7	Mira	187	M
U Arietis	03	11.0	+14	48	7.2–15.2	Mira	371	M
R Aurigae	05	17.3	+53	35	6.7–13.9	Mira	458	M
Epsilon Aurigae	05	02.0	+43	49	2.9–3.8	Algol	9892	F+B
R Boötis	14	37.2	+26	44	6.2–13.1	Mira	223	M
W Boötis	14	43.4	+26	32	4.7–5.4	Semi-regular?	450?	M
X Camelopardalis	04	45.7	+75	06	7.4–14.2	Mira	144	K–M
R Cancri	08	16.6	+11	44	6.1–11.8	Mira	362	M
X Cancri	08	55.4	+17	14	5.6–7.5	Semi-regular	195?	C
*R Canis Majoris	07	19.5	−16	24	5.7–6.3	Algol	1.1	F
*VY Canis Majoris	07	23.0	−25	46	6.5–9.6	Unique	–	M
*FW Canis Majoris	07	24.7	−16	12	5.0–5.5	Gamma Cas	–	B
S Canis Minoris	07	32.7	+08	19	6.6–13.2	Mira	333	M
R Canum Ven.	13	49.0	+39	33	6.5–12.9	Mira	329	M
R Carinae	09	32.2	−62	47	3.9–10.5	Mira	309	M
S Carinae	10	09.4	−61	33	4.5–9.9	Mira	149	K–M
l Carinae	09	45.2	−62	30	3.3–4.2	Cepheid	35.5	F–K
Eta Carinae	10	45.1	−59	41	−0.8–7.9	Irregular	–	Pec

Star	RA		Declination		Range	Type	Period (days)	Spectrum
	h	m	°	′				
R Cassiopeiae	23	58.4	+51	24	4.7–13.5	Mira	430	M
S Cassiopeiae	01	19.7	+72	37	7.9–16.1	Mira	612	S
W Cassiopeiae	00	54.9	+58	34	7.8–12.5	Mira	406	C
Gamma Cas.	00	56.7	+60	43	1.6–3.0	Irregular	–	B
Rho Cassiopeiae	23	54.4	+57	30	4.1–6.2	Semi-regular	–	F–K
R Centauri	14	16.6	–59	55	5.3–11.8	Mira	546	M
S Centauri	12	24.6	–49	26	7–8	Semi-regular	65	C
T Centauri	13	41.8	–33	36	5.5–9.0	Semi-regular	90	K–M
S Cephei	21	35.2	+78	37	7.4–12.9	Mira	487	C
T Cephei	21	09.5	+68	29	5.2–11.3	Mira	388	M
Delta Cephei	22	29.2	+58	25	3.5–4.4	Cepheid	5.4	F–G
Mu Cephei	21	43.5	+58	47	3.4–5.1	Semi-regular	730	M
U Ceti	02	33.7	–13	09	6.8–13.4	Mira	235	M
W Ceti	00	02.1	–14	41	7.1–14.8	Mira	351	S
*Omicron Ceti	02	19.3	–02	59	2.0–10.1	Mira	332	M
R Chamaeleontis	08	21.8	–76	21	7.5–14.2	Mira	335	M
T Columbae	05	19.3	–33	42	6.6–12.7	Mira	226	M
R Comae Ber.	12	04.3	+18	47	7.1–14.6	Mira	363	M
R Coronae Bor.	15	48.6	+28	09	5.7–14.8	R Coronae Bor.	–	C
S Coronae Bor.	15	21.4	+31	22	5.8–14.1	Mira	360	M
T Coronae Bor.	15	59.6	+25	55	2.0–10.8	Recurrent nova	–	M+Pec
V Coronae Bor.	15	49.5	+39	34	6.9–12.6	Mira	358	C
W Coronae Bor.	16	15.4	+37	48	7.8–14.3	Mira	238	M
R Corvi	12	19.6	–19	15	6.7–14.4	Mira	317	M
R Crucis	12	23.6	–61	38	6.4–7.2	Cepheid	5.8	F–G
R Cygni	19	36.8	+50	12	6.1–14.4	Mira	426	S
U Cygni	20	19.6	+47	54	5.9–12.1	Mira	463	C
W Cygni	21	36.0	+45	22	5.0–7.6	Semi-regular	131	M
RT Cygni	19	43.6	+48	47	6.0–13.1	Mira	190	M
SS Cygni	21	42.7	+43	35	7.7–12.4	Dwarf nova	50±	K+Pec
CH Cygni	19	24.5	+50	14	5.6–9.0	Symbiotic	–	M+B
Chi Cygni	19	50.6	+32	55	3.3–14.2	Mira	408	S
R Delphini	20	14.9	+09	05	7.6–13.8	Mira	285	M
U Delphini	20	45.5	+18	05	5.6–7.5	Semi-regular	110?	M
EU Delphini	20	37.9	+18	16	5.8–6.9	Semi-regular	60	M
Beta Doradus	05	33.6	–62	29	3.5–4.1	Cepheid	9.8	F–G
R Draconis	16	32.7	+66	45	6.7–13.2	Mira	246	M
T Eridani	03	55.2	–24	02	7.2–13.2	Mira	252	M
R Fornacis	02	29.3	–26	06	7.5–13.0	Mira	389	C
R Geminorum	07	07.4	+22	42	6.0–14.0	Mira	370	S

Star	RA		Declination		Range	Type	Period (days)	Spectrum
	h	m	°	'				
U Geminorum	07	55.1	+22	00	8.2–14.9	Dwarf nova	105±	Pec+M
*Zeta Geminorum	07	04.1	+20	34	3.6–4.2	Cepheid	10.2	F–G
*Eta Geminorum	06	14.9	+22	30	3.2–3.9	Semi-regular	233	M
S Gruis	22	26.1	−48	26	6.0–15.0	Mira	402	M
S Herculis	16	51.9	+14	56	6.4–13.8	Mira	307	M
U Herculis	16	25.8	+18	54	6.4–13.4	Mira	406	M
Alpha Herculis	17	14.6	+14	23	2.7–4.0	Semi-regular	−	M
68, u Herculis	17	17.3	+33	06	4.7–5.4	Algol	2.1	B+B
R Horologii	02	53.9	−49	53	4.7–14.3	Mira	408	M
U Horologii	03	52.8	−45	50	6–14	Mira	348	M
R Hydrae	13	29.7	−23	17	3.5–10.9	Mira	389	M
U Hydrae	10	37.6	−13	23	4.3–6.5	Semi-regular	450?	C
VW Hydri	04	09.1	−71	18	8.4–14.4	Dwarf nova	27±	Pec
R Leonis	09	47.6	+11	26	4.4–11.3	Mira	310	M
R Leonis Minoris	09	45.6	+34	31	6.3–13.2	Mira	372	M
R Leporis	04	59.6	−14	48	5.5–11.7	Mira	427	C
Y Librae	15	11.7	−06	01	7.6–14.7	Mira	276	M
RS Librae	15	24.3	−22	55	7.0–13.0	Mira	218	M
Delta Librae	15	01.0	−08	31	4.9–5.9	Algol	2.3	A
R Lyncis	07	01.3	+55	20	7.2–14.3	Mira	379	S
R Lyrae	18	55.3	+43	57	3.9–5.0	Semi-regular	46?	M
RR Lyrae	19	25.5	+42	47	7.1–8.1	RR Lyrae	0.6	A–F
Beta Lyrae	18	50.1	+33	22	3.3–4.4	Eclipsing	12.9	B
U Microscopii	20	29.2	−40	25	7.0–14.4	Mira	334	M
*U Monocerotis	07	30.8	−09	47	5.9–7.8	RV Tauri	91	F–K
V Monocerotis	06	22.7	−02	12	6.0–13.9	Mira	340	M
R Normae	15	36.0	−49	30	6.5–13.9	Mira	508	M
T Normae	15	44.1	−54	59	6.2–13.6	Mira	241	M
R Octantis	05	26.1	−86	23	6.3–13.2	Mira	405	M
S Octantis	18	08.7	−86	48	7.2–14.0	Mira	259	M
V Ophiuchi	16	26.7	−12	26	7.3–11.6	Mira	297	C
X Ophiuchi	18	38.3	+08	50	5.9–9.2	Mira	329	M
RS Ophiuchi	17	50.2	−06	43	4.3–12.5	Recurrent nova	−	OB+M
U Orionis	05	55.8	+20	10	4.8–13.0	Mira	368	M
W Orionis	05	05.4	+01	11	5.9–7.7	Semi-regular	212	C
Alpha Orionis	05	55.2	+07	24	0.0–1.3	Semi-regular	2335	M
S Pavonis	19	55.2	−59	12	6.6–10.4	Semi-regular	381	M
Kappa Pavonis	18	56.9	−67	14	3.9–4.8	Cepheid	9.1	G
R Pegasi	23	06.8	+10	33	6.9–13.8	Mira	378	M
Beta Pegasi	23	03.8	+28	05	2.3–2.7	Irregular	−	M

Star	RA h	m	Declination °	'	Range	Type	Period (days)	Spectrum
X Persei	03	55.4	+31	03	6.0–7.0	Gamma Cas	–	O9.5
Beta Persei	03	08.2	+40	57	2.1–3.4	Algol	2.9	B
Rho Persei	03	05.2	+38	50	3.3–4.0	Semi-regular	50?	M
Zeta Phoenicis	01	08.4	–55	15	3.9–4.4	Algol	1.7	B+B
R Pictoris	04	46.2	–49	15	6.4–10.1	Semi-regular	171	M
*RS Puppis	08	13.1	–34	35	6.5–7.7	Cepheid	41.4	F-G
L² Puppis	07	13.5	–44	39	2.6–6.2	Semi-regular	141	M
T Pyxidis	09	04.7	–32	23	6.5–15.3	Recurrent nova	7000±	Pec
U Sagittae	19	18.8	+19	37	6.5–9.3	Algol	3.4	B+G
WZ Sagittae	20	07.6	+17	42	7.0–15.5	Dwarf nova	1,900±	A
R Sagittarii	19	16.7	–19	18	6.7–12.8	Mira	270	M
RR Sagittarii	19	55.9	–29	11	5.4–14.0	Mira	336	M
RT Sagittarii	20	17.7	–39	07	6.0–14.1	Mira	306	M
RU Sagittarii	19	58.7	–41	51	6.0–13.8	Mira	240	M
RY Sagittarii	19	16.5	–33	31	5.8–14.0	R Coronae Bor.	–	G
RR Scorpii	16	56.6	–30	35	5.0–12.4	Mira	281	M
RS Scorpii	16	55.6	–45	06	6.2–13.0	Mira	320	M
RT Scorpii	17	03.5	–36	55	7.0–15.2	Mira	449	S
S Sculptoris	00	15.4	–32	03	5.5–13.6	Mira	363	M
R Scuti	18	47.5	–05	42	4.2–8.6	RV Tauri	146	G–K
R Serpentis	15	50.7	+15	08	5.2–14.4	Mira	356	M
S Serpentis	15	21.7	+14	19	7.0–14.1	Mira	372	M
T Tauri.	04	22.0	+19	32	9.3–13.5	Irregular	–	F–K
SU Tauri	05	49.1	+19	04	9.1–16.9	R Coronae Bor.	–	G
Lambda Tauri	04	00.7	+12	29	3.4–3.9	Algol	4.0	B+A
R Trianguli	02	37.0	+34	16	5.4–12.6	Mira	267	M
R Ursae Majoris	10	44.6	+68	47	6.5–13.7	Mira	302	M
T Ursae Majoris	12	36.4	+59	29	6.6–13.5	Mira	257	M
U Ursae Minoris	14	17.3	+66	48	7.1–13.0	Mira	331	M
R Virginis	12	38.5	+06	59	6.1–12.1	Mira	146	M
S Virginis	13	33.0	–07	12	6.3–13.2	Mira	375	M
SS Virginis	12	25.3	+00	48	6.0–9.6	Semi-regular	364	C
R Vulpeculae	21	04.4	+23	49	7.0–14.3	Mira	137	M
Z Vulpeculae	19	21.7	+25	34	7.3–8.9	Algol	2.5	B+A

R and FW Canis Majoris

Comparison stars:

A	= 4.96
B	= 5.45
C	= 5.46
D	= 5.78
E	= 6.05
F	= 6.09
G	= 6.6
H	= 6.77

VY Canis Majoris

Comparison stars:

C	= 7.0
D	= 7.1
E	= 8.1
F	= 8.4
G	= 8.8
H	= 9.4

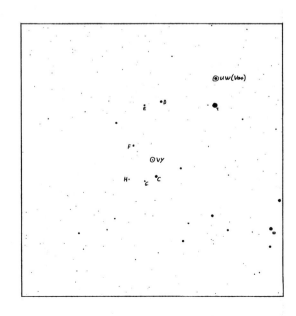

Mira

Comparison stars:

Alpha (α)	= 2.52
	(off map)
Gamma (γ)	= 3.46
Delta (δ)	= 4.06
Nu (ν)	= 4.87
N	= 5.34
P	= 5.41
R	= 6.00
S	= 6.32
T	= 6.49
U	= 7.19
W	= 8.06
X	= 8.42
y	= 9.00
z	= 9.33

Eta and Zeta Geminorum

Comparison stars:

Epsilon (ε) Gem	= 2.98
Zeta (ζ) Tau	= 3.03
Xi (χ) Gem	= 3.34
Lambda (λ) Gem	= 3.59
Nu (ν) Gem	= 4.14
1 Gem	= 4.15

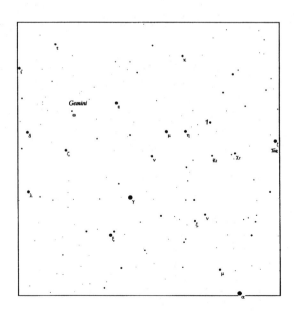

U Monocerotis

Comparison stars:

C	= 5.72
D	= 5.85
E	= 6.00
F	= 6.62
G	= 6.97
H	= 7.51
K	= 7.81
L	= 8.03

RS Puppis

Comparison stars:

A	= 6.4
B	= 6.4
C	= 7.0
D	= 7.4
E	= 7.6
F	= 8.2
G	= 8.3

Mira Stars: Maxima, 2000

JOHN ISLES

Below are the predicted dates of maxima for Mira stars that reach magnitude 7.5 or brighter at an average maximum. Individual maxima can in some cases be brighter or fainter than average by a magnitude or more, and all dates are only approximate. The positions, extreme ranges and mean periods of these stars can be found in the preceding list of interesting variable stars.

Star	Mean magnitude at maximum	Dates of maxima
R Andromedae	6.9	Aug. 19
W Andromedae	7.4	Sep. 25
R Aquarii	6.5	June 5
R Aquilae	6.1	Jan. 24, Nov. 4
R Boötis	7.2	May 19, Dec. 29
R Cancri	6.8	Oct. 4
S Canis Minoris	7.5	Nov. 24
R Carinae	4.6	Oct. 26
S Carinae	5.7	Jan. 7, June 5, Nov. 1
R Cassiopeiae	7.0	Oct. 26
R Centauri	5.8	Jan. 27, Oct. 8
T Cephei	6.0	June 20
U Ceti	7.5	July 31
Omicron Ceti	3.4	Sep. 25
T Columbae	7.5	Apr. 25, Dec. 7
S Coronae Borealis	7.3	Oct. 10
V Coronae Borealis	7.5	Apr. 10
R Corvi	7.5	Apr. 26
R Cygni	7.5	Oct. 20
RT Cygni	7.3	Mar. 8, Sep. 14
R Geminorum	7.1	Nov. 18
R Horologii	6.0	Feb. 3

Star	Mean magnitude at maximum	Dates of maxima
U Horologii	7	Dec. 12
R Hydrae	4.5	June 23
R Leonis	5.8	May 12
R Leonis Minoris	7.1	Sep. 24
R Leporis	6.8	May 14
RS Librae	7.5	July 23
V Monocerotis	7.0	Apr. 19
R Normae	7.2	Sep. 24
T Normae	7.4	Mar. 26, Nov. 22
V Ophiuchi	7.5	Mar. 26
X Ophiuchi	6.8	July 14
U Orionis	6.3	Nov. 9
R Sagittarii	7.3	May 24
RR Sagittarii	6.8	Oct. 2
RT Sagittarii	7.0	Mar. 7
RU Sagittarii	7.2	July 24
RR Scorpii	5.9	Jan. 19, Oct. 26
RS Scorpii	7.0	June 5
S Sculptoris	6.7	Nov. 30
R Serpentis	6.9	Jan. 18
R Trianguli	6.2	Apr. 3, Dec. 26
R Ursae Majoris	7.5	Feb. 20, Dec. 18
R Virginis	6.9	Jan. 6, May 31, Oct. 23
S Virginis	7.0	Nov. 21

Some Interesting Double Stars

R. W. ARGYLE

The positions given below correspond to epoch 2000.0.

Star	RA		Declin-ation	Magni-tudes	Separation arc seconds	PA	Cata-logue	Comments
	h	m	° ′			°		
β Tuc	00	31.5	−62 58	4.4, 4.8	27.1	169	LCL119	Both again difficult doubles.
η Cas	00	49.1	+57 49	3.4, 7.5	12.8	317	Σ60	Easy. Creamy, bluish.
36 And	00	55.0	+23 38	6.0, 6.4	0.9	309	Σ73	Period 168 years. Both yellow. Slowly opening.
ζ Psc	01	13.7	+07 35	5.6, 6.5	23.1	63	Σ100	Yellow, reddish-white.
ρ Eri	01	39.8	−56 12	5.8, 5.8	11.5	191	Δ5	Period 483 years.
γ Ari	01	53.5	+19 18	4.8, 4.8	7.5	1	Σ180	Very easy. Both white.
α Psc	02	02.0	+02 46	4.2, 5.1	1.8	272	Σ202	Binary. Period 933 years.
γ And	02	03.9	+42 20	2.3, 5.0	9.6	63	Σ205	Yellow, blue. Relatively fixed.
γ² And				5.1, 6.3	0.4	103	OΣ38	BC. Needs 30 cm.
ι Cas AB	02	29.1	+67 24	4.9, 6.9	3.0	227	Σ262	AB is long-period binary. Period 840 years.
ι Cas AC				4.9, 8.4	7.2	118		
ω For	02	33.8	−28 14	5.0, 7.7	10.8	245	HJ 3506	Common proper motion.
γ Cet	02	43.3	+03 14	3.5, 7.3	2.6	298	Σ299	Not too easy.
θ Eri	02	58.3	−40 18	3.4, 4.5	8.3	90	Pz2	Both white.
ε Ari	02	59.2	+21 20	5.2, 5.5	1.5	208	Σ333	Binary. Both white.
Σ331 Per	03	00.9	+52 21	5.3, 6.7	12.0	85	–	Fixed.
α For	03	12.1	−28 59	4.0, 7.0	4.4	298	HJ 3555	Period 314 years. B variable?
f Eri	03	48.6	−37 37	4.8, 5.3	8.2	215	Δ16	Pale yellow. Fixed.
32 Eri	03	54.3	−02 57	4.8, 6.1	6.9	348	Σ470	Fixed.

Star	RA		Declination	Magnitudes	Separation arc seconds	PA	Catalogue	Comments
	h	m	° '			°		
1 Cam	04	32.0	+53 55	5.7, 6.8	10.3	308	Σ550	Fixed.
ι Pic	04	50.9	−53 28	5.6, 6.4	12.4	58	Δ18	Good object for small apertures. Fixed.
κ Lep	05	13.2	−12 56	4.5, 7.4	2.2	357	Σ661	Visible in 7.5 cm.
β Ori	05	14.5	−08 12	0.1, 6.8	9.5	204	Σ668	Companion once thought to be close double.
41 Lep	05	21.8	−24 46	5.4, 6.6	3.4	93	HJ 3752	Deep yellow pair in a rich field.
η Ori	05	24.5	−02 24	3.8, 4.8	1.7	78	Da5	Slow-moving binary.
λ Ori	05	35.1	+09 56	3.6, 5.5	4.3	44	Σ738	Fixed.
θ Ori AB	05	35.3	−05 23	6.7, 7.9	8.6	32	Σ748	Trapezium in M42.
θ Ori CD				5.1, 6.7	13.4	61		
σ Ori AC	05	38.7	−02 36	4.0, 10.3	11.4	238	Σ762	Quintuple. A is a close double.
σ Ori ED				6.5, 7.5	30.1	231		
ζ Ori	05	40.7	−01 57	1.9, 4.0	2.4	164	Σ774	Can be split in 7.5 cm.
η Gem	06	14.9	+22 30	var., 6.5	1.6	256	β1008	Well seen with 20 cm. Primary orange.
12 Lyn AB	06	46.2	+59 26	5.4, 6.0	1.8	74	Σ948	AB is binary, period 706 years.
12 Lyn AC				5.4, 7.3	8.7	309		
γ Vol	07	08.7	−70 30	3.9, 5.8	14.1	298	Δ42	Very slow binary.
h3945 CMa	07	16.6	−23 19	4.8, 6.8	26.8	51	−	Contrasting colours.
δ Gem	07	20.1	+21 59	3.5, 8.2	5.8	225	Σ1066	Not too easy. Yellow, pale blue.
α Gem	07	34.6	+31 53	1.9, 2.9	3.9	65	Σ1110	Widening. Easy with 7.5 cm.
κ Pup	07	38.8	−26 48	4.5, 4.7	9.8	318	H III 27	Both white.
ζ Cnc AB	08	12.2	+17 39	5.6, 6.0	0.8	85	Σ1196	A is a close double.
ζ Cnc AB-C				5.0, 6.2	5.9	74		
δ Vel	08	44.7	−54 43	2.1, 5.1	0.7	191	I 10	Difficult close pair. Period about 100 years.
ε Hya	08	46.8	+06 25	3.3, 6.8	2.9	298	Σ1273	PA slowly increasing.
38 Lyn	09	18.8	+36 48	3.9, 6.6	2.8	230	Σ1338	Almost fixed.
ν Car	09	47.1	−65 04	3.1, 6.1	5.0	128	Rmk 11	Fixed. Fine in small telescopes.

Star	RA		Declin-ation	Magni-tudes	Separation arc seconds	PA	Cata-logue	Comments
	h	m	° ′			°		
γ Leo	10	20.0	+19 50	2.2, 3.5	4.6	125	Σ1424	Binary. Period 619 years. Both orange.
s Vel	10	32.0	−45 04	6.2, 6.5	13.5	218	Pz3	Fixed.
μ Vel	10	46.8	−49 26	2.7, 6.4	2.5	58	R155	Period 116 years. Widest in 1996.
54 Leo	10	55.6	+24 45	4.5, 6.3	6.6	111	Σ1487	Slowly widening. Pale yellow and white.
ξ UMa	11	18.2	+31 32	4.3, 4.8	1.8	274	Σ1523	Binary, period 60 years. Opening. Needs 10 cm.
π Cen	11	21.0	−54 29	4.3, 5.0	0.3	142	I879	Binary, period 39.2 years. Very close. Needs 35 cm
ι Leo	11	23.9	+10 32	4.0, 6.7	1.7	117	Σ1536	Period 192 years.
N Hya	11	32.3	−29 16	5.8, 5.9	9.5	210	H III 96	Fixed.
D Cen	12	14.0	−45 43	5.6, 6.8	2.8	243	Rmk14	Orange and white. Closing.
α Cru	12	26.6	−63 06	1.4, 1.9	4.0	112	Δ252	Third star in a low-power field.
γ Cen	12	41.5	−48 58	2.9, 2.9	1.0	347	HJ4539	Period 84 years. Closing. Both yellow.
γ Vir	12	41.7	−01 27	3.5, 3.5	1.5	259	Σ1670	Binary. Period 168 years.
β Mus	12	46.3	−68 06	3.7, 4.0	1.3	43	R207	Both white. Closing.
μ Cru	12	54.6	−57 11	4.3, 5.3	34.9	17	Δ126	Fixed. Both white.
α CVn	12	56.0	+38 19	2.9, 5.5	19.3	229	Σ1692	Easy. Yellow, bluish.
J Cen	13	22.6	−60 59	4.6, 6.5	60.0	343	Δ133	Fixed. A is a close pair.
ζ UMa	13	24.0	+54 56	2.3, 4.0	14.4	152	Σ1744	Very easy. Naked-eye pair with Alcor.
3 Cen	13	51.8	−33 00	4.5, 6.0	7.9	106	H III 101	Both white. Closing slowly.
α Cen	14	39.6	−60 50	0.0, 1.2	14.1	222	Rhd 1	Finest pair in the sky. Period 80 years. Closing.
ζ Boo	14	41.1	+13 44	4.5, 4.6	0.8	300	Σ1865	Both white. Closing, highly inclined orbit.
ε Boo	14	45.0	+27 04	2.5, 4.9	2.9	343	Σ1877	Yellow, blue. Fine pair.

Star	RA		Declin- ation	Magni- tudes	Separation arc seconds	PA	Cata- logue	Comments
	h	m	° ′			°		
54 Hya	14	46.0	−25 27	5.1, 7.1	8.3	122	H III 97	Closing slowly.
μ Lib	14	49.3	−14 09	5.8, 6.7	1.9	2	β106	Becoming wider. Fine in 7.5 cm.
ξ Boo	14	51.4	+19 06	4.7, 7.0	6.6	318	Σ1888	Fine contrast. Easy.
44 Boo	15	03.8	+47 39	5.3, 6.2	2.2	53	Σ1909	Period 246 years.
π Lup	15	05.1	−47 03	4.6, 4.7	1.7	67	HJ 4728	Widening.
μ Lup AB	15	18.5	−47 53	5.1, 5.2	1.0	308	Δ180	AB closing?
μ Lup AC				4.4, 7.2	23.2	129	HJ 4543	AC almost fixed.
γ Cir	15	23.4	−59 19	5.1, 5.5	0.9	12	HJ 4787	Closing. Needs 20 cm. Long-period binary.
η CrB	15	32.0	+32 17	5.6, 5.9	0.8	63	Σ1937	Both yellow. Period 41 years, near widest separation.
δ Ser	15	34.8	+10 33	4.2, 5.2	4.0	175	Σ1954	Long-period binary.
γ Lup	15	35.1	−41 10	3.5, 3.6	0.8	274	HJ 4786	Period 147 years. Needs 20 cm.
ξ Lup	15	56.9	−33 58	5.3, 5.8	10.2	49	Pz4	Fixed.
σ CrB	16	14.7	+33 52	5.6, 6.6	7.0	236	Σ2032	Long-period binary. Both white.
α Sco	16	29.4	−26 26	1.2, 5.4	2.9	273	Gnt 1	Red, green. Difficult from mid-northern latitudes.
λ Oph	16	30.9	+01 59	4.2, 5.2	1.4	29	Σ2055	Period 129 years. Fairly difficult in small apertures.
ζ Her	16	41.3	+31 36	2.9, 5.5	0.7	12	Σ2084	Fine, rapid binary. Period 34 years.
μ Dra	17	05.3	+54 28	5.7, 5.7	2.0	17	Σ2130	Long-period binary. Slowly closing.
α Her	17	14.6	+14 24	var., 5.4	4.6	105	Σ2140	Red, green. Binary.
36 Oph	17	15.3	−26 35	5.1, 5.1	4.8	327	SHJ 243	Period 549 years.
ρ Her	17	23.7	+37 08	4.6, 5.6	4.1	318	Σ2161	Slowly widening.
95 Her	18	01.5	+21 36	5.0, 5.1	6.4	257	Σ2264	Colours thought variable in C19.
70 Oph	18	05.5	+02 30	4.2, 6.0	3.7	149	Σ2272	Opening. Easy in 7.5 cm.
h5014 CrA	18	06.8	−43 25	5.7, 5.7	1.7	346	−	Closing slowly. Orbit poorly known. Needs 10 cm.

Star	RA		Declin-ation	Magni-tudes	Separation arc seconds	PA	Cata-logue	Comments
	h	m	° ′			°		
OΣ358 Her	18	35.9	+16 58	6.8, 7.0	1.7	155	–	Period 292 years.
ε¹ Lyr	18	44.3	+39 40	5.0, 6.1	2.6	350	Σ2382	Quadruple system with ε². Both pairs visible in 7.5 cm.
ε² Lyr	18	44.3	+39 40	5.2, 5.5	2.3	82	Σ2383	
θ Ser	18	56.2	+04 12	4.5, 5.4	22.4	104	Σ2417	Fixed. Very easy.
γ CrA	19	06.4	–37 04	4.8, 5.1	1.3	55	HJ 5084	Beautiful pair. Period 122 years.
β Cyg AB	19	30.7	+27 58	3.1, 5.1	34.3	54	ΣI 43	Glorious. Yellow, blue-greenish.
β Cyg Aa				3.1, 4.0	0.4	132	MCA 55	Discovered in 1976. Closing slowly.
δ Cyg	19	45.0	+45 08	2.9, 6.3	2.6	225	Σ2579	Slowly widening.
ε Dra	19	48.2	+70 16	3.8, 7.4	3.2	17	Σ2603	Slow binary.
γ Del	20	46.7	+16 07	4.5, 5.5	9.2	266	Σ2727	Easy. Yellowish.
λ Cyg	20	47.4	+36 29	4.8, 6.1	0.9	8	OΣ413	Difficult binary in small apertures.
ε Equ AB	20	59.1	+04 18	6.0, 6.3	0.8	285	Σ2737	Fine triple. AB is closing.
ε Equ AC				6.0, 7.1	10.3	66		
61 Cyg	21	06.9	+38 45	5.2, 6.0	30.6	150	Σ2758	Nearby binary. Both orange. Period 722 years.
θ Ind	21	19.9	–53 27	4.5, 7.0	6.8	271	HJ 5258	Pale yellow and reddish. Long-period binary.
μ Cyg	21	44.1	+28 45	4.8, 6.1	1.8	307	Σ2822	Period 713 years.
ξ Cep	22	03.8	+64 37	4.4, 6.5	8.1	275	Σ2863	White and blue. Long-period binary.
53 Aqr	22	26.6	–16 45	6.4, 6.6	1.8	8	SHJ 345	Long-period binary. Closing.
ζ Aqr	22	28.8	–00 01	4.3, 4.5	1.9	186	Σ2909	Slowly widening.
Σ3050 And	23	59.4	+33 43	6.6, 6.6	1.9	331	–	Period 350 years.

Some Interesting Nebulae, Clusters and Galaxies

Object	RA		Declin-ation		Remarks
	h	m	°	′	
M.31 Andromedae	00	40.7	+41	05	Andromeda Galaxy, visible to naked eye.
H.VIII 78 Cassiopeiae	00	41.3	+61	36	Fine cluster, between Gamma and Kappa Cassiopeiae.
M.33 Trianguli	01	31.8	+30	28	Spiral. Difficult with small apertures.
H.VI 33–4 Persei	02	18.3	+56	59	Double Cluster; Sword-handle.
Δ142 Doradus	05	39.1	−69	09	Looped nebula round 30 Doradus. Naked-eye. In Large Magellanic Cloud.
M.1 Tauri	05	32.3	+22	00	Crab Nebula, near Zeta Tauri.
M.42 Orionis	05	33.4	−05	24	Orion Nebula. Contains the famous Trapezium, Theta Orionis.
M.35 Geminorum	06	06.5	+24	21	Open cluster near Eta Geminorum.
H.VII 2 Monocerotis	06	30.7	+04	53	Open cluster, just visible to naked eye.
M.41 Canis Majoris	06	45.5	−20	42	Open cluster, just visible to naked eye.
M.47 Puppis	07	34.3	−14	22	Mag. 5.2. Loose cluster.
H.IV 64 Puppis	07	39.6	−18	05	Bright planetary in rich neighbourhood.
M.46 Puppis	07	39.5	−14	42	Open cluster.
M.44 Cancri	08	38	+20	07	Praesepe. Open cluster near Delta Cancri. Visible to naked eye.
M.97 Ursae Majoris	11	12.6	+55	13	Owl Nebula, diameter 3′. Planetary.
Kappa Crucis	12	50.7	−60	05	'Jewel Box'; open cluster, with stars of contrasting colours.
M.3 Can. Ven.	13	40.6	+28	34	Bright globular.
Omega Centauri	13	23.7	−47	03	Finest of all globulars. Easy with naked eye.
M.80 Scorpii	16	14.9	−22	53	Globular, between Antares and Beta Scorpii.
M.4 Scorpii	16	21.5	−26	26	Open cluster close to Antares.
M.13 Herculis	16	40	+36	31	Globular. Just visible to naked eye.

Object	RA		Declin-ation		Remarks
	h	m	°	′	
M.92 Herculis	16	16.1	+43	11	Globular. Between Iota and Eta Herculis.
M.6 Scorpii	17	36.8	−32	11	Open cluster; naked eye.
M.7 Scorpii	17	50.6	−34	48	Very bright open cluster; naked eye.
M.23 Sagittarii	17	54.8	−19	01	Open cluster nearly 50′ in diameter.
H.IV 37 Draconis	17	58.6	+66	38	Bright planetary.
M.8 Sagittarii	18	01.4	−24	23	Lagoon Nebula. Gaseous. Just visible with naked eye.
NGC 6572 Ophiuchi	18	10.9	+06	50	Bright planetary, between Beta Ophiuchi and Zeta Aquilae.
M.17 Sagittarii	18	18.8	−16	12	Omega Nebula. Gaseous. Large and bright.
M.11 Scuti	18	49.0	−06	19	Wild Duck. Bright open cluster.
M.57 Lyrae	18	52.6	+32	59	Ring Nebula. Brightest of planetaries.
M.27 Vulpeculae	19	58.1	+22	37	Dumbbell Nebula, near Gamma Sagittae.
H.IV 1 Aquarii	21	02.1	−11	31	Bright planetary near Nu Aquarii.
M.15 Pegasi	21	28.3	+12	01	Bright globular, near Epsilon Pegasi.
M.39 Cygni	21	31.0	+48	17	Open cluster between Deneb and Alpha Lacertae. Well seen with low powers.

Our Contributors

Chris Lintott, now at Cambridge University, has been an active member of the British Astronomical Association for several years, and has been co-editor of the Association's Student Newsletter.

Dr Paul Murdin is Head of Astronomy at the Particle Physics and Astronomy Research Council (PPARC) and Director of Science at the British National Space Centre. He is, of course, one of our most regular and valued contributors.

Dr G. J. H. McCall, one of the world's leading specialists in the study of meteorites, spent some time in Western Australia, but now lives in England.

Dr Fred Watson is Astronomer in Charge at the Anglo-Australian Observatory in New South Wales, where he is responsible for the scientific output of the Anglo-Australian Telescope and the United Kingdom Schmidt Telescope.

Nigel Bannister, a graduate of Leicester University, has specialized in the study of white dwarf stars, and has been undertaking research with the Jacobus Kapteyn Telescope and the Isaac Newton telescope at La Palma.

R. W. Arbour is an amateur astronomer with his own observatory in Hampshire. He specializes in hunting for supernovae, and has several discoveries to his credit.

Dr Helen Walker carries out her research at the Rutherford–Appleton Laboratory in Oxfordshire, and has been paying special attention to infrared astronomy.

Professor Chris Kitchin is Director of the University of Hertfordshire Observatory. He is an astrophysicist who does much to encourage popular interest in astronomy.

Dr Allan Chapman is our leading astronomical historian. He as at Oxford University, and has published many original papers, both popular and technical.

Chas Parker worked for many years at the Royal Greenwich Observatory, ultimately as Press Officer, but left when the RGO was moved to Cambridge. He is now a freelance writer, and helped to establish a hands-on science centre in the old telescope buildings at Herstmonceux.

The William Herschel Society maintains the museum established at 19 New King Street, Bath – the only surviving Herschel House. It also undertakes activities of various kinds. New members would be welcome; those interested are asked to contact the Secretary at the museum.

Astronomical Societies in the British Isles

British Astronomical Association
Assistant Secretary: Burlington House, Piccadilly, London WIV 9AG.
Meetings: Lecture Hall of Scientific Societies, Civil Service Commission Building, 23 Savile Row, London W1. Last Wednesday each month (Oct.–June). 5 p.m. and some Saturday afternoons.

Association for Astronomy Education
Secretary: Teresa Grafton, The Association for Astronomy Education, c/o The Royal Astronomical Society, Burlington House, Piccadilly, London WIV 0NL.

Astronomy Ireland
Secretary: Tony Ryan, PO Box 2888, Dublin 1, Ireland.
Meetings: 2nd and 4th Mondays of each month. Telescope meetings, every clear Saturday.

Federation of Astronomical Societies
Secretary: Clive Down, 10 Glan-y-Llyn, North Cornelly, Bridgend County Borough, CF33 4EF.

Junior Astronomical Society of Ireland
Secretary: K. Nolan, 5 St Patrick's Crescent, Rathcoole, Co. Dublin.
Meetings: The Royal Dublin Society, Ballsbridge, Dublin 4. Monthly.

Aberdeen and District Astronomical Society
Secretary: Ian C. Giddings, 95 Brentfield Circle, Ellon, Aberdeenshire AB41 9DB.
Meetings: Robert Gordon's Institute of Technology, St Andrew's Street, Aberdeen. Friday 7.30 p.m.

Abingdon Astronomical Society (was **Fitzharry's Astronomical Society**)
Secretary: Chris Holt, 9 Rutherford Close, Abingdon, Oxon OX14 2AT.
Meetings: All Saints' Methodist Church Hall, Dorchester Crescent, Abingdon, Oxon. 2nd Monday Sept.–June, 8 p.m.

Altrincham and District Astronomical Society
Secretary: Derek McComiskey, 33 Tottenhan Drive, Manchester M23 9WH.
Meetings: Timperley Village Club. 1st Friday Sept.–June, 8.00 p.m.

Andover Astronomical Society
Secretary: Mrs S. Fisher, Staddlestones, Aughton, Kingston, Marlborough, Wiltshire, SN8 3SA.
Meetings: Grately Village Hall. 3rd Thursday each month, 7.30 p.m.

Astra Astronomy Section
Secretary: c/o Duncan Lunan, Flat 65, Dalraida House, 56 Blythswood Court, Anderston, Glasgow G2 7PE
Meetings: Airdrie Arts Centre, Anderson Street, Airdrie. Weekly.

Astrodome Mobile School Planetarium
Contact: Peter J, Golding, 39 Alexandra Avenue, Gillingham, Kent ME7 2LP.

Aylesbury Astronomical Society
Secretary: Alan Smith, 182 Morley Fields, Leighton Buzzard, Bedfordshire LU7 8WN.
Meetings: 1st Monday in Month. Details from Secretary.

Bassetlaw Astronomical Society
Secretary: Andrew Patton, 58 Holding, Worksop, Notts S81 0TD.
Meetings: Rhodesia Village Hall, Rhodesia, Worksop, Notts. On 2nd and 4th Tuesdays of month at 7.45 p.m.

Batley & Spenborough Astronomical Society
Secretary: Robert Morton, 22 Links Avenue, Cleckheaton, West Yorks BD19 4EG.
Meetings: Milner K. Ford Observatory, Wilton Park, Batley. Every Thursday, 8.00 p.m.

Bedford Astronomical Society
Secretary: Mrs L. Harrington, 24 Swallowfield, Wyboston, Bedfordshire, MK44 3AE.
Meetings: Bedford School, Burnaby Rd, Bedford. Last Wednesday each month.

Bingham & Brookes Space Organization
Secretary: N. Bingham, 15 Hickmore's Lane, Lindfield, W. Sussex.

Birmingham Astronomical Society
Secretary: Peter Bolas, 4 Moat Bank, Burton-on-Trent, Staffordshire, DE15 0QJ.
Meetings: Room 146, Aston University, last Tuesday each month, Sept. to June (except Dec., moved to 1st week in Jan.).

Blackburn Leisure Astronomy Section
Secretary: Mr H. Murphy, 20 Princess Way, Beverley, East Yorkshire, HU17 8PD.
Meetings: Blackburn Leisure Welfare. Mondays 8.00 p.m.

Blackpool & District Astronomical Society
Secretary: Terry Devon, 30 Victory Road, Blackpool, Lancashire, FY1 3JT.
Meetings: St Kentigens Social Centre, Blackpool. 1st Wednesday each month, 8.00 p.m.

Bolton Astronomical Society
Secretary: Peter Miskiw, 9 Hedley Street, Bolton, Lancashire, BL1 3LE.
Meetings: Ladybridge Community Centre, Bolton. 1st and 3rd Tuesdays Sept.–May, 7.30 p.m.

Border Astronomical Society
Secretary: David Pettit, 14 Shap Grove, Carlisle, Cumbria, CA2 5QR.
Meetings: The Observatory, Trinity School, Carlisle. Alternate Thursdays, 7.30 p.m.

Boston Astronomers
Secretary: Mrs Lorraine Money, 18 College Park, Horncastle, Lincolnshire, LN9 6RE
Meetings: Blackfriars Arts Centre, Boston. 2nd Monday each month, 7.30 p.m.

Bradford Astronomical Society
Contact: Mrs J. Hilary Knaggs, 6 Meadow View, Wyke, Bradford BD12 9LA
Meetings: Eccleshill Library, Bradford. Alternate Mondays, 7.30 p.m.

Braintree, Halstead & District Astronomical Society
Secretary: Mr J.R. Green, 70 Dorothy Sayers Drive, Witham, Essex, CM8 2LU.
Meetings: BT Social Club Hall, Witham Telephone Exchange. 3rd Thursday each month, 8 p.m.

Breckland Astronomical Society (was **Great Ellingham and District Astronomy Club**)
Contact: Martin Wolton, Willowbeck House, Pulham St Mary, Norfolk, IP21 4QS.
Meetings: Great Ellingham Recreation Centre, Watton Road (B1077), Great Ellingham, 2nd Friday each month, 7.15 p.m.

Bridgend Astronomical Society
Secretary: Clive Down, 10 Glan-y-Llyn, Broadlands, North Cornelly, Bridgend County, CF33 4EF.
Meetings: Bridgend Bowls Centre, Bridgend, 1st and 3rd Friday monthly, 7.30 p.m.

Bridgwater Astronomical Society
Secretary: W. L. Buckland, 104 Polden Street, Bridgwater, Somerset.
Meetings: Room D10, Bridgwater College, Bath Road Centre, Bridgwater. 2nd Wednesday each month, Sept.–June.

Bridport Astronomical Society
Secretary: Mr G. J. Lodder, 3 The Green, Walditch, Bridport, Dorset, DT6 4LB.
Meetings: Walditch Village Hall, Bridport. 1st Sunday each month, 7.30 p.m.

Brighton Astronomical and Scientific Society
Secretary: Ms T. Fearn, 38 Woodlands Close, Peacehaven, East Sussex, BN10 7SF.
Meetings: St Johns Church Hall, Hove. 1st Tuesday each month, 7.30 p.m.

Bristol Astronomical Society
Secretary: Dr John Pickard, 'Fielding', Easter Compton, Bristol BS35 5SJ.
Meetings: Frank Lecture Theatre, University of Bristol Physics Dept., alternate Fridays in term time, and Westbury Park Methodist Church Rooms, North View, other Fridays.

Cambridge Astronomical Association
Secretary: Brian Lister, 80 Ramsden Square, Cambridge CB4 2BL.
Meetings: Institute of Astronomy, Madingley Road, 3rd Friday each month.

Cardiff Astronomical Society
Secretary: D. W. S. Powell, 1 Tal-y-Bont Road, Ely, Cardiff, CF5 5EU.
Meetings: Dept. of Physics and Astronomy, University of Wales, Newport Road Cardiff. Alternate Thursdays, 8 p.m.

Castle Point Astronomy Club
Secretary: Andrew Turner, 3 Canewdon Hall Close, Canewdon, Essex SS4 3PY.
Meetings: St Michael's Church Hall, Daws Heath. Wednesdays, 8 p.m.

Chelmsford Astronomers
Secretary: Brendan Clark, 5 Borda Close, Chelmsford, Essex.
Meetings: Once a month.

Chester Astronomical Society
Secretary: Mrs S. Brooks, 39 Halton Road, Great Sutton, South Wirral, LL66 2UF.
Meetings: All Saints Parish Church, Chester. Last Wednesday each month except Aug. and Dec., 7.30 p.m.

Chester Society of Natural Science, Literature and Art
Secretary: Paul Braid, 'White Wing', 38 Bryn Avenue, Old Colwyn, Colwyn Bay, Clwyd.
Meetings: Grosvenor Museum, Chester. Fortnightly.

Chesterfield Astronomical Society
Secretary: Mr Robert McGregor, 34 Higher Albert Street, Chesterfield, Derbyshire, S41 7QE.
Meetings: Barnet Observatory, Newbold, Each Friday.

Clacton & District Astronomical Society
Secretary: C. L. Haskell, 105 London Road, Clacton-on-Sea, Essex.

Cleethorpes & District Astronomical Society
Secretary: C. Illingworth, 38 Shaw Drive, Grimsby, S. Humberside.
Meetings: Beacon Hill Observatory, Cleethorpes. 1st Wednesday each month.

Cleveland & Darlington Astronomical Society
Secretary: Dr John McCue, 40 Bradbury Road Norton, Stockton-on-Tees, TS20 1LE.
Meetings: Thorpe Thewles Parish Hall, near Stockton-on-Tees. Monthly. 2nd Friday.
Colchester Amateur Astronomers
Secretary: F. Kelly, 'Middleton', Church Road, Elmstead Market, Colchester, Essex.
Meetings: William Loveless Hall, High Street, Wivenhoe. Friday evenings. Fortnightly.
Cork Astronomy Club
Secretary: Charles Coughlan, 12 Forest Ridge Crescent, Wilton, Cork, Ireland.
Meetings: 1st Monday Sept.–May (except bank holidays).
Cornwall Astronomy Society
Secretary: J. M. Harvey, 1 Tregunna Close, Porthleven, Cornwall TR13 9LW.
Meetings: Godolphin Club, Wendron Street, Helston, Cornwall, 2nd and 4th Thursday of each month, 7.30 for 8 p.m.
Cotswold Astronomical Society
Secretary: Alan Cahill, 51 Fieldfare, Abbeydale, Gloucester GL4 4WH.
Meetings: Church House, Painswick Road, Cheltenham. 2nd Saturday each month, 8.00 p.m.
Coventry & Warwicks Astronomical Society
Secretary: V. Cooper, 5 Gisburn Close, Woodloes Park, Warwick.
Meetings: Coventry Technical College. 1st Friday each month, Sept.–June.
Crawley Astronomical Society
Secretary: Ron Gamer, 1 Pevensey Close, Pound Hill, Crawley, West Sussex RH10 7BL.
Meetings: Ifield Community Centre, Ifield Road, Crawley. 3rd Friday each month, 7.30 p.m.
Crayford Manor House Astronomical Society
Secretary: Roger Pickard, 28 Appletons, Hadlow, Kent TM1 0DT.
Meetings: Manor House Centre, Crayford. Monthly during term-time.
Croydon Astronomical Society
Secretary: John Murrell, 17 Dalmeny Road, Carshalton, Surrey.
Meetings: Lecture Theatre, Royal Russell School, Combe Lane, South Croydon. Alternate Fridays, 7.45 p.m.
Derby & District Astronomical Society
Secretary: Kevin Woodward, 3 Swiss Cottages, Chevin Road, Belper, Derbyshire.
Meetings: Friends Meeting House, Derby. 1st Friday each month, 7.30 p.m.
Doncaster Astronomical Society
Secretary: John Chapple, 5 Orchard Mews, Cusworth, Doncaster DN5 8HQ.
Meetings: Corporation Brewery Tap public house, 2nd and 4th Wednesdays each month.
Dumfries Astronomical Society
Secretary: Mr J. Sweeney, 3 Lakeview, Powfoot, Annan, DG13 5PG.
Meetings: Gracefield Arts Centre, Edinburgh Road, Dumfries. 3rd Tuesday Aug.–May, 7.30 p.m.
Dundee Astronomical Society
Secretary: G. Young, 37 Polepark Road, Dundee, Tayside, DD1 5QT.
Meetings: Mills Observatory, Balgay Park, Dundee. 1st Friday each month, 7.30 p.m. Sept.–Apr.
Easington and District Astronomical Society
Secretary: T. Bradley, 52 Jameson Road, Hartlepool, Co. Durham.

Meetings: Easington Comprehensive School, Easington Colliery. Every 3rd Thursday throughout the year, 7.30 p.m.

Eastbourne Astronomical Society
Secretary: Peter Gill, 18 Selwyn House, Eastbourne, East Sussex, BN21 2LF.
Meetings: St Aiden's Church Hall, 1 Whitley Road, Eastbourne. 1st Saturday each month, 7.30 p.m.

East Lancashire Astronomical Society
Secretary: D. Chadwick, 16 Worston Lane, Great Harwood, Blackburn BB6 7TH.
Meetings: As arranged. Monthly.

East Riding Astronomers
Secretary: Tony Scaife, 15 Beech Road, Elloughton, Brough, North Humberside, HU15 1JX.
Meetings: As arranged.

Astronomical Society of Edinburgh
Secretary: Graham Rule, 105/19 Causewayside, Edinburgh EH9 1QG.
Meetings: City Observatory, Calton Hill, Edinburgh. 1st Friday each month, 8.00 p.m.

Edinburgh University Astronomical Society
Secretary: c/o Dept. of Astronomy, Royal Observatory, Blackford Hill, Edinburgh.

Ewell Astronomical Society
Secretary: G. O'Mara, 46 Stanton Close, Epsom KT19 9NP.
Meetings: Minor Hall, Bourne Hall, Spring Street, Ewell. 1st Friday of each month except August, 7.45 p.m.

Exeter Astronomical Society
Secretary: Tim Sedgwick, Old Dower House, Half Moon, Newton St Cyres, Exeter, Devon, EX5 5AE.
Meetings: The Meeting Room, Wynards, Magdalen Street, Exeter. 1st Thursday of month.

Farnham Astronomical Society
Secretary: Laurence Anslow, 'Asterion', 18 Wellington Lane, Farnham, Surrey, GU9 9BA.
Meetings: Church House, Union Road, Farnham. 2nd Monday each month, 7.45 p.m.

Furness Astronomical Society
Secretary: Richard Aldridge, 56 Hartington Street, Barrow-in-Furness, Cumbria LA14 5SR.
Meetings: Trinity Church Centre, Warwick Street, Barrow-in-Furness. 1st Friday each month.

Fylde Astronomical Society
Secretary: 28 Belvedere Road, Thornton, Lancs.
Meetings: Stanley Hall, Rossendale Avenue South. 1st Wednesday each month.

Astronomical Society of Glasgow
Secretary: Mr Robert Hughes, Apartment 8/4, 75 Plean Street, Glasgow G14 0YW.
Meetings: University of Strathclyde, George St, Glasgow. 3rd Thursday each month, Sep.–Apr., 7.30 p.m.

Greenock Astronomical Society
Secretary: Carl Hempsey, 49 Brisbane Street, Greenock.
Meetings: Greenock Arts Guild, 3 Campbell Street, Greenock.

Grimsby Astronomical Society
Secretary: R. Williams, 14 Richmond Close, Grimsby, South Humberside.
Meetings: Secretary's home. 2nd Thursday each month, 7.30 p.m.

Guernsey: La Société Guernesiaise Astronomy Section
Secretary: Ken Staples, 4 Le Felconte, St Peters, Guernsey GY7 9QB.
Meetings: The Observatory, St Peters, Tuesdays, 8 p.m.

Guildford Astronomical Society
Secretary: A. Langmaid, 22 West Mount, The Mount, Guildford, Surrey, GU2 5HL.
Meetings: Guildford Institute, Ward Street, Guildford. 1st Thursday each month, except Aug., 7.30 p.m.

Gwynedd Astronomical Society
Secretary: Mr Ernie Greenwood, 18 Twrcelyn Street, Llanerchymedd, Anglesey LL74 8TL.
Meetings: Dept. of Electronic Engineering, Bangor University. 1st Thursday each month except August, 7.30 p.m.

The Hampshire Astronomical Group
Secretary: Geoff Mann, 11 Fir Tree Gardens, Horndean, Waterlooville, Hampshire PO8 9HF.
Meetings: Clanfield Memorial Hall. Each Friday, 7.30 p.m.

Hanney & District Astronomical Society
Secretary: Bob Church, 47 Upthorpe Drive, Wantage, Oxfordshire, OX12 7DG.
Meetings: Last Thursday each month, 8.00 p.m.

Astronomical Society of Haringey
Secretary: Jerry Workman, 91 Greenslade Road, Barking, Essex, IG11 9XF.
Meetings: Palm Court, Alexandra Palace. 3rd Wednesday each month, 8 p.m.

Harrogate Astronomical Society
Secretary: Brian Bonser, 114 Main Street, Little Ouseburn, TO5 9TG.
Meetings: National Power HQ, Beckwith Knowle, Harrogate. Last Friday each month.

Hastings and Battle Astronomical Society
Secretary: Mrs Karen Parkhurst, 30 Bredon Rise, Hastings, East Sussex, TN34 3QC.
Meetings: St Clements Hall, Priory Road, Saturdays, 7.30 p.m.

Havering Astronomical Society
Secretary: Frances Ridgley, 133 Severn Drive, Upminster, Essex RM14 1PP.
Meetings: Cranham Community Centre, Marlborough Gardens, Cranham, Essex. 3rd Wednesday each month, 7.30 p.m.

Heart of England Astronomical Society
Secretary: John Williams, 100 Stanway Road, Shirley, Solihull, B90 3JG.
Meetings: Furnace End Village, every Thursday.

Hebden Bridge Literary & Scientific Society, Astronomical Section
Secretary: Peter Jackson, 44 Gilstead Lane, Bingley, West Yorkshire, BD16 3NP.
Meetings: Hebden Bridge Information Centre, Last Wednesday, Sept.–May.

Herschel Astronomy Society
Secretary: Kevin Bishop, 106 Holmsdale, Crown Wood, Bracknell, Berkshire, RG12 3TB.
Meetings: Eton College, 2nd Friday each month, 7.30 p.m.

Highlands Astronomical Society
Secretary: Richard Green, 11 Drumossie Avenue, Culcabock, Inverness IV2 3SJ.
Meetings: The Spectrum Centre, Inverness. 1st Tuesday each month, 7.30 p.m.

Hinckley & District Astronomical Society
Secretary: Mr S. Albrighton, 4 Walnut Close, The Bridleways, Hartshill, Nuneaton, Warwickshire, CV10 0XH.

Meetings: Burbage Common Visitors Centre, Hinckley. 1st Tuesday Sept.–May, 7.30 p.m.

Horsham Astronomy Group (was **Forest Astronomical Society**)
Secretary: Mr A. R. Clarke, 93 Clarence Road, Horsham, West Sussex, RH13 5SL.
Meetings: 1st Wednesday each month.

Howards Astronomy Club
Secretary: H. Ilett, 22 St Georges Avenue, Warblington, Havant, Hants.
Meetings: To be notified.

Huddersfield Astronomical and Philosophical Society
Secretary: R. A. Williams, 43 Oaklands Drive, Dalton, Huddersfield HD5 8PR.
Meetings: 4a Railway Street, Huddersfield. Every Friday, 7.30 p.m.

Hull and East Riding Astronomical Society
Secretary: Tony Scaife, 15 Beech Road, Elloughton, Brough, North Humberside, HU15 1JX.
Meetings: Wyke 6th Form College, Bricknell Avenue, Hull. 2nd Tuesday each month, Oct.–Apr., 7.30 p.m.

Ilkeston & District Astronomical Society
Secretary: Mark Thomas, 2 Elm Avenue, Sandiacre, Nottingham NG10 5EJ.
Meetings: The Function Room, Erewash Museum, Anchor Row, Ilkeston. 2nd Tuesday monthly, 7.30 p.m.

Ipswich, Orwell Astronomical Society
Secretary: R. Gooding, 168 Ashcroft Road, Ipswich.
Meetings: Orwell Park Observatory, Nacton, Ipswich. Wednesdays 8 p.m.

Irish Astronomical Association
Secretary: Barry Loane, 4 Belfast Road, Newtownards, Co. Down, NG10 5EJ.
Meetings: Ashby Building, Stranmillis Road, Belfast. Alternate Wednesdays, 7.30 p.m.

Irish Astronomical Society
Secretary: James O'Connor, PO Box 2547, Dublin 15, Ireland.
Meetings: Ely House, 8 Ely Place, Dublin 2. 1st and 3rd Monday each month.

Isle of Man Astronomical Society
Secretary: James Martin, Ballaterson Farm, Peel, Isle of Man IM5 3AB.
Meetings: The Manx Automobile Club, Hill Street, Douglas. 1st Thursday of each month, 8.00 p.m.

Isle of Wight Astronomical Society
Secretary: J. W. Feakins, 1 Hilltop Cottages, High Street, Freshwater, Isle of Wight.
Meetings: Unitarian Church Hall, Newport, Isle of Wight. Monthly.

Keele Astronomical Society
Secretary: Natalie Webb, Department of Physics, University of Keele, Keele, Staffordshire, ST5 5BG.
Meetings: As arranged during term time.

Kettering and District Astronomical Society
Asst. Secretary: Steve Williams, 120 Brickhill Road, Wellingborough, Northants.
Meetings: Quaker Meeting Hall, Northall Street, Kettering, Northants. 1st Tuesday each month. 7.45 p.m.

King's Lynn Amateur Astronomical Association
Secretary: P. Twynman, 17 Poplar Avenue, RAF Marham, King's Lynn.
Meetings: As arranged.

Lancaster and Morecambe Astronomical Society
Secretary: Miss E. Haygarth, 27 Coulston Road, Bowerham, Lancaster.

Meetings: Midland Hotel, Morecambe. 1st Wednesday each month except Jan. 7.30 p.m.

Lancaster University Astronomical Society
Secretary: c/o Students Union, Alexandra Square, University of Lancaster.
Meetings: As arranged.

Laymans Astronomical Society
Secretary: John Evans, 10 Arkwright Walk, The Meadows, Nottingham.
Meetings: The Popular, Bath Street, Ilkeston, Derbyshire. Monthly.

Leeds Astronomical Society
Secretary: Ray Emery, 39 Churchfield Lane, Rothwell, Leeds LS26 0NA.
Meetings: Centenary House, North Street. 2nd Wednesday each month, 7.30 p.m.

Leicester Astronomical Society
Secretary: Dr P. J. Scott, 21 Rembridge Close, Leicester LE3 9AP.
Meetings: Judgemeadow Community College, Marydene Drive, Evington, Leicester. 2nd and 4th Tuesdays each month, 7.30 p.m.

Letchworth and District Astronomical Society
Secretary: Eric Hutton, 14 Folly Close, Hitchin, Herts.
Meetings: As arranged.

Lewes Amateur Astronomers
Secretary: Christa Sutton, 8 Tower Road, Lancing, West Sussex, BN15 9HT.
Meetings: The Bakehouse Studio, Lewes. Last Wednesday each month.

Limerick Astronomy Club
Secretary: Tony O'Hanlon, 26 Ballycannon Heights, Meelick, Co. Clare, Ireland.
Meetings: Limerick Senior College, Limerick, Ireland. Monthly (except June and Aug.), 8 p.m.

Lincoln Astronomical Society
Secretary: David Swaey, 'Everglades', 13 Beaufort Close, Lincoln LN2 4SF.
Meetings: The Lecture Hall, off Westcliffe Street, Lincoln. 1st Tuesday each month.

Liverpool Astronomical Society
Secretary: Mr K. Clark, 31 Sandymount Drive, Wallasey, Merseyside L45 0LJ.
Meetings: Lecture Theatre, Liverpool Museum, 3rd Friday each month, 7.00 p.m.

Norman Lockyer Observatory Society
Secretary: Mr G. E. White, 6 Burrow Close, Newton Poppleford, Sidmouth, Devon, EX10 0BS.
Meetings: Norman Lockyer Observatory, Sidmouth, Fridays and 2nd Monday each month, 7.30 p.m.

Loughton Astronomical Society
Secretary: 14a Manor Road, Wood Green, London N22 4YJ
Meetings: 1st Theydon Bois Scout Hall, Loughton Lane, Theydon Bois. Weekly.

Lowestoft and Great Yarmouth Regional Astronomers (LYRA) Society
Secretary: Simon Briggs, 28 Sussex Road, Lowestoft, Suffolk.
Meetings: Community Wing, Kirkley High School, Kirkley Run, Lowestoft. 3rd Thursday each month, 7.30 p.m.

Luton & District Astronomical Society
Secretary: Mr G. Mitchell, 47 Rossfold Road, Luton LU3 3HJ.
Meetings: Putteridge Bury, Luton. Last Friday each month, 7.30 p.m.

Lytham St Annes Astronomical Association
Secretary: K. J. Porter, 141 Blackpool Road, Ansdell, Lytham St Annes, Lancs.

Meetings: College of Further Education, Clifton Drive South, Lytham St Annes. 2nd Wednesday monthly Oct.–June.

Macclesfield Astronomical Society
Secretary: Mrs Cherry Moss, 164a Chester Road, Macclesfield, Cheshire, SK11 8PT.
Meetings: Jodrell Bank Science Centre, 1st Tuesday each month.

Maidenhead Astronomical Society
Secretary: Tim Haymes, Hill Rise, Knowl Hill Common, Knowl Hill, Reading RG10 9YD.
Meetings: Stubbings Church Hall, near Maidenhead, 1st Friday Sept.–June.

Maidstone Astronomical Society
Secretary: Stephen James, 4 The Cherry Orchard, Haddow, Tonbridge, Kent.
Meetings: Nettlestead Village Hall, 1st Tuesday in month except July and Aug. 7.30 p.m.

Manchester Astronomical Society
Secretary: Mr J. H. W. Davidson, Godlee Observatory, UMIST, Sackville Street, Manchester M60 1QD.
Meetings: At the Observatory, Thursdays, 7.00 p.m.

Mansfield and Sutton Astronomical Society
Secretary: Angus Wright, Sherwood Observatory, Coxmoor Road, Sutton-in-Ashfield, Nottinghamshire NG17 5LF.
Meetings: Sherwood Observatory, Coxmoor Road. Last Tuesday each month, 7.30 p.m.

Mexborough and Swinton Astronomical Society
Secretary: Mark R. Benton, 14 Sandalwood Rise, Swinton, Mexborough, South Yorkshire, S64 8PN.
Meetings: Swinton WMC, Thursdays, 7.30 p.m.

Mid-Kent Astronomical Society
Secretary: Peter Bassett, 167 Shakespeare Road, Gillingham, Kent, ME7 5QB.
Meetings: Riverside Country Park, Lower Rainham Road, Gillingham. 2nd and last Fridays each month, 7.45 p.m.

Milton Keynes Astronomical Society
Secretary: Mark Hurn, 23 Wallread Gardens, Loughton, Milton Keynes.
Meetings: Rectory Cottage, Bletchley. Alternate Tuesdays.

Moray Astronomical Society
Secretary: Richard Pearce, 1 Forsyth Street, Hopeman, Elgin, Moray, Scotland.
Meetings: Village Hall Close, Co. Elgin.

Newbury Amateur Astronomical Society
Secretary: Miss Nicola Evans, 'Romaron', Bunces Lane, Burghfield Common, Reading RG7 3DG.
Meetings: United Reformed Church Hall, Cromwell Place, Newbury. 2nd Friday of month, Sept.–June.

Newcastle-on-Tyne Astronomical Society
Secretary: C. E. Willits, 24 Acomb Avenue, Seaton Delaval, Tyne and Wear.
Meetings: Zoology Lecture Theatre, Newcastle University, Monthly.

North Aston Space & Astronomical Club
Secretary: W. R. Chadburn, 14 Oakdale Road, North Aston, Sheffield.
Meetings: To be notified.

Northamptonshire Natural History Society (Astronomy Section)
Secretary: Dr Nick Hewitt, 4 Daimler Close, Northampton NN3 5JT

Meetings: Humfrey Rooms, Castilian Terrace, Northampton, 2nd and 4th Mondays, most months, 7.30 p.m.

Northants Amateur Astronomers

Secretary: Mervyn Lloyd, 76 Havelock Street, Kettering, Northamptonshire.

Meetings: 1st and 3rd Tuesday each month, 7.30 p.m.

North Devon Astronomical Society

Secretary: P. G. Vickery, 12 Broad Park Crescent, Ilfracombe, Devon EX34 8DX.

Meetings: Methodist Hall, Rhododendron Avenue, Sticklepath, Barnstaple. 1st Wednesday each month, 7.15 p.m.

North Dorset Astronomical Society

Secretary: J. E. M. Coward, The Pharmacy, Stalbridge, Dorset.

Meetings: Charterhay, Stourton, Caundle, Dorset. 2nd Wednesday each month.

North Downs Astronomical Society

Secretary: Martin Akers, 36 Timber Tops, Lordswood, Chatham, Kent, ME5 8XQ.

Meetings: Vigo Village Hall. 3rd Thursday each month. 7.30 p.m.

North-East London Astronomical Society

Secretary: Mr B. Beeston, 38 Abbey Road, Bush Hill Park, Enfield EN1 2QN.

Meetings: Wanstead House, The Green, Wanstead. 3rd Sunday each month (except Aug.), 3.00 p.m.

North Gwent Astronomical Society

Secretary: J. Powell, 14 Lancaster Drive, Gilwern, nr Abergavenny, Gwent NP7 0AA.

Meetings: Gilwern Community Centre, 15th of each month, 7.30 p.m.

North Staffordshire Astronomical Society

Secretary: Mr R. L. Daw, 6 Hall Drive, Weston Coyney, Stoke-on-Trent, Staffordshire, ST3 5PF.

Meetings: Pitfield Centre, Brampton Road, Newcastle, Staffs. 1st Wednesday of each month, 7.15 p.m.

North Western Association of Variable Star Observers

Secretary: Jeremy Bullivant, 2 Beaminster Road, Heaton Mersey, Stockport, Cheshire.

Meetings: Four annually.

Norwich Astronomical Society

Secretary: Frank Lawlor, 'Farnworth', Poringland Road, Upper Stoke Holy Cross, Norwich NR14 8NW

Meetings: Seething Observatory, Toad Lane, Thwaite St Mary, Norfolk. Every Friday, 7.30 p.m.

Nottingham Astronomical Society

Secretary: C. Brennan, 40 Swindon Close, The Vale, Giltbrook, Nottingham NG16 2WD.

Meetings: Djanogly City Technology College, Sherwood Rise (B682). 1st and 3rd Thursdays each month, 7.30 p.m.

Oldham Astronomical Society

Secretary: P. J. Collins, 25 Park Crescent, Chadderton, Oldham.

Meetings: Werneth Park Study Centre, Frederick Street, Oldham. Fortnightly, Friday.

Open University Astronomical Society

Secretary: Jim Lee, c/o above, Milton Keynes.

Meetings: Open University, Walton Hall, Milton Keynes. As arranged.

Orpington Astronomical Society

Secretary: Dr Ian Carstairs, 38 Brabourne Rise, Beckenham, Kent BR3 2SG.

Meetings: High Elms Nature Centre, High Elms Country Park, High Elms Road, Farnborough, Kent. 4th Thursday each month, Sept.–July, 7.30. p.m.

Papworth Astronomy Club
Secretary: Keith Tritton, Magpie Cottage, Fox Street, Great Gransden, Sandy, Bedfordshire, SG19 3AA.
Meetings: Bradbury Progression Centre, Church Lane, Papworth Everard, near Huntingdon. 1st Wednesday each month, 7.00 p.m.

Pendle Astronomical Society
Secretary: Kevin Pickup, 25 Lancaster Street, Colne, Lancashire.
Meetings: Parish Hall, Sacred Heart, Colne. 1st Tuesday each month, 7.30 p.m.

Peterborough Astronomical Society
Secretary: Sheila Thorpe, 6 Cypress Close, Longthorpe, Peterborough.
Meetings: 1st Thursday every month at 7.30 p.m.

Plymouth Astronomical Society
Secretary: Alan G. Penman, 12 St Maurice View, Plympton, Plymouth, Devon, PL7 IFQ.
Meetings: Glynis Kingham Centre, YMCA Annex, Lockyer Street, Plymouth, 2nd Friday each month, 7.30 p.m.

PONLAF
Secretary: Matthew Hepburn, 6 Court Road, Caterham, Surrey, CR3 5RD.
Meetings: Room 5, 6th Floor, Tower Block, University of North London. Last Friday each month during term time, 6.30 p.m.

Port Talbot Astronomical Society (was **Astronomical Society of Wales**)
Secretary: Mr J. Hawes, 15 Lodge Drive, Baglan, Port Talbot, West Glamorgan SA12 8UD.
Meetings: Port Talbot Arts Centre, 1st Tuesday each month, 7.15 p.m.

Portsmouth Astronomical Society
Secretary: G. B. Bryant, 81 Ringwood Road, Southsea.
Meetings: Monday, fortnightly.

Preston & District Astronomical Society
Secretary: P. Sloane, 77 Ribby Road, Wrea Green, Kirkham, Preston, Lancs.
Meetings: Moor Park (Jeremiah Horrocks) Observatory, Preston. 2nd Wednesday, last Friday each month. 7.30 p.m.

The Pulsar Group
Secretary: Barry Smith, 157 Reridge Road, Blackburn, Lancs.
Meetings: Amateur Astronomy Centre, Clough Bank, Bacup Road, Todmorden, Lancs. 1st Thursday each month.

Reading Astronomical Society
Secretary: Mrs Ruth Sumner, 22 Anson Crescent, Shinfield, Reading RG2 8JT.
Meetings: St Peter's Church Hall, Church Road, Earley. 3rd Friday each month, 7 p.m.

Renfrew District Astronomical Society (formerly **Paisley A.S.**)
Secretary: Mark Pollock, 14 Mains Wood, Erskine, PA8 7JW.
Meetings: Coats Observatory, Oakshaw Street, Paisley, Fridays, 7.30 p.m.

Richmond & Kew Astronomical Society
Secretary: Stewart McLaughlin, 41a Bruce Road, Mitcham, Surrey CR4 2BJ.
Meetings: Richmond Adult College, Parkshot, Richmond, Surrey, and the King's Observatory, Old Deer Park, Richmond, Surrey. Bimonthly.

Rower Astronomical Club
Secretary: Mary Kelly, Knockatore, The Rower, Thomastown, Co. Kilkenny, Ireland.
Salford Astronomical Society
Secretary: Mrs Kath Redford, 2 Albermarle Road, Swinton, Manchester M27 5ST.
Meetings: The Observatory, Chaseley Road, Salford, Wednesdays.
Salisbury Astronomical Society
Secretary: Mrs R. Collins, 3 Fairview Road, Salisbury, Wiltshire, SP1 1JX.
Meetings: Glebe Hall, Winterbourne Earls, Salisbury. 1st Tuesday each month.
Sandbach Astronomical Society
Secretary: Phil Benson, 8 Gawsworth Drive, Sandbach, Cheshire.
Meetings: Sandbach School, as arranged.
Sawtry & District Astronomical Society
Secretary: Brooke Norton, 2 Newton Road, Sawtry, Huntingdon, Cambridgeshire, PE17 5UT.
Meetings: Greenfields Cricket Pavilion, Sawtry Fen. Last Friday each month.
Scarborough & District Astronomical Society
Secretary: Mrs S. Anderson, Basin House Farm, Sawdon, Scarborough, N. Yorks.
Meetings: Scarborough Public Library. Last Saturday each month, 7–9 p.m.
Scottish Astronomers Group
Secretary: Dr Ken Mackay, Hayford House, Cambusbarron, Stirling, FK7 9PR.
Meetings: North of Hadrian's Wall, twice yearly.
Sheffield Astronomical Society
Secretary: Mr Andrew Green, 11 Lyons Street, Sheffield S4 7QS.
Meetings: Twice monthly at Mayfield Environmental Education Centre, David Lane, Fulwood, Sheffield.
Shetland Astronomical Society
Secretary: Chris McGinlay, Roselynn, Levenwick, Shetland.
Meetings: Clickimin Horizons Café. 1st Thursday of each month, Sept.–Apr., 6 p.m.
Shropshire Astronomical Society
Contact: David Woodward, 20 Station Road, Condover, Shrewsbury ST5 7BQ.
Meetings: The Gateway Arts & Education Centre, Shrewsbury. Occasional Fridays, 7.30 p.m.
Sidmouth and District Astronomical Society
Secretary: M. Grant, Salters Meadow, Sidmouth, Devon.
Meetings: Norman Lockyer Observatory, Salcombe Hill. 1st Monday in each month.
Society for Popular Astronomy (was **Junior Astronomical Society**)
Secretary: Guy Fennimore, 36 Fairway, Keyworth, Nottingham, NG12 5DU.
Meetings: Last Saturday in Jan., Apr., July, Oct., 2.30 p.m. in London.
Solent Amateur Astronomers
Secretary: Ken Medway, 443 Burgess Road, Swaythling, Southampton SO16 3BL.
Meetings: Room 2, Oaklands Community School, Fairisle Road, Lordshill, Southampton. 3rd Tuesday each month, 7.30 p.m.
Southampton Astronomical Society
Secretary: John Thompson, 4 Heathfield, Hythe, Southampton.
Meetings: Conference Room 3, the Civic Centre, Southampton, 2nd Thursday each month (except August), 7.30 p.m.
South Downs Astronomical Society
Secretary: J. Green, 46 Central Avenue, Bognor Regis, West Sussex.
Meetings: Assembly Rooms, Chichester. 1st Friday in each month.

South-East Essex Astronomical Society
Secretary: C. P. Jones, 92 Long Riding, Basildon, Essex.
Meetings: Lecture Theatre, Central Library, Victoria Avenue, Southend-on-Sea. Generally 1st Thursday in month, Sept.–May, 7.30 p.m.

South-East Kent Astronomical Society
Secretary: Andrew McCarthy, 25 St Paul's Way, Sandgate, near Folkestone, Kent, CT20 3NT.
Meetings: Monthly.

South Lincolnshire Astronomical & Geophysical Society
Secretary: Ian Farley, 12 West Road, Bourne, Lincolnshire, PE10 9PS.
Meetings: Adult Education Study Centre, Pinchbeck. 3rd Wednesday each month, 7.30 p.m.

Southport Astronomical Society
Secretary: Patrick Brannon, Willow Cottage, 90 Jacksmere Lane, Scarisbrick, Ormskirk, Lancashire, L40 9RS.
Meetings: Monthly Sept.–May, plus observing sessions.

Southport, Ormskirk and District Astronomical Society
Secretary: J. T. Harrison, 92 Cottage Lane, Ormskirk, Lancs L39 3NJ.
Meetings: Saturday evenings, monthly as arranged.

South Shields Astronomical Society
Secretary: c/o South Tyneside College, St George's Avenue, South Shields.
Meetings: Marine and Technical College. Each Thursday, 7.30 p.m.

South Somerset Astronomical Society
Secretary: G. McNelly, 11 Laxton Close, Taunton, Somerset.
Meetings: Victoria Inn, Skittle Alley, East Reach, Taunton. Last Saturday each month, 7.30 p.m.

South-West Cotswolds Astronomical Society
Secretary: C. R. Wiles, Old Castle House, The Triangle, Malmesbury, Wilts.
Meetings: 2nd Friday each month, 8 p.m. (Sept.–June).

South-West Hertfordshire Astronomical Society
Secretary: Tom Walsh, 'Finches', Coleshill Lane, Winchmore Hill, Amersham, Buckinghamshire, HP7 0NP.
Meetings: Rickmansworth. Last Friday each month, Sept.–May.

Stafford and District Astronomical Society
Secretary: Miss L. Hodkinson, 6 Elm Walk, Penkridge, Staffordshire, ST19 5NL.
Meetings: Weston Road High School, Stafford. Every 3rd Thursday, Sept.–May, 7.15 p.m.

Stirling Astronomical Society
Secretary: Hamish MacPhee, 10 Causewayhead Road, Stirling FK9 5ER
Meetings: Smith Museum & Art Gallery, Dumbarton Road, Stirling. 2nd Friday each month, 7.30 p.m.

Stoke-on-Trent Astronomical Society
Secretary: M. Pace, Sundale, Dunnocksfold Road, Alsager, Stoke-on-Trent.
Meetings: Cartwright House, Broad Street, Hanley. Monthly.

Stratford-upon-Avon Astronomical Society
Secretary: Robin Swinbourne, 18 Old Milverton, Leamington Spa, Warwickshire, CV32 6SA.
Meetings: Tiddington Home Guard Club. 4th Tuesday each month, 7.30 p.m.

Sunderland Astronomical Society
Contact: Don Simpson, 78 Stratford Avenue, Grangetown, Sunderland SR2 8RZ.
Meetings: Friends Meeting House, Roker. 1st, 2nd and 3rd Sundays each month.

Sussex Astronomical Society
Secretary: Mrs C. G. Sutton, 75 Vale Road, Portslade, Sussex.
Meetings: English Language Centre, Third Avenue, Hove. Every Wednesday, 7.30–9.30 p.m. Sept.–May.

Swansea Astronomical Society
Secretary: Maurice Convey, 132 Eaton Crescent, Uplands, Swansea SA1 4QR.
Meetings: Lecture Room C, Mathematics and Physics Building, University of Swansea. 2nd and 4th Thursdays each month, 7.00 p.m.

Tavistock Astronomical Society
Secretary: Mrs Ellie Coombes, Rosemount, Under Road, Gunnislake, Cornwall PL18 9JL.
Meetings: Science Laboratory, Kelly College, Tavistock. 1st Wednesday each month, 7.30 p.m.

Thames Valley Astronomical Group
Secretary: K. J. Pallet, 82a Tennyson Street, South Lambeth, London SW8 3TH.
Meetings: As arranged.

Thanet Amateur Astronomical Society
Secretary: P.F. Jordan, 85 Crescent Road, Ramsgate.
Meetings: Hilderstone House, Broadstairs, Kent. Monthly.

Torbay Astronomical Society
Secretary: Tim Moffatt, 31 Netley Road, Newton Abbot, Devon, TQ12 2LL.
Meetings: Torquay Boys' Grammar School, 1st Thursday in month; and Town Hall, Torquay, 3rd Thursday in month, Oct.–May, 7.30 p.m.

Tullamore Astronomical Society
Secretary: Sean McKenna, 145 Arden Vale, Tullamore, Co. Offaly, Ireland.
Meetings: Tullamore Vocational School. Tuesdays, Oct.–June, 8 p.m.

Tyrone Astronomical Society
Secretary: John Ryan, 105 Coolnafranky Park, Cookstown, Co. Tyrone.
Meetings: Contact Secretary.

Usk Astronomical Society
Secretary: Bob Wright, Llwyn Celyn, 75 Woodland Road, Croesyceiliog, Cwmbran, NP44 2OX.
Meetings: Usk Community Education Centre, Maryport Street. Each Thursday during school term, 7.00 p.m.

Vectis Astronomical Society
Secretary: J. W. Smith, 27 Forest Road, Winford, Sandown, Isle of Wight, PO36 0JY.
Meetings: Lord Louis Library Meeting Room, Newport. 4th Friday each month except Dec., 7.30 p.m.

Vigo Astronomical Society
Secretary: Robert Wilson, 43 Admers Wood, Vigo Village, Meopham, Kent DA13 0SP.
Meetings: Vigo Village Hall, as arranged.

Webb Society
Secretary: M. B. Swan, Carrowreagh, Kilshanny, Kilfenora, Co. Clare, Ireland.

Wellingborough District Astronomical Society
Secretary: S. M. Williams, 120 Brickhill Road, Wellingborough, Northants.
Meetings: 2nd Wednesday each month. Gloucester Hall, Church Street, Wellingborough, 7.30 p.m.

Wessex Astronomical Society
Secretary: Leslie Fry, 14 Hanhum Road, Corfe Mullen, Dorset.
Meetings: Allendale Centre, Wimborne, Dorset. 1st Tuesday of each month.

West Cornwall Astronomical Society
Secretary: Robin Hughes, 93 Atlantic Way, Portatowan, Cornwall, TR4 8AH
Meetings: Helston Football Club, 3rd Thursday each month, and St Michalls Hotel, 1st Wednesday each month, 7.30 p.m.

West of London Astronomical Society
Secretary: Tom H. Ella, 25 Boxtree Road, Harrow Weald, Harrow, Middlesex.
Meetings: Monthly, alternately at Uxbridge and North Harrow. 2nd Monday in month, except Aug.

West Midlands Astronomical Association
Secretary: Miss S. Bundy, 93 Greenridge Road, Handsworth Wood, Birmingham.
Meetings: Dr Johnson House, Bull Street, Birmingham. As arranged.

West Yorkshire Astronomical Society
Secretary: Pete Lunn, 21 Crawford Drive, Wakefield, West Yorkshire.
Meetings: Rosse Observatory, Carleton Community Centre, Carleton Road, Pontefract, each Tuesday, 7.15 p.m.

Whitby and District Astronomical Society
Secretary: Rosemary Bowman, The Cottage, Larpool Drive, Whitby, North Yorkshire, YO22 4ND.
Meetings: Mission to Seamen, Haggersgate, Whitby. 2nd Tuesday of the month, 7.30 p.m.

Whittington Astronomical Society
Secretary: Peter Williamson, The Observatory, Top Street, Whittington, Shropshire.
Meetings: The Observatory, every month.

Wiltshire Astronomical Society
Secretary: Simon Barnes, 25 Woodcombe, Melksham, Wilts SN12 6HA.
Meetings: St Andrews Church Hall, Church Lane, off Forest Road, Melksham, Wilts.

Wolverhampton Astronomical Society
Secretary: Mr M. Bryce, Iona, 16 Yellow Hammer Court, Kidderminster, Worcestershire, DY10 4RR.
Meetings: Beckminster Methodist Church Hall, Wolverhampton. Alternate Mondays, Sept.–Apr., extra dates in summer, 7.30 p.m.

Worcester Astronomical Society
Secretary: Mr S. Bateman, 12 Bozward Street, Worcester WR2 5DE.
Meetings: Room 117, Worcester College of Higher Education, Henwick Grove, Worcester. 2nd Thursday each month, 8.00 p.m.

Worthing Astronomical Society
Contact: G. Boots, 101 Ardingly Drive, Worthing, West Sussex, BN12 4TW.
Meetings: Heene Church Rooms, Heene Road, Worthing. 1st Wednesday each month (except Aug.). 7.30 p.m.

Wycombe Astronomical Society

Secretary: Mr P. Tgeherne, 34 Honeysuckle Road, Widner End, High Wycombe, Buckinghamshire, HP15 6BW.

Meetings: Woodrow High House, Amersham. 3rd Wednesday each month, 7.45 p.m.

York Astronomical Society

Secretary: Martin Whipp, 3 Marehall Close, Clifton Moore, York YO3 4WA.

Meetings: Goodricke College, York University. 1st and 3rd Fridays each month, 7.30 p.m.

Any society wishing to be included in this list of local societies or to update details is invited to write to the Editor (c/o Macmillan, 25 Eccleston Place, London SW1W 9NF), so that the relevant information may be included in the next edition of the *Yearbook*.